Y0-AIE-139

66238

D
DAEDALUS
SCIENCE AND CULTURE
C.
6.00

Date Due

JAN 15 '69

**The Library
Nazareth College of
Rochester, New York**

PRINTED IN U.S.A

SCIENCE AND CULTURE

A STUDY OF COHESIVE
AND DISJUNCTIVE FORCES

EDITED BY GERALD HOLTON

HOUGHTON MIFFLIN COMPANY BOSTON
THE RIVERSIDE PRESS CAMBRIDGE

1965

First Printing   R

66238

Copyright © 1965 by the American Academy
of Arts and Sciences

All rights reserved including the right to
reproduce this book or parts thereof in any form

Library of Congress Catalog Card Number: 65-19315

With the exception of "The Thematic Imagination in Science"
by Gerald Holton and "The Integrity of Science," the essays
in this book first appeared, several of them in somewhat
different form, in the Winter 1965 issue of *Dædalus*, the
Journal of the American Academy of Arts and Sciences

Printed in the United States of America

CONTENTS

vii   GERALD HOLTON
       Introduction

Definitions

1   HARRY LEVIN
      Semantics of Culture

14   JAMES S. ACKERMAN
      On *Scientia*

24   EDMUND R. LEACH
      Culture and Social Cohesion: An Anthropologist's View

39   TALCOTT PARSONS
      Unity and Diversity in the Modern Intellectual Disciplines: The Role of the Social Sciences

On Coherences and Transformations

70   HARVEY BROOKS
      Scientific Concepts and Cultural Change

88   GERALD HOLTON
      The Thematic Imagination in Science

109   DON K. PRICE
      The Established Dissenters

Contents

145   GYORGY KEPES
The Visual Arts and the Sciences: A Proposal for Collaboration

163   MARGARET MEAD
The Future as the Basis for Establishing a Shared Culture

On Disjunction and Alienation

184   OSCAR HANDLIN
Science and Technology in Popular Culture

199   ERIC WEIL
Science in Modern Culture

218   HERBERT MARCUSE
Remarks on a Redefinition of Culture

236   DANIEL BELL
The Disjunction of Culture and Social Structure: Some Notes on the Meaning of Social Reality

251   RENÉ DUBOS
Science and Man's Nature

273   ROBERT S. MORISON
Toward a Common Scale of Measurement

291   The Integrity of Science
A Report by the American Association for the Advancement of Science Committee on Science in the Promotion of Human Welfare

333   Notes on Contributors

337   Index

GERALD HOLTON

Introduction

SOME QUESTIONS are interesting because they have quick answers; others, because they do not. The important problems of contemporary science, for example, are largely of the first kind. They typically have a half-life of a few years before they are solved. The problems to which the authors in this issue devote themselves—what is the meaning of "culture," what is the state of our culture, and particularly what is the place of science in it—are of the second kind. They are important because every age has to frame its key questions anew and try to wrestle with them in its own way.

At once there arises the difficulty of finding a widely acceptable meaning for the main concepts needed in a discussion—for example, the concept "culture" itself. Thus, in their introduction to the volume *Culture: A Critical Review of Concepts and Definitions*, the anthropologists A. L. Kroeber and Clyde Kluckhohn quoted Lowell's confession:

> I have been entrusted with the difficult task of speaking about culture. But there is nothing in the world more elusive. One cannot analyze it, for its components are infinite. One cannot describe it, for it is a Protean in shape. An attempt to encompass its meaning in words is like trying to seize the air in the hand, when one finds that it is everywhere except in one's grasp.[1]

And the authors add wistfully: "One sometimes feels that A. Lawrence Lowell's remark about the humanistic concept of culture is almost equally applicable to the anthropological."

In addition to the unsatisfactory state of the terminology itself, there is the burden of history that sits heavily on any unresolved dialogue. For some time it has been clear to many that the most recent debates on science and culture were arriving at a stalemate which left matters not very different from what they had been before the Rede Lecture of 1959 stirred up the well-remembered furor noted briefly in three or four of the following essays. An enormous amount of work remains to be done. The relationships between the humanities, the social sciences, the natural sciences, and the creative arts, and in particular between the research functions of the first three, have recently been the subject of much interest but not of enough serious investigation. For example, the ways in which progress in one area may depend upon discovery in another are scarcely understood. The extent to which new disciplines depend upon the transfer of methods and of personnel from many older disciplines is only now beginning to be explored. It is frequently difficult to know to which of the traditional areas new disciplines belong; and the problem of "sharing knowledge" becomes more complex each day.

These questions, if properly pursued, lead to a fundamental re-examination of the concept of culture in the light of the situation that exists today. The controversies between Matthew Arnold and Thomas Huxley in the nineteenth century, or between T. S. Eliot and his critics, or between Snow and Leavis more recently, serve to remind us how necessary it is for each period to rethink what culture is—to re-examine it in each of its multiple senses and to identify the forces and mechanisms that change it.

In this light, a sound question would typically be "How may we define culture in such a way that the sciences are not automatically thought to be a disturbing component in our culture?" This is, however, not the way the question is usually posed. The preferred rhetoric starts by positing a dichotomy. We can see this hereditary defect as early as Matthew Arnold's essay "Culture and Anarchy" (1869) in which he maintained that culture is "a study of perfection. It moves by the force, not merely or primarily of the scientific passion for pure knowledge, but also of the moral and social passion for doing good." Science, "the mere endeavour to see and learn the truth for our own personal satisfaction," can be tolerated insofar as it prepares the way for the "great aim of culture, the aim of setting ourselves to ascertain what perfection is and to make it prevail." But if taken seriously, for its own sake, "it looks selfish, petty, and unprofitable." Of course, this, too, had been said many times before, and occasionally more convincingly by philosophers and more movingly by poets. In *Anna Karenina*, written just three years after the publication of Arnold's essay, Tolstoy saw the

Introduction

irreconcilable claims of traditional culture and new science in the soul of even an "unbeliever," Konstantin Levin:

> Ever since, by his beloved brother's deathbed, Levin had first glanced into the questions of life and death in the light of these new convictions, as he called them, which had during the period from his twentieth to his thirty-fourth year imperceptibly replaced his childish and youthful beliefs—he had been stricken with horror, not so much of death, as of life, without any knowledge of whence, and why, and how, and what it was. The physical organization, its decay, the indestructibility of matter, the law of the conservation of energy, evolution, were the words which usurped the place of his old belief. These words and the ideas associated with them were very well for intellectual purposes. But for life they yielded nothing, and Levin felt suddenly like a man who has changed his warm fur cloak for a muslin garment, and, going for the first time into the frost is immediately convinced, not by reason, but by his whole nature, that he is as good as naked, and that he must infallibly perish miserably.

If the question of the place of science in our culture is seen only in this way, there is perhaps nothing new or more persuasive to be added, and all continuation of the discussion would be repetitious.

I

Indeed, attempts to put the discussion on another plane seem continually to bog down. It is very significant that the tedious diatribes against and sweeping eulogies of the Rede Lecture are usually concerned with the relative merits of scientific and literary knowledge and are not (or at best only parenthetically) concerned with the reason originally advanced by its author for the thesis. It seems to be difficult to focus attention on the fact that the lecture was not a plea for or against one group of academics; rather, the question raised was what to do "in a time when science is determining much of our destiny, that is, whether we live or die." The lecture was only secondarily a plea for the intellectual betterment of nonscientists, or for closing the "gap" between scientists and others. Instead, the book is primarily an apocalyptical treatise on the need for a political utopia. The "gulf of mutual incomprehension" between literary intellectuals at one extreme and scientists at the other is, the author believed, "disastrous for a living culture"; but the disaster he had in mind is most threatening in the realm of geopolitics.

This does not refer simply to the increasing competition from the Soviet world. There is a second large and widening gap, that between the rich, industrialized countries, which are getting richer, and the poor countries, which are getting poorer. We are told that *if* we can accelerate the process of scientific revolution everywhere, we shall see our way through the three major menaces before us, "H-bomb war, overpopulation, and the gap between the rich and the poor." To achieve a stable state of international order, we are asked to change our culture in order that it may supply more intelligent administrators, educators, etc., to operate the world-wide scientific revolution without which we are not likely to survive the three major threats.

The plea may have been right; it may have been wrong. Even if it turns out to have been only partly right, the disaster projected for our time is so large that we would have been well advised to pay more attention to the warning, even though we may be inclined to view it merely as a part of a long tradition that looks to science and technology for powers to avert threatening adversity.

But any attempt to place the discussion on such a level creates another difficulty. The dire state of affairs is supposed to be remedied by an injection of a larger scientific and technological component into our culture, yet the recent advances in science and technology are themselves identified as the forces responsible for the state of affairs in the first place. These are the agencies that have been contributing to the enormous increase in the rate of innovation and social change, and that have helped to perfect new weapons that make the possibility of instantaneous destruction of Western civilization a real and continued threat. Thus, it would seem that we are asked to seek safety by delivering ourselves more fully to the very forces that appear to be responsible for the crisis.

While we may intuitively feel that the choice is unpleasant, it is perhaps not necessarily so paradoxial as it seems. A number of social or physical systems offer models in which stability, when disrupted by the introduction of a new factor, can be re-established at some level only by increasing the role of the new factor even further. Examples that come readily to mind are the introduction of literacy or industrialization or political emancipation into a traditional primitive society. Or, again, when an ionized atom begins to capture an electron, energy in the form of photons will in general continue inexorably to be radiated from the system until the electron has passed through the various energy levels to the ground state, at which point the quantum numbers symbolizing the system have the smallest values and the system is again stable.

Introduction

The recent trend of the discussion of science and culture, I believe, may also be an example of a cybernetic process which, when initiated at one level, runs its course until—hopefully—it reaches its new level. The recent and continuing flood of publications implies that our age is still trying to make up its mind about the place of science and is trying to do so by accommodating old as well as new factors. However one may assess the quality of the recent debate, it engaged the attention of such a large and concerned audience that it constituted a major international literary controversy of the post-war period. And because we are still very much aware of a gnawing dissatisfaction, we should take every opportunity during this transition phase to inject thoughtful material into the inquiry. This, at any rate, is the hope and function of the collection of essays in this volume.

The authors in this volume have had a significant advantage over other writers on this general topic: The great majority of them saw and discussed one another's preliminary drafts before writing their essays. Thanks to a grant from the National Science Foundation, the Editors of *Dædalus*, the journal of the American Academy of Arts and Sciences, were able to hold at the House of the Academy a Conference which yielded first drafts of most of the chapters in this book. These essays (originally published in the Winter 1965 issue of *Dædalus*) were intended not as final pronouncements, but as documents of the time, both in what they say and in what they feel unnecessary to say. And at the Academy Conference held prior to the commissioning of the final essays, this very diverse group of about thirty-five men and women,* including scientists, scholars in the humanities, creative artists, social scientists, and administrators, found fairly quickly one area of substantial agreement. It was the feeling that the relationship between the sciences and the humanities may well become considerably more strained in the immediate future. This estimate did not neglect the many new and old areas of mutual help[2] nor the fact that there has always been some back-

* Those who attended the Academy Conference included: James S. Ackerman, Daniel Bell, Frederick Burkhardt, Douglas Bush, Bruce Chalmers, Benjamin DeMott, S. R. Graubard, Lillian Hellman, Hudson Hoagland, Gerald Holton, Gyorgy Kepes, Leon Kirchner, Harold D. Lasswell, William Letwin, Herbert Marcuse, Margaret Mead, Robert K. Merton, Elting Morison, Robert S. Morison, F. S. C. Northrop, Talcott Parsons, Don K. Price, Edward M. Purcell, W. V. Quine, Ivor A. Richards, Walter A. Rosenblith, B. F. Skinner, Krister Stendahl, Julius Stratton, George Wald, and Harry Woolf.

ground noise of mutual invective.[3] Here we are speaking of something new. As one concerned scientist expressed it, "we may not have seen anything yet of the row that is really going to develop."[4] For example, one may expect drastic advances in the possibilities of increasing control over the human environment as well as over psychological and physiological functions (as by the action of drugs and the transplantation of organs); and this will have "a deep effect on what it is to be a human being." A sociologist agreed completely: "I think that the development of the in-between sphere [where both the sciences and the humanities have claims] is going to force many, many fights; they have been developing rapidly, and we have seen only the barest beginning of what is coming." Another social scientist felt that such a conflict may cause "the entire intellectual enterprise to come under severe attacks in the next years." A historian agreed that there is a storm brewing. One symptom (and an aggravating cause), he felt, was already discernible, namely the increasingly divergent curricula for the education of scientists and nonscientists.

A scholar in the field of public administration pointed out that similar warning signs are evident in areas outside the sciences: "Some of the subjects that have been thought of as rather harmless exercises in pure scholarship on the nonscientific side may take on great importance for our ideology and our self-control." A literary critic and poet added: "There is a mounting sense of tension; I am quite sure that those who have stressed it have been right. We are at the beginning of trouble." The Conference members did not by any means consider themselves an embattled group of intellectuals. It therefore came as rather a surprise, at least for me, to find how widely the sense of coming emergency was shared. Some of this feeling is reflected in the papers, particularly those toward the end of the present volume.

II

The essays have been arranged in three general groups. The first four essays, by Harry Levin, James S. Ackerman, Edmund R. Leach, and Talcott Parsons, are substantially concerned with definitions of terms and with historic developments. Harry Levin's urbane essay "Semantics of Culture" reviews some of the debates as well as the chief meanings given to the term "culture" itself. He implies that the recent fate of the term mirrors the trend of our culture.

Introduction

He indicates the great variety of current usages; for example, a number of threefold differentiations (culture as the transmittable core of high knowledge, culture as anthropologists study it, and culture as sociologists use the term; or high-, low-, and middle-brow culture; or the sciences, social sciences, and humanities; etc.), as well as a number of twofold differentiations (culture as personal activity and as a body of works to be studied; the elitistic or Brahminic culture of scholars, creative artists, and scientists on the one hand, versus that of the Philistines on the other; the culture of scientists on one hand, and that of all others on the other; etc.).

At the Conference, other dissatisfactions were expressed in addition to Mr. Levin's gently implied criticism of the current uses of the term. Two are of particular interest: that the industrialized West has for too long resisted expanding the operational meaning of culture to include the contributions from the Middle and Far East; and that we have delayed too long in considering what culture means in a period of rapidly emerging world community. In this connection, Margaret Mead's intent in her essay is to stimulate thinking about new points of view that the future may demand.

One reason for putting James S. Ackerman's paper immediately after Mr. Levin's is that it seemed to most participants at the Conference to introduce a basic point, the crucial distinction between technique or art on the one hand and *scientia* on the other. While at any given time a great number of fundamentally different techniques or areas of technical competence exist, occasionally a gifted person can progress beyond his own art and share in or contribute to the *scientia*, namely that single, evolving structure of ideas and of images that characterizes his time. (Examples of such seminal ideas are the coupling of complementary traits and the use of probabilistic concepts to express complex relationships.) If there is an unbalance today, Mr. Ackerman holds, it may be between the preponderance of attention to technique versus the lack of realization of what the contemporary *scientia* is and how it pervades the attitudes of scientist, artist, and humanist-scholar alike, even though they are working on very different materials and in different languages. Perhaps this imbalance reflects merely the openness of access to techniques, while the creators of new fundamental images who occasionally emerge from the trained mass are necessarily few.

Our *scientia* does not need to be rescued or newly established; it exists as surely now as, in a different way, it existed in medieval Europe. Moreover, on that level there is at all times a freemasonry of intellectuals and artists. As they always have done, they may now also be feeling isolated, even from the technicians in their own field, and they may think of themselves as standing on fragments of the total culture, on tiny islands. But they immediately recognize their counterparts when they meet, and they do not feel apologetic about the restrictions on their discourse imposed by the differences of the techniques through whose mastery they have come to share in the same *scientia*. Thus Sigmund Freud, writing to Albert Einstein in 1932 (in the exchange of letters published later under the title *Why War?*), said with his usual perception: "It may perhaps seem to you as though our theories are a kind of mythology and, in the present case, not even an agreeable one. But does not every science come in the end to a kind of mythology like this? Cannot the same be said today of your own physics?"

At the Academy Conference, a psychologist whose work has transformed his whole specialty field expressed everyone's impatience with attempts at *Gleichschaltung* on the level of mere technique:

> I don't think that any one of us expects that everyone should take all knowledge or art as his province. I don't enjoy the Chinese theater, and I don't feel a bit handicapped. Every time I pick up an issue of the *Scientific American,* I realize how much of science I don't know anything at all about; but I don't feel guilty. We can't really be interested in unity in the sense that we are all going to share the same knowledge, the same art. . . . I hope that we are not going to set ourselves up as salesmen of method, hoping to be able to "help" the physicist by getting him to look at music, or help the musician by getting him to take an interest in physics.

As another expressed it, detailed professional knowledge of the other's specialty field is not necessary for acknowledging common elements in science and scholarship—fidelity in observation, loyalty to the text, "troth to truth," above all, mutual respect and tolerance. Of the tension between recognized commonalities and the necessary differences, Robert Oppenheimer wrote in the first issue of *Dædalus* (Winter 1958), ". . . the unity we can seek lies really in two things. One is that the knowledge which comes to us at such a terrifyingly, inhumanly rapid rate, has some order in it. . . . The second is simply this: We can have each other to dinner."

Of course, when it comes to discerning consequences for education that follow from this point of view, one must be careful

Introduction

not to apply prescriptions valid for those who can contribute at the level of *scientia* indiscriminately also to the larger mass of those who will have to function at a quite different level. If it is true, as has recently been claimed, that "modern man must specialize or die," and if all he does is specialize, then most men will not know in what respect they are modern, or human, or alive. While those who make the most elevated efforts to comprehend and organize reality, by this very activity, share in one another's different thoughts, what is it that is shared by the ordinary don, the educated technician, the average citizen? What *should* it be?

Given the fact that the company assembled at the Academy Conference contained a preponderance of university people, the question of education was not long forgotten, although most of the papers were not to deal specifically with it. The Conference returned often to educational prescriptions, and at least a few words should be said here about some of these exchanges. No one doubted that high culture itself would cease to exist if there were not a shared respect for courageous specialization, for the requirement that an educated man have direct contact with work of the highest quality in order that he may understand some one thing profoundly. But nobody thought the task of education—as against training—should stop there.

One of the informal drafts prepared for the Conference presented a position widely accepted by the symposiasts. Culture properly defined for the purpose of educational questions, Franklin L. Ford wrote,

... implies the most ambitious and the most exacting intellectual effort and aesthetic endeavor in every discipline. Thus defined, it also presupposes at least some exchange among the disciplines, some reciprocal curiosity and appreciation. In short, it necessarily involves a continuing tension between the centrifugal thrust of specialized exploration and a centripetal tug toward synthesis, toward the central area of shared concerns. What is worrying us now? Is it not precisely the suspicion that the centrifugal has triumphed over the centripetal, that the essential tension has disappeared—and with it, culture itself?

As we contemplate this possibility, chilling in its implied finality, why do we tend so readily to focus our concern on the position of science? ... Part of the answer seems to me to be that it is in discussing science that all who are concerned, scientist and nonscientist alike, see most clearly before them the threat that a synthesis of the human comprehension of the world may never again be possible, that culture as a thing shared may be lost forever to our species. ... The all-important breakdown, I maintain, came in an area far less dramatic and far less commonly noted than those of religion or interpersonal relations. It came in the loss of adequate communication across the interior boundaries of our culture, and it came at the most elementary level of communication, in language itself.

... I have identified communication as crucial to the entire problem; let me suggest that one step which might be taken would be a direct attack on the problem of language itself and that what is involved is no casuistic retreat into an argument over words and their meanings. Culture is always dependent and always will depend on how much that one knows can be explained to another, or to put it more realistically, how many of the central concerns agitating one portion of the community can be appreciated at least in general terms by other sectors.

The language of science, it seems to me, definitely needs help. . . . Quite clearly, I think we are facing the need not to redefine culture, but rather to re-enunciate a very old definition, one which incorporates both specialization and some determination to share its result.[5]

Approaching the question of definitions from an anthropologist's viewpoint, Edmund R. Leach at the very outset touches on the same point as Mr. Ford: The primary problem is to preserve the possibility of wide and unambiguous communication. "Culture can survive only where one human generation can transmit its accumulated knowledge to the next"; and later, ". . . my recurrent emphasis is upon culture as a communications system. Granted this approach, language itself has a certain primacy as compared to any of the other polymorph aspects of culture. . . . Mutual intelligibility is a fundamental necessity for any cohesive social group." It comes then as no surprise that at the end of the essay the scientist's frequent inability—or unwillingness—to communicate his "secret knowledge" is seen to exacerbate "a very serious kind of social incoherence."

The last of the four introductory essays concerned with definitions is Talcott Parsons' review of the role of the social sciences in the development of contemporary culture. After tracing the history of the conception that our culture is being fragmented and of attempts at synthesis, he finds that the most fruitful view of the contemporary situation is to recognize the existence and ecological function of differentiated variants. Thus he concludes that now neither a monolithic nor a dualistic view of culture "is tenable as a frame of reference for the modern level of sophistication." The social sciences have emerged as mediating or coupling connections between those two other pursuits which exclude, on the one hand, the category of subjectivity and individuality of meaning and, on the other, the predominance of analytical generality.

Introduction

This fundamentally optimistic analysis was persuasively argued at the Conference, where Mr. Parsons noted three elements that cut across subject-matter divisions: common methodological concepts in the broad sense, such as the relativistic approach; methodological devices, such as computers; and even the very tendency to seek dichotomies (e.g., between *Geistes-* and *Naturwissenschaften,* a distinction becoming more and more untenable, as demonstrated, for example, by the success of the scientific study of language itself).

III

If one cannot hope for a unified culture in which the philosopher and the engineer communicate often and easily about each other's work—as we surely now know we cannot—what is it that one can legitimately ask for? If not unity or harmony in the sense of a considerable degree of identity and homogeneity of terminology and a consciously, widely shared orientation, what else instead? On this point, the symposium adopted what seems to me a fundamental, fruitful point of view, one which is reflected in the division of the remaining papers into two groups as shown in the Table of Contents: the first group is concerned with coherence-making elements, the second with disjunction and alienation.

Accepting, as underlying an implicit common *scientia,* the existence and need for great variety and differentiation of techniques and orientations, the basic question is whether these pieces—any two of which, taken separately, may well be incompatible—do or do not fit together in some kind of congruent way. It is the structure of society that either facilitates such organic coherence or militates against it. And the desired coherence would obviously have to be on a level somewhere between a kind of totalitarian sameness at one extreme, of which Herbert Marcuse's paper warns, and at the other extreme a chaos of unengaged elements, or even the "universal uniformity" that saddened and chilled Tocqueville when he contemplated the possible future of an America containing "this countless multitude of beings, shaped in each other's likeness, amidst whom nothing rises and nothing falls."

As a sociologist put it at the Conference: "For me the central question is, what kind of reorganization of the way we live our lives and fulfill our roles ... makes for greater or less congruence between the various parts of our culture." The model, then, is not one

GERALD HOLTON

of specialties competing for dominance, or even for acceptance as separate equals. It is rather of an organism in which diverse elements have to cooperate in an articulated way, in which there may indeed be only a delicate balance that decides whether the milieu which one part sets up for the others is viable or lethal. On this basis it might be argued that whatever the historic facts of the case are, the present question is not whether, say, the sciences do or should challenge the traditional predominance of the humanities, but rather how to discern and nourish what it is that each needs from the other for the proper development of its own sphere, however defined.[6]

The set of five essays on coherences and transformations takes by and large a favorable view concerning the possibilities of nurturing the coherence-making aspects. Harvey Brooks first shows evidences that "both scholarship and practical affairs have increasingly adopted the spirit and mode of thought of the natural sciences" for useful purposes and then gives a number of convincing contemporary examples where "the actual concepts and ideas of science have entered into other disciplines and into our culture generally" or have a potential for producing such transformations.

This is certainly not to say that the expansion of influence is necessarily a one-way process. On the contrary, as my own paper argues, it can be shown that the transforming themes of science (such as "energy") are potent precisely because they are rooted in a more basic imaginative faculty, one that operates with a relatively unspecialized vocabulary of fundamental themata. Hence, when a really effective theme has gained entrance into another discipline, it must be suspected that it was not an alien import from science, but rather has returned to familiar ground which was prepared to receive it. And, with a little training one can discern that the basic thematic imagination is quite similar inside and outside the sciences.

This situation points up a need not at all unique to the sciences—the need to have not only patronage, but also an educated audience. The lesson is contained in Don K. Price's important analysis of the way both the sciences and the humanities have in the last few decades unwittingly collaborated in destroying in their several ways the old comfortable American assumption that political progress is inevitable and automatic. This essay and the one by Gyorgy Kepes use very different methods when confronting the question of how highly specialized, science-based knowledge can be translated

Introduction

into effective action outside the sciences—in one case into political decision, in the other into artistic creation. In arriving at exemplars that indicate some answers, both papers demonstrate that the power of certain scientific concepts is not that they add a conceptual tool or skill needed to solve a problem in a defined area, but that they trigger a transforming extension of the area itself by changing the whole range of possible thought or action.

Again, the accent in both presentations is on gains registered by the application of scientific ideas; but it is a net balance reached by considering results on two sides of the ledger. Thus, Mr. Price supports by a careful analysis the view which he expressed at the Conference that "by getting itself established...as the principal official means of determining the truth, science now brings up in acute form some constitutional problems of a kind that the United States thought it had successfully disposed of forever by a disestablishment of the church." And Mr. Kepes spoke of correspondingly fundamental problems which the progress of science and technology raises for the artist. One of these is the increasing difficulty of preserving a sense of human scale or, for that matter, of solitariness necessary for artistic creation. Another is the—sometimes threatening—challenge to the artist to explore new ways of seeing the world. Indeed, the most characteristic element of contemporary art, he thought, is the courage of the best practitioners to "go back to the almost invisible roots of all artistic creation, and perhaps to create works that previous generations could not, because their challenge was not so fundamental and so menacing as ours."

Each of the five essays in this group has in it an element of hopeful extrapolation; the last of them, that by Margaret Mead, is fully and frankly future-directed. The subject, indeed, is nothing less than the proper way to construct a future in which Herbert Read's prescription would come true. He said, in his essay "To Hell With Culture,"

> ... Culture in a natural society will not be a separate and distinguishable thing—a body of learning that can be put into books and museums and mugged up in your spare time. Just because it will not exist as a separate entity, it would be better to stop using the word "culture." We shall not need it in the future and it will only confuse the present issue. Culture belongs to the past: the future will not be conscious of its culture.[7]

IV

Whatever the reaction which the specific details of Miss Mead's proposal provoke, one aspect is certain to be noted: It is the primacy of concern with the actual, individual, living person. Writing even with passion about the "human being" may still be writing about an abstraction. But in this essay, at the midpoint of the issue, we have come to a fulcrum from which the two halves, like the arms of a lever, extend in different directions: As it turned out, the papers in the first half tended, with occasional exceptions, to deal with the beneficent interactions, the symbiotic exchanges of concept, the forces of coherence at work in groups and disciplines. And while they are, it seems to me, seminal contributions for any future consideration of the topic, Konstantin Levin might say that they are "very well for intellectual purposes." On the other hand, the essays in the second half, with certain exceptions, are asking whether contemporary ideas after all are sufficient for the individual life.

The papers by Messrs. Handlin, Weil, Marcuse, Bell, Dubos, and Morison, are in varying degrees concerned with the forces of disjunction in our society and in our culture, the causes of alienation and anomie of the individual—often but not always ascribed to the growth of science. Some of our authors are not sanguine that the agencies of coherence, even if they could be nourished and elaborated, will be sufficiently strong or meaningful. Bringing these essays together with the others does, therefore, reflect to a large degree the whole current spectrum of opinion on the valid place for science.

And that spectrum is indeed wide and colorful! Anyone who cares even moderately for a wider understanding of science continually finds new evidence of troubled concern in the hearts of friends and strangers alike, ranging from uneasiness to violent outrage.[8]

It would be quite wrong to dismiss seriously meant comments as the symptoms of misinformation or lack of proper training. The earnestness, the variety, the persistence, the honest purpose in the majority of cases cannot be treated as the merely frivolous statements should be. Nor can one fail to listen to a cause simply because it has been championed so long—in this case, for over two thousand years. It may have been natural that in the *Phaedo* Socrates should have thought of another philosopher who also had been accused of impiety—Anaxagoras. But what Socrates at the very end of his

Introduction

last day was saying to his friends had another motive: When he was young, Socrates warned, he had had a great appetite for the study called natural science, and had thought Anaxagoras would be a suitable teacher. But these fine hopes were soon dashed: The man talked only of things like air and ether and water and other absurdities. He left the real cause untouched, the soul unattended.

Almost every one of these final essays is a plea to take seriously the lower, darker side of the balance; and there are a number of themes common to several of the essays, which will now be considered together. Two of these themes have to be particularly noted: the view that modern science is an inextricable ally of a monstrous technology that threatens man's physical existence; and the view that modern science is the growth medium of a monstrous ideology that threatens man's philosophical existence.

Oscar Handlin's paper goes to the heart of the first point by establishing the historic context within which "the machine" became, to many, a threat, and "science" became identified with the technological enterprise which insists that machines are "the fruits of science." To anyone actively working in science, it is always initially astonishing to discover how closely in the public mind science and technology are confused and identified on entirely spurious grounds. But, like many of the benign as well as maleficent reactions recorded here, the supposed threat of the machine is, of course, a notion of long standing. When rapid railroad transportation was introduced on a large scale in Western and Central Europe, the voices that spoke of "the dark, Satanic mills" now also began to wonder about coal, iron, and steam. And, as a historian reminded us at the Conference, they asked "what they had to do with things that were true and beautiful and of good report. Or they asserted, as Huxley did, that they were not impressed by the power, natural resources, knowledge, or machinery that greatly extended man's competence. 'The great issue,' as Huxley put it, 'about which hangs a true sublimity and the terror of over-hanging fate is, what are you going to do with all these things?'"

This last sentence, to many intellectuals today—to an increasing number, it seems to me—is still the great issue. As a culture-changing instrumentality of irresistible and unmatched power, the thrust of technology seems to them to be on an erratic and unpredictable path, turning up in seemingly random succession, now an undreamt-of gift, now a nightmarish horror, and now a brash vulgarity.[9]

xxi

Matters are made worse by the painful fact that there are still very few statesmen of technology, persons who could either help this impartial giant to select its goals or at least explain clearly to those who are concerned why this cannot be done. As a result, the main governing forces seem to many now to be just two: the desire for private gain among those who make calculated small decisions that can escalate into unexpected large ones, and the needs of the military establishment. By and large, these two forces are less and less trusted to achieve good ends on their own. As Herbert Read said, with due acknowledgment of the fact that industrialization may be the only hope of the poor: "The technological revolution lacks any moral or aesthetic foundation."[10]

This judgment seems to reflect a widespread sentiment, one so strong that, in addition to the papers published in this group, an equal number of participants in the Conference brought position drafts expressing similar concerns. This situation in itself may indicate that the fundamental message of Eric Ashby's *Technology and the Academics* is applicable to our time and place. There is no doubt that technology has not made itself acceptably understood.

This matter enters our issue also because of the widespread inability of intellectuals as well as the wider public to find a basic difference between technology and science. A number of fairly evident causes come to mind to explain this confusion; one is the fear of an overwhelming intrusion of "civilization," with its technological burden of meaning, into "culture," with its original humanistic meaning. Mr. Marcuse's paper speaks of this with passion: "When the most abstract achievements of mathematics and theoretical physics satisfy so adequately the needs of IBM and of the Atomic Energy Commission, it is time to ask whether such applicability is not inherent in the concepts of science itself." Looking at the threats to the integrity of science from the inside, the final paper in this volume, the controversial and searchingly introspective report of the Committee on Science in the Promotion of Human Welfare of the American Association for the Advancement of Science, finds that "a social decision to accomplish a particular technological aim is often made in advance of the necessary scientific knowledge," and it projects dire consequences of the growth of large military and political pressures on the enterprise of "pure" science. There is evidence of a more demoralizing effect of these developments on some scientists, as reflected in the remarks of

Introduction

Max Born, who wrote in the Preface of his collection of essays *Physics in My Generation* (1956):

> ... In 1921 I believed—and I shared this belief with most of my contemporary physicists—that science produced an objective knowledge of the world, which is governed by deterministic laws. The scientific method seemed to me superior to other, more subjective ways of forming a picture of the world—philosophy, poetry, and religion; and I even thought the unambiguous language of science to be a step towards a better understanding between human beings.
>
> In 1951 I believed in none of these things. The border between object and subject had been blurred, deterministic laws had been replaced by statistical ones, and although physicists understood one another well enough across all national frontiers they had contributed nothing to a better understanding of nations, but had helped in inventing and applying the most horrible weapons of destruction.

The current rapidity of conversion from pure search to exploitable application is, of course, striking; frequently only a few years intervene between a basic advance in physics or biochemistry and the development of a whole new industry or world-wide medical specialty. But again, the fact that this sequence of events is regarded as so important and is so assiduously fostered must be seen against the background of a long tradition of its own. That application may follow basic discovery is neither a necessity of nature nor in itself very interesting. It is the old and widespread habit of regarding the latter as subservient to the former which makes it significant, especially in this country. A tight coupling of science and technology has been so deeply imbedded in our thinking that a large-scale change of mind would seem to be quite difficult. We can find evidence of this everywhere and from the earliest period. It is illustrated by some paragraphs from the explanatory Preface to the first volume of the *Memoirs* of the American Academy of Arts and Sciences, published in 1785:

> This country being young, and few among us having such affluence and leisure as to admit of their applying much time to the cultivation of the sciences, and to the making of improvements in arts, manufactures, agriculture, &c. it will not, at present, be expected, that this Academy should vie with similar institutions in old countries, where they have peculiar advantage for such prosecutions. Yet, it is hoped, that the following papers will not be reckoned useless, nor prove unacceptable to the public.
>
> The astronomical and mathematical papers, in this volume, will, perhaps, be the least entertaining of any in the collection, and will have

the smallest number of readers. However, they are useful in such a work. Few, if any of them, contain deep speculations and obstruse researches and calculations; but they are chiefly of the practical kind. The astronomical pieces principally exhibit such observations and deductions, as are subservient to the cause of geography and navigation, the improvement of which is of great importance to this country. . . .

It is the part of a patriot-philosopher to pursue every hint—to cultivate every enquiry, which may eventually tend to the security and welfare of his fellow citizens, the extension of their commerce, and the improvement of those arts, which adorn and embellish life.[11]

The strength and tenacity of this tradition in the United States is indicated by the fact that the President, at a meeting of a group of scientists and engineers at the White House on October 6, 1964, said, "I have guided my course by a view I once read from an early American journal," and then cited the last paragraph above.

It is possible to conceive of a society in which the sophisticated technological by-products of scientific advance are reserved *only* for fashioning more and better tools for furthering pure scientific research. In this hypothetical society, where technology is the handmaiden only of science, reactors and computers would never be taken from their original places in the laboratory. Science would progress at a lower and slower level but would not be impossible. If this were the case, the whole discussion in this final group of thoughtful papers would have to be rather different. If the Baconian knot that binds science, technology, and society together were cut, this would partly relieve Mr. Bell's concern with cultural disjunction, Mr. Dubos' concern with the growing mismatch between man's nature and man's behavior, and Dr. Morison's concern with the growing anomie of modern man.

But the knot cannot be cut;[12] and if it were, the relief would be only partial. For even then, there would remain a variety of disjunctive mechanisms. And the most important of these is the *philosophical* portent that modern science is widely thought to have for our time. This is the final and possibly most significant point that arises from a consideration of this last group of papers.

V

Perhaps the most unique characteristic of modern science is the generally accepted thema of the unlimited possibility of *doing* science, the belief that nature is inexhaustibly knowable. Kepler found support for this belief in equating the mind of God and of

Introduction

man on those subjects which can be understood in the exact sciences. In our day, Heisenberg has said: "Exact science also goes forward in the belief that it will be possible in every new realm of experience to understand nature."

To recapture the exuberant enthusiasm of science, one should not go to a well-established contemporary physical science, but perhaps to a field when it was still young. In the journals of the seventeenth and eighteenth centuries, we can find, side by side, what we would now consider very heterogeneous material—descriptions of a violent thunderstorm, statistics of and speculations on the causes of death in a certain village, notes on microscopic or telescopic wonders, on the colors in chemical reactions, observations on the propagation of light, on the growth and types of reptiles, on the origin of the world. The heterogeneity speaks of a marvelous and colorful efflorescence of interests and an unselfconscious exuberance that verges sometimes on aimless play. The scientists of the time seem to us to have run from one astonishing and delightful discovery to the next like happy children surrounded by gifts.

As the terminology has grown more sophisticated, this wonderful feeling has become less evident to those not directly involved in science. And it also has become less wide-ranging in scientific circles as the work of the scientist has become more and more specialized. But from the platform of his specialized science, he can more than ever feel that Nature bars no questions, that what can be imagined also can be—no, must be—investigated.

But behind this apparently atomistic fragmentation of attention has been a monistic aim. The seventeenth- and eighteenth-century researcher did not see the myriads of separate and disparate investigations around him as unrelated items in a randomly built catalogue of natural knowledge. Coupled with the theme of the universal accessibility of nature has been the old motivating methodological theme of an underlying *Einheit der Naturwissenschaften* —both a unity and a singularity of natural knowledge. The paths to an understanding of nature may be infinite (as the success of even the most specialized interests indicates), and each of these paths is expected to have difficult but not insurmountable barriers. But all the paths have been vaguely thought to lead to *a* goal, *an* understanding of *one* nature, a delimited though no doubt complex rational corpus which some day a man's mind would be able to make his own (as the layman today says, somewhat frightened, "one great formula" that tells everything there is to know about nature).[13]

These two connected themata of unlimited outer accessibility and delimited inner meaning can be vaguely depicted by the device of a maze having in its outer walls innumerable entrances, through each of which one can hopefully reach, sooner or later, the one mystery which lies at the center.

But another possibility has suggested itself more and more insistently: that at the inner-most chamber of the maze one would find *nothing*. Writing in the fateful year of 1905, J. Larmor, one of Newton's successors as Lucasian Professor of Mathematics at Cambridge, saw it coming:

> There has been of late a growing trend of opinion, prompted in part by general philosophical views in the direction that the theoretical constructions of physical science are largely factitious, that instead of presenting a valid image of the relation of things on which further progress can be based, they are still little better than a mirage.[14]

The final encounter, he seems to cry out, cannot be with a mere shadow, or, worse still, with a narcissistic self-reflection of one's own thought processes.

Yet, on the face of it, it is not necessary to believe that knowledge of nature must turn out to be organizable in a philosophically satisfactory way. "We have no right to assume that any physical law exists," Max Planck once said. From a suitable distance, we cannot soundly claim that the historic development of science has proved nature to be understandable in a unique way—as distinct from documentable, manipulable, predictable within limits, or technically exploitable. What has happened is that the ground of the unknown has continually been shifted, the allegory has continually changed. David Hume expressed this in 1773:

> While Newton seemed to draw off the veil from some of the mysteries of nature, he showed at the same time the imperfections of this mechanical philosophy; and thereby restored her ultimate secrets to that obscurity in which they ever did and ever will remain.[15]

In the empirical sciences, we are far from able to prove that we have been approaching an increasing understanding of the type that characterized the development of, say, some branches of mathematics. Our interests and tools change, but not in a linear, inevitable way. For example, the historic development, from organismic science to a mechanistic and then to the mathematical style, *could* have taken place in the opposite direction. And the ontological status of scientific knowledge itself has been turned completely upside down since the beginning of the twentieth century. The experimental detail is now not simply the token of a real world; on the contrary, it is all that we can be more or less sure about at the moment.

Karl Popper summarizes this view in these words:

> I think that we shall have to get accustomed to the idea that we must not look upon science as a "body of knowledge," but rather as a system of hypotheses; that is to say, as a system of guesses or anticipations which in principle cannot be justified, but with which we work as long as they stand up to tests, and of which we are never justified in saying that we know that they are "true" or "more or less certain" or even "probable."[16]

Our justification for these hypotheses is that they have a hold on our imagination and that they help us to deal with our experience. On this basis, all the scientist needs to say, if anyone should ask him what he is doing, is: *hypotheses fingo*. This is precisely what Lodge, Larmor, Poincaré, and so many others could not accept— the new thematic hypothesis fundamental to the scientific revolution of the first ten years of our century.

And in this pursuit, what is it that one can ultimately encounter? Heisenberg has written that "changes in the foundations of modern science may perhaps be viewed as symptoms of shifts in the fundamentals of our existence which then express themselves simultaneously in many places, be it in changes in our way of life or our usual thought forms...." And the shift he singles out is "that for the first time in the course of history, man on earth faces only himself, that he finds no longer any other partner or foe." In science, too, "the object of research is no longer nature in itself but rather nature exposed to man's questioning, and to this extent man here also meets himself."[17]

This, then, is a main trend in the contemporary philosophy of science—resulting from a merging of the two strongest philosophical movements, existentialism and positivism—which appears to me to underlie the uneasiness expressed by many who see in science a disjunctive and alienating component. The physicist and mathematician, Hermann Weyl, expressed a similar conclusion in a moving way:

> In existentialism is proclaimed a philosophical position which perhaps is better coordinated with the structure of modern scientific knowledge than Kantian idealism in which the epistemological positions of Democri-

tus, Descartes, Galileo, and Newton appeared to have found their full philosophical expression.

... When Bertrand Russell and others tried to resolve mathematics into pure logic, there was still a remnant of meaning in the form of simple logical concepts; but in the formalism of Hilbert, this remnant disappeared. On the other hand, we need *signs*, real signs, as written with chalk on the blackboard or with pen on paper. We must understand what it means to place one stroke after the other. It would be putting matters upside down to reduce this naively and grossly understood ordering of signs in space to some purified spatial conception and structure, such as that which is expressed in Euclidean geometry. Rather, we must support ourselves here on the natural understanding in handling things in our natural world around us. Not pure ideas in pure consciousness, but concrete signs lie at the base, signs which are for us recognizable and reproducible despite small variations in detailed execution, signs which by and large we know how to handle.

As scientists, we might be tempted to argue thus: "As we know" the chalk mark on the blackboard consists of molecules, and these are made up of charged and uncharged elementary particles, electrons, neutrons, etc. But when we analyzed what theoretical physics means by such terms, we saw that these physical things dissolve into a symbolism that can be handled according to some rules. The symbols, however, are in the end again concrete signs, written with chalk on the blackboard. You notice the ridiculous circle. . . .[18]

From the beginning to the present day, science has been shaped and made meaningful not only by its specific, detailed findings but even more fundamentally by its thematic hypotheses. The reigning themata until about the mid-nineteenth century have been expressed perhaps most characteristically by the mandala of a static, homocentric, hierarchically ordered, harmoniously arranged cosmos, rendered in sharply delineated lines as in those of Copernicus' own handwriting. It was a finite universe in time and space; a divine temple, God-given, God-expressing, God-penetrated, knowable through a difficult process similar to that necessary for entering the state of Grace—by the works of the spirit and the hand. While not complete knowledge, it was as complete as the nature of things admits in this mortal life.

This representation was slowly supplanted by another, increasingly so in the last half of the nineteenth century. The universe became unbounded, "restless" (to use the fortunate description of Max Born), a weakly coupled ensemble of infinitely many separate, individually sovereign parts and events. While evolving, it is continually interrupted by random discontinuities on the cosmologi-

Introduction

cal scale as well as on the submicroscopic scale. The clear lines of the earlier mandala have been replaced by undelineated, fuzzy smears, similar perhaps to the representation of distribution of electron clouds around atomic nuclei.

And now a significant number of our most thoughtful scholars seems to fear that a third mandala is rising to take precedence over both of these—the labyrinth with the empty center, where the investigator meets only his own shadow and his blackboard with his own chalk marks on it, his own solutions to his own puzzles. And this philosophical threat is thought to be matched, as is being suggested by several articles in this issue, by the physical threat considered as originating from a blind, aimless, self-motivating, ever-growing engine of technology.

It therefore is not surprising that those who think of our culture and our persons as caught between these two tendencies find little comfort in the beauty of scientific advances, in the recital of coherence-making forces, or in promises that the lamp of science will light the way to a greater society. Not until their doubts are allayed will there be any hope for achieving the rapprochement needed for finding a more positive and valid place for science in our culture.

Acknowledgments

We have noted before the essential financial support by the National Science Foundation that made it possible to commission most of these essays and bring together most of the authors. In addition, this volume owes a great deal to a Planning Committee whose membership included Bernard Bailyn, Harvey Brooks, Franklin L. Ford, Stephen R. Graubard, Harry Levin, Talcott Parsons, W. V. Quine, and George Wald.

To Dr. Graubard, the Editor of the Academy and of the journal *Dædalus*, I wish to express my special thanks for his devoted and effective help with all the problems involved in bringing the authors to the Academy Conference and assembling a group of essays of this richness and variety. At every step he has been a wise counselor and active collaborator. If the volume contributes to an enlightened discussion of the role of science in contemporary society, it will in large measure be owing to the thought and time he has given to it in its preparation.

References

1. A. L. Kroeber and Clyde Kluckhohn, *Culture: A Critical Review of Concepts and Definitions* (New York: Alfred A. Knopf, Inc. and Random House, Inc., 1963, originally published 1952), p. 7.

2. For one of the informative articles of this kind, see the recent essay by the chairman of the U. S. Atomic Energy Commission, Glenn T. Seaborg, "Science and Humanities: A New Level of Symbiosis," *Science, Vol. 144* (June 5, 1964), pp. 1199-1203.

3. To choose examples from a safely distant past, the biologist Rudolph Virchow could write in 1847 that, while not an enemy of philosophy as such, he distrusted the "cocksure, all-knowing, self-satisfied philosophy of the '40's"; and at about the same time, the physiologist, Carl Vogt, could write calmly that one day "thoughts would have about the same relation to the brain as bile to liver and urine to the kidney." Quoted in Everett Mendelsohn, "The Biological Sciences in the Nineteenth Century: Some Problems and Sources," *History of Science, Vol. 3* (1964), pp. 43-44.

4. Unless otherwise indicated, the following quotations have been taken from the "Transcript of the Conference on A Redefinition of Culture," American Academy of Arts and Sciences.

5. In the last fifteen or twenty years, more and more of the thoughtful statesmen-scientists of the caliber of I. I. Rabi have been concerned with making scientific knowledge and attitudes more accessible to nonscientists in a way that stresses the links that do exist between science and the other parts of our culture. For a recent example, see the lengthy interview with Mr. Rabi in the *New York Times*, October 28, 1964.

   The same point of view toward the educational (as against training) function of scientific instruction is now emerging quite generally and may in due course overturn the view of many scientists of the old school who are preoccupied with a narrower, self-contained presentation of science to scientists and nonscientists alike. For recent evidences of the rise of new views, see, for example, the proceedings of two International Conferences on Education in Physics: S. C. Brown et al., (Ed.), *Why Teach Physics?* (Cambridge: The M.I.T. Press, 1964). S. C. Brown and N. Clarke, (Ed.), *International Education in Physics* (New York: Technology Press and John Wiley, 1960). Also Robert Hoopes (Ed.), *Science in General Education* (Rochester, Mich.: Oakland University Publ., 1963), and the forthcoming Report on the Boulder (Colo.) Conference of the Commission on College Physics.

6. It is salutary to see, for instance, that reports of the President's Science Advisory Committee (for example, of November 15, 1960) occasionally give expression to the conception that the health and growth of science itself is metabolically linked with the health and growth of the nonscientific professions. And conversely, the Commission on the Humanities adopted the same proposition in the opening paragraphs of its first report (April 30, 1964).

   Ours may, incidentally, be an auspicious time to take up this point of

Introduction

view, for while the absolute number of professional people in this country is expected to double in the next three or four decades, the *relative* number of persons trained in the sciences, engineering, and the humanities and arts is expected to remain almost constant, appearing to have reached an equilibrium state after several decades of relative decrease of the latter group. This expectation emerges from manpower studies such as the recent projections made by the National Science Foundation. Comparing earned baccalaureate degrees with the percentage of persons reaching age 22, the data and projections are as follows:

Year	1901-10		1962		1980		2000	
Population Age 22 (in 1000's)	16,811		2,300		4,142		5,609	
Category of Earned Baccalaureate Degrees	%	Relat. Prop.	%	Relat. Prop.	%	Relat. Prop.	%	Relat. Prop.
ALL FIELDS	1.46	100	17.76	100	26.00	100	34.00	100
HUMANITIES AND ARTS	0.48	33	2.26	13	3.41	13	4.35	13
SCIENCE	0.32	22	4.51	25	6.76	26	9.04	27
ENGINEERING	0.07	5	1.65	9	2.49	10	3.48	10

(Projections for higher degrees are roughly comparable.) Based on "Comparisons of Earned Degrees Awarded 1901-62 with Projections to 2000," *National Science Foundation Publication NSF 64-2* (January 13, 1964), p. 13.

7. Herbert Read, *To Hell with Culture, and Other Essays on Art and Society* (New York: Schocken Books, 1963), pp. 12-13.

8. To illustrate, one could take almost at random some phrases from writings such as those that happened to have come across my desk in the last few weeks. They are fairly representative. (No doubt it is in the nature of the case that the opposite type of statement—say a glowing defense of technocracy—is comparatively rarely found nowadays.)
 ". . . Scientists are the worst kind of academic politicians. . . . The narrower the field in which a man must tell the truth, the wider is the area in which he is free to lie." (Robert M. Hutchins, *Science, Scientists, and Politics,* 1963). "One current and widely held view of the future is that in 1984 'the scientists' will have elevated themselves into an elite in which they treat all the rest of us not merely as social inferiors, but as racial inferiors . . . [and that we shall be treated by them as] either pets or cattle." (This was said by one of the authors in this volume in commenting on a passage in his essay). "I believe that a free-wheeling scientific culture, self-governed and uninformed by other, external value-systems is revealing an irresponsibility that was inevitable since the days of Galileo." (Hilbert Schenck, Jr., *The Centennial Review,* 1964).

9. The aesthetic offensiveness of technological products and promises is possibly going to be the sensation that lasts the longest, since it is reinforced in so many different ways. The General Motors Futurama exhibit at the

1964 New York World's Fair somehow summed it up in one scene. On an average day, over 90,000 persons took a ride past model landscapes, including one of a deep tropical forest; meanwhile the narrator, according to the script, was saying: ". . . An equatorial land where nature flourishes more abundantly and at greater variety than in any other region of the world. (2 sec. music sweep.) Yet, nowhere else have man's productive efforts been so challenged and for so long. Now technology has found a way to penetrate and to control the wild profusion of this wonderworld. A jungle road is built in one continuous operation! First—a searing ray of light—the laser beam—cuts through the trees. Then, a giant machine—a factory on wheels—grinds up the stumps and jungle growth—sets the firm foundation—forms the surface slabs—sets them in place—and the roadway bed is paved!

"These forest highways now are bringing to the innermost depths of the tropic world the goods and materials of progress and prosperity—creating productive communities that can enter profitably the markets of the world. . . ." (Narration for Futurama Ride, General Motors Corporation, 4th revision, March 2, 1964.)

10. Herbert Read, *op. cit.*, p. 183.

11. *Memoirs of the American Academy of Arts and Sciences*, Vol. I (1785), p. viii.

12. Lewis Mumford asked in his paper, significantly entitled "Science as Technology," at the celebration of the 400th anniversary of the birth of Francis Bacon (*Proceedings, American Philosophical Society*, Vol. 105, No. 5 [October 13, 1961], p. 511): "Has the time not come, then—in technology as in every aspect of the common life—to re-examine our accepted axioms and practical imperatives, and to release science itself from the humanly impoverished and under-dimensioned mythology of power that Francis Bacon helped to promote?" But there are few hints how it might be done. And we remember that even in the absence of a well-developed technology, science has often been seen as the proper agency for social reform. Thus, as Walter F. Cannon points out in "John Herschel and the Idea of Science" (*Journal of the History of Ideas*, Vol. 22 [1961], pp. 215-239), Herschel's widely hailed *Preliminary Discourse on the Study of Natural Philosophy* (1830), published during the agitation for the Reform Bill, urged that the attitude of science can guide one to the proper approach to legislation. Herschel wrote (*Discourse*, 7):

"Why should we despair that the reason which has enabled us to subdue all nature to our purpose should (if permitted and assisted by the providence of God) achieve a far more difficult conquest; and ultimately find some means of enabling the collective wisdom of mankind to bear down on those obstacles which individual short-sightedness, selfishness, and passion, oppose to all improvements, and by which the highest hopes are continually blighted, and the fairest prospects marred."

13. In this way we may possibly have been hoping to return to the primitive or childlike state of "Einheitswirklichkeit," a primitive "Ganzheitserfahrung

Introduction

der grossen Welt," as against the later-learned "Ich-Welt," the fragmented "Partialwelt," or "Objektwelt," to use the terms of Erich Neumann in *Der Schöpferische Mensch* (Zürich: Rhein-Verlag, 1959), pp. 105-109. I have developed some of this material in more detail in *Eranos-Jahrbuch XXXI* (Zürich: Rhein-Verlag, 1962), pp. 351-425.

14. J. Larmor, in the Preface to *Science and Hypothesis* by H. Poincaré (republished New York: Dover Publications, 1952), p. xii.

15. David Hume, *The History of England, Vol. 8* (1773), p. 332.

16. K. R. Popper, *The Logic of Scientific Discovery* (New York: Basic Books, Inc., 1959), p. 317.

17. Werner Heisenberg, "The Representation of Nature in Contemporary Physics," *Dædalus*, Summer, 1958, pp. 103-104 and 105.

18. H. Weyl, *Eranos-Jahrbuch XVI* (Zürich: Rhein-Verlag, 1949), pp. 382 and 427-428.

SCIENCE
AND CULTURE

HARRY LEVIN

Semantics of Culture

"Every day, Sancho," said Don Quixote, "you are becoming less foolish and more sensible." "It must be that some of your worship's good sense is rubbing off on me," Sancho replied. "Lands which by themselves are dry and barren, if they are manured and cultivated, bring forth good fruit. I mean to say that your worship's conversation is the manure that has been spread upon the barren ground of my dry wit; the time that I have spent in your service and company has been the cultivation . . ."

And the harvest is, in short, a liberal education: the development of human personality through a systematic exposure to higher knowledge. Sancho Panza, as usual, sees farther ahead than his condescending master; his wit is truly as dry as the arid plain of La Mancha; and his earthy metaphor serves to place our problem in its elemental context. In the Spanish text of Cervantes the key-word is *cultivación*; its exact counterpart was not introduced into the English language until much later, because the word *culture* itself was still close enough to the soil so that it could designate a process rather than a product. *Culture,* imported from France as a synonym for tillage or husbandry, figures from the early fifteenth century—so unambiguously that the prefix in *agri-culture* did not need to be added for nearly two hundred years. Meanwhile English writers were not slow in extending a metaphorical application to the training of the intellect, which had been implicit from the original Latin in the Ciceronian "*cultura animi.*" The Oxford English Dictionary cites a phrase employed by Sir Thomas More in 1510: "the culture and profit of their minds." Thomas Hobbes, who equated the education of children with "the culture of their minds" in his *Leviathan,* likewise referred to culture as training of the body under the Hellenizing influence of his translation from Thucydides. Subsequent meaning seems to have been broadened and sublimated to the point where the concept could be defined, by the Oxford editors, as nothing less than "the intellectual side of civilization."

French usage came to specify the object that was cultivated; thus the article in Diderot's *Encyclopédie* is limited to *"culture des terres"*; but the *Dictionnaire de L'Académie Francaise* of 1777 subjoins to its agricultural definition a figurative sense: *". . . se dit aussi au figuré, du soin qu'on prend des arts et de l'esprit."* The word had already taken its artistic and intellectual turn when the Germans borrowed it from France; it is one of the ironies of linguistic history that *Kultur,* so heavily charged with the overtones of Teutonic nationalism, should have started out as a gallicism, and gradually changed its initial C to the more agressive K. It preserved a uniquely patriotic aura for Thomas Mann, pamphleteering during the first World War, as opposed to the forces of *Zivilisation* on the other side: music and philosophy versus rhetoric and politics. Oswald Spengler shortly thereafter could take, as his touchstone for *Kulturgeschichte,* the difference between vitalistic cultures (Greece, Germany) and petrifying civilizations (Rome, America). In Russia it would seem that the term *kul'tura* has harbored certain western associations, sometimes merely denoting material amenities or—perhaps more characteristically—the absence of them: Gogol characterizes a slovenly inn as "uncultured because of the bedbugs." One of the sharpest issues between Stalin and Trotsky was whether Soviet culture should become proletarian and regional, or whether a Marxist culture should not be classless and international. The upshot was a victory for the social control of culture, rather than for the cultural regeneration of society.

Clearly, we are involved with one of those terms that have a way of touching off controversies. The *Kulturkampf* that reverberates at the moment is one which, over the past five years, has emerged from the common rooms of Cambridge University to enlist antipathies and sympathies throughout the educational institutions of the English-speaking world. It cannot really be said to have been started by Sir Charles Snow, whose Rede Lecture of 1959 on *The Two Cultures and the Scientific Revolution* was—in its good intentions—about as blandly unexceptionable as a commencement speech. Its earnest plea for intercommunication across the high table, as between exponents of the scientific and the humanistic disciplines, had frequently been voiced before and has been since, notably by J. R. Oppenheimer. The fact that it slightly chided "the traditional intellectuals," while retaining full confidence in the scientists, explains some reactions to it *pro* and *contra* but does not invalidate its attempt to strike a bicultural equipoise. Its incontrovertible argument came under the overlooked second half of its title, its recogni-

Semantics of Culture

tion of the need to face the epochal changes wrought by science in our time. More problematic was its assumption of parity between a play of Shakespeare and the Second Law of Thermodynamics as twin tests of cultural literacy. Most educated laymen are vaguely aware of the general significance of the latter, even if they cannot recite Carnot's mathematical formula; whereas there are advanced physicists who, one gathers, have their doubts about it.

Energy was indeed transformed into heat three years afterward, when F.R. Leavis delivered his Parthian valedictory on the occasion of his retirement from a university lectureship in English at Cambridge, *Two Cultures? The Significance of C. P. Snow*. Granted that Sir Charles's views deserved to be more rigorously examined, it was not auspicious that the examiner began by pronouncing his subject "beneath contempt" on literary grounds, and proceeded to support his *ad hominem* arguments with the kind of intramural dogmatizing that has aroused the fervor of young disciples and the skepticism of professional scholars throughout the course of an embattled pedagogic career. But, when so equable and broad-minded a critic as Lionel Trilling too joins issue with Sir Charles, we realize that *The Two Cultures* deserves at least one of the names that Dr. Leavis has called it: it is a portent. Beneath its well-meaning truisms there lurks one striking novelty, which has scarcely been tested by all the discussion: the implication that science can stand by itself as a culture. This assumes not only a total separation from the humanities but also an internal unity among the sciences. Anyone who has ever engaged in academic shop-talk will admit, with regret, that it all too soon reaches limits beyond which specialists in different fields —or even in differing branches of the same field, say mathematics or physics—find it difficult to communicate. And anyone who has tried to follow the public debate on the uses of nuclear energy will find it hard to believe that all scientists share the same premises.

However, there is nothing new in the basis of the controversy, and Mr. Trilling puts it into clarifying perspective when he reminds us that it was Matthew Arnold who gave the Rede Lecture in 1882. That became his well-known essay, "Literature and Science," much better known to most students of literature than the address to which it was intended as a rejoinder, "Science and Culture," by Thomas Henry Huxley. Huxley was arguing, six years after the founding of the Cavendish Laboratory, for the introduction of the sciences into higher education, and against what he was not alone in regarding as a snobbish monopoly on the part of the classics. From a practical standpoint, and in the light of later developments, he does not sound unduly contentious when he maintains that "for the purposes of offering real culture, scientific education is at least as effective as an exclusively literary education." He does make certain naively positivistic assumptions, which scientific progression has since discarded, but which enabled Arnold to counterclaim that the layman needs to be acquainted only with the factual results of investigation and not with its experimental methods. Huxley stood closer to Arnold than to us in his Victorian belief that a secular revelation was near at hand. Insofar as he was proposing a more up-to-date version of revealed truth, he did not foresee how soon its momentary substance would be outdated by its inherent nature. The scientific revolution he heralded would make any given body of facts less significant than a continuing point of view.

Arnold was defending that position which he had made peculiarly his own in *Culture and Anarchy* (1869), where he saw culture both as a form of personal activity ("the study and pursuit of perfection") and as a collection of works to be studied ("the best which has been thought and said in the world"). He himself was committed to fighting a rear-guard action; his schoolmasterly voice got shriller as he felt himself constrained to repeat his old-fashioned lesson; and he must bear responsibility for making culture a curricular shibboleth, so that literary critics continue to bridle when they hear others using the word for purposes of their own. Hence they spurn the hand that Sir Charles has offered. They might do better by making common cause with our scientific colleagues, their fellow intellectuals after all, against the true Arnoldian enemy, the Philistines; for, if Arnold's prescription now looks as inapplicable as Huxley's overconfident materialism, his diagnosis of those anarchic influences which disorganize modern life seems clairvoyant, not to say understated. His pair of metaphors for the esthetic and cognitive objects of culture, Sweetness and Light, was derived from a hard-boiled parable by Jonathan Swift, stating the case for the Ancients in opposition to the Moderns; but the connotation has softened appreciably, like Beauty and Truth themselves when jingled into a slogan. Similarly, the adjective *cultured*—or, for that matter, *refined*, which was once synonymous with *civilized*—has been relegated to the genteel vocabulary of the women's clubs.

Mark Twain's chapter on gingerbread architecture, "Castles and Culture," in *Life on the Mississippi* expresses our native American suspicion of culture-faking, along with a grass-roots feeling that culture must be an importation to this country, more often than not from Great Britain. Consequently, such a culture-vulture as Ezra Pound can speak ambivalently of what he spells "kulchuh," while a proponent of artistic modernism, Sir Herbert Read, can entitle a book *To Hell with Culture!* Yet self-improvement has always run the risks of falling into mere imitation or sheer affectation, and genuine culture has been kept alive by migrations as well as by traditions. Cultural deracination has taken various forms, many of them vain efforts to turn back the clock. The relative simplicity of the past, contrasted with the complexity of the present by Henry Adams and other Americans, instilled a mood of historical nostalgia. Still others, for whom the contrast was primarily geographical, artists and writers in search of picturesque backgrounds, expatriated themselves to the Old World like Henry James. T. S. Eliot seems to be both the exemplar and the preceptor of this retrospective movement in the twentieth century. His *Notes Toward a Definition of Culture* (1948) glance down at the problem from a hierarchical eminence, virtually identifying it with religion and ignoring science altogether. It is doubtless a consciously ironic anachronism that these notes should have been jotted down in the aftermath of the second World War, when the next decade would be witnessing outbursts of angry young men, inroads of Americanization, and redefinitions of English culture by such levellers as Richard Hoggart and Raymond Williams.

Yet Mr. Eliot, unlike his Jamesian predecessors, has never romanticized his vista of latter-day England. His cultural orthodoxy does not necessarily fix its abode in cathedrals or castles, thatched cottages or ivy-covered ruins.

It includes all the characteristic activities and interests of a people: Derby Day, Henley Regatta, Cowes, the twelfth of August, a cup final, the dog races, the pin table, the dart board, Wensleydale cheese, boiled cabbage cut into sections, beetroot in vinegar, nineteenth-century Gothic churches and the music of Elgar. The reader can make his own list.

Mr. Eliot's personal list is a good index of the thorough degree to which he has been acculturated. For whom but an Englishman would the opening of the grouse-shooting season (the twelfth of August) be a meaningful and magic date? On the other hand, it may well take a foreign-born subject of the Queen to discern and savor the distinctively English quality in things that might seem merely undistinguished to those of us who are not connoisseurs. Of course, we could itemize their American counterparts: the World Series, the Rose Bowl, miniature golf, cheeseburgers, ice cream sundaes, supermarkets, motels. Archaeologists of the future may speculate as to what sacrificial rites or orgiastic ceremonies might have been performed in our backyard barbecues and drive-in cinemas. Much that we might consider endemic, however, has become international. Pinball machines are a craze in Tokyo; a jukebox supplies the atmosphere for a novel by Jean-Paul Sartre; and our commercial hegemony is greeted abroad as "coca-colonization." The paradoxical notion of popular culture, standing midway between folklore and mass-communication, would seem to round out the etymology of the word by bringing it down to earth again—and to the lowbrow strata underlying the highbrow superstructures. The danger lies not in such stratification when it is clearly marked, but in the confounding of layers and the compounding of those tasteless amalgams which Virginia Woolf denounced as middlebrow.

The mutual incomprehension between scientists and scholars, so long as they more or less peacefully coexist within the educational establishment, is by no means as unsettling as the gap between their aggregate minority of trained minds and the great majority of untrained minds. Here is a real disjunction between the two cultures. It has been the focus of Dwight Macdonald's candid gaze for some two decades, during which he has diametrically shifted his critical viewpoint. In "A Theory of Popular Culture," which Mr. Eliot regarded as the best alternative to his own theory, Mr. Macdonald looked hopefully ahead toward some sort of integration between—to employ his categories—the masses and the classes. In his revised analysis, "Masscult and Midcult," he demonstrates and illustrates the extent to which popularization has become vulgarization. Drawing an analogy from the modern dairy, he tells us that our culture has been homogenized; the cream that should have found its place at the top has been diluted to a thin uniformity. It is reassuring to have so able a journalist as Mr. Macdonald on our side, but we professors cannot afford to be quite so intransigent. We are too painfully conscious that the study of perfection must work its way through a sequence of imperfect states. Since education proceeds from the lower to the upper levels of thought, teachers are never shocked by the large numbers who flounder complacently somewhere in the middle. Moreover, it seems rather sentimental to posit an uppermost level so aloof and inviolate from contact that we cannot imagine how anyone ever got there.

But, with all due reservation, the seriousness of the dilemma ought not to be minimized, and statisticians attest it more loudly

Semantics of Culture

than critics. It has not eluded Dr. Gallup's monitors, who polled the American public on cultural interests a year or two ago and produced the following paradigm:

	Men	Women
Went to theater	15	20
Went to concert	10	16
Visited art museum	17	17
Read a book all the way through	42	50
Paint in oils, watercolors	6	11
Play musical instrument	10	11
Went to football game	31	17
Went bowling	27	21
Watch TV westerns	74	61
Read comic strips	49	44

Not much Shakespeare here, and no Laws of Thermodynamics. The phraseology is revealing, inasmuch as it has to be specified in words of one syllable that half of the women—and somewhat less than half of the men—read at least one book "all the way through" during the year. We should not be surprised that the curve of taste ascends from the sporadic practice of painting and music, through the desuetude of the theatrical medium, to the popularity of the comic strip and the quasi-universal appeal of the televised western film. What is most significant, if not more surprising, is that the divergence of the sexes, within the broader pattern, corresponds to our cultural dichotomy. It would appear that our mores are still tribal; our squaws go in for the arts and our braves for athletics. Additional figures show that the incidence of patronage for the theater and the concert-hall is considerably higher than average among college graduates. The correlation should be encouraging for educators, so far as it goes; and the United States government promises further encouragement through a National Culture Foundation, which should raise the Gallup percentages—and possibly reduce the sexual imbalances—by officially sponsoring performances at Washington. Sponsorship of this kind has hitherto been something less than an instrument of national policy, especially when compared to France, whose *services culturels* have proved so strategic in upholding French prestige during periods of declining political impact.

Our field of observation is one which, operationally speaking, has no little effect in determining the vantage-point of the observer. George Orwell's meat—comic postcards, advertising media—would have been Matthew Arnold's poison. High culture has traditionally been the proud possession of an elite, a mandarin class: the Arnoldian "remnant" suggests, as Oxford itself did to Arnold, defensive battles in losing causes. Its Oxonian canon has been a noble one, well worth fighting for: indubitable "Greats," *litterae humaniores,* the Greco-Roman heritage. It has been a mark of caste as well. It has constituted a good deal more than an ornamental framework of reference; for centuries it provided the West with its norms of behavior, prototypes of action, and criteria for evaluation; hence its reduction to simply another learned specialty has been a loss for culture in general. Through the greater part of European history, the collected ideas and surviving experiences of classical antiquity have functioned as the basic educational program, *paideia,* which comprised for Werner Jaeger the one, the only culture. Ethnologists were bound to regard that view as too ethnocentric. J. G. Frazer, who might be said to have annotated the classics by amassing barbarian lore, signalized a transition in this respect. If there was now a plurality of cultures, the next step was to recognize a relativism of standards. A culture-bound Euro-American might still risk the value judgment that Jaeger's Hellenes were more relevant and interesting to himself and his fellow citizens than Malinowski's Trobriand Islanders, or echo the nineteenth-century parochialism of Tennyson: "Better fifty years of Europe than a cycle of Cathay."

Nonetheless it gives one pause to read a recent and fascinating book by Peter Matthiessen, *Under the Mountain Wall,* a first-hand account of a Stone Age people living in valleys isolated by the New Guinea mountains, the Kurelu. Their tools, it seems, are utterly primitive; their clothes are all but non-existent; but, like duelling students at German universities, they like to show off their wounds. As for their weaponry, it is so ineffectual—bows and arrows and bamboo spears—that their wars are essentially sporting events; the fighters are greatly outnumbered by the spectators; and the game is called if anyone gets killed. Denizens of a nuclear-powered culture may be prompted to ask themselves Herman Melville's question, "Who ain't a cannibal?" The relativistic approach of the anthropologists is well presented through a survey issued under the auspices of the Peabody Museum at Harvard and lately reissued in paperback, *Culture: A Critical Review of Concepts and Definitions,* by A. L. Kroeber and Clyde Kluckhohn, who between them very nearly succeeded in capturing our term for social science. Moving from cultures in the plural toward a broadly central conception, they unavoidably differ from their humanistic forerunners by stressing the collective at the expense of the individual. The older outlook stressed the dynamic aspect of self-cultivation rather than the static transmission of behavioral patterns. Culture was a goal to be strenuously achieved rather than a *donnée* to be passively accepted. It was not simply a state or condition but, in the formulation of Dr. Johnson's dictionary, which quotes Richard Steele's periodical, the "Art of improvement or melioration."

Arnold and the Arnoldians, for all their ethical aims, had more and more tended to shift their emphasis from the individual's pursuit of perfection to the accumulated corpus of great books, from the act of cultivation to the cult of received opinion. The human being remains the measure of the humanities; yet they are likewise subject to those pressures, technological, economic, and otherwise, which lead us to project an image of man being acted upon rather than of man acting for himself. Under the limiting circumstances, the anthropological attitude toward culture has a good deal to recommend it, particularly as it was spelled out by E. B. Tylor in *Primitive Culture* (1871): ". . . that complex whole which includes knowledge, belief, art, law, morals, custom, and any other capabilities and habits acquired by man as a member of society." The key-phrase repeated by several of Kroeber and Kluckhohn's other spokesmen is "complex whole." That science should play a role of ever-increasing importance within this aggregation of varied concerns, none of them wholly autonomous, should almost go without saying. But that it should be, or ever become, a culture by itself is even less tenable than the proposition—which only a Wildean paradox could defend—that art alone makes culture. Futhermore, it is dangerous and divisive to interject the number two, as Sir Charles Snow duly warned us when he did so. It would be better to acknowledge the coexistence of further subcultures, a multi-cultural pluralism—or better still, *e pluribus unum,* one large heterogeneous culture, democratically split up into numerous professional lobbies.

This is a less discouraging and, I believe, a more realistic model than Sir Charles's tense polarity, and he himself is a lively illustration of the fact that the two worlds can converge. Much of that convergence, it should be noted, has taken place for him within the humane or humanistic or humanitarian sphere: in the recruitment and supervision of scientists and in fiction or drama about them. It seems to be an intrinsic feature of the situation that most of the dialogue between the sciences and the humanities must take place within the latter domain, not only because of our humanistic ignorance—which we trust such converse will modify—but because all scientists are human beings before they are anything else. We may rate the laws of thermodynamics with the plays of Shakespeare, if we are giving out posthumous Nobel Prizes for incommensurable achievements; but *King Lear* happens to be an accessible experience to everyone who knows the language, since it seems to address us so directly, while one must have learned a special language in order to appreciate Carnot. Obviously, one may experience the phenomena he has described without the benefit of his descriptions, which are laws because of their very detachment from our existence. Art is such by virtue of that characteristic which the Scholastics called quiddity, that whatness which makes an object its unique self, and which is in itself more interesting than anything that we could say about it. If applied science is what we like to call *know-how*, then theoretical science is *know-why*—another line of adverbial inquiry—and art seeks answers to the substantive questions, *what* (Montaigne's "What do I know?") and ultimately *who* (Who am I? Who are you?).

In his last book, *Literature and Science*, the late Aldous Huxley reaffirmed the viability of certain middle roads. Under the conciliatory heading, "The Art of Science," in a special issue of the (London) *Times Literary Supplement*, Sir Charles Snow has amplified and modified his earlier case. He has withdrawn his thermodynamic test. His reconsidered criterion for scientific literacy would be taken from biology rather than from physics. This would bring it somewhat closer to the layman's orbit of curiosity, and the term *culture* already has its own currency in the biological sphere. He would also now admit the possibility of a third culture, to be hopefully drawn from the social sceinces; and, if his allusion to that *tertium quid* is tactfully vague, this should help to obviate further reprisals from both the scientists and the humanists. One could be reminded of Molière's philosopher, who tried to adjudicate the conflicting claims of M. Jourdain's rival tutors, and ended by finding himself in the thick of the free-for-all. Yet there may be a mediating factor in the social scientists' acceptance of science as an ideal, which is frankly approximated much more often than it is successfully attained. Physical scientists, one suspects, could make the same admission without losing face. The actual attainment of such an ideal is, in its searchingly analytic nature, beyond the apprehension of most other men. We must and do admire it; but Sir Charles cannot have it both ways; by that very token, we cannot blame ourselves and most other men for not apprehending it.

Semantics of Culture

The structure of scientific knowledge is vertical, so that its investigators progress through research to discovery, building on the work of their predecessors and guiding their students from one stage to the next. To mark a rough geometrical distinction, it might be counterstated that the structure of humanistic knowledge is horizontal; it is so broadly based and so widely spread that everyone must touch it at some point, however rudimentarily. To think of the two modes of knowledge as existing on the same plane is, in consequence, something of a fallacy. Their relationship could be more consistently outlined by a pyramidal diagram. At its base would be programs in General Education, which colleges have developed to counterbalance the mounting drives toward specialization. "Woe to the specialist who is not a pretty fair generalist," Samuel Butler admonished, "and to the generalist who is not also a bit of a specialist." Insofar as the scientists are the specialists, they need the generality of the humanities; but there is another sense in which the reverse may be true, and the specializing humanists need to come to terms with the mechanisms of the universe. Such adjustments and corrections are mutually possible as long as the several branches of learning are represented on the same faculties. The very words we use can either unite or divide, and their histories are records of unification or subdivision. Thus the German rubric, *Wissenschaft,* subsumes all lines of scholarly inquiry and confers the nominal status of a science on them.

Understandably, the Latin *scientia* did not differentiate between book-learning and the other kinds: arts and sciences nestled together, and were interchangeably labelled, in the medieval Trivium and Quadrivium. Nor did its English derivative until well into the eighteenth century, when *science* was more narrowly applied to what had previously figured as natural or experimental philosophy; and it was not until the mid-nineteenth century that its practitioners would be singled out as *scientists*. These semantic shifts run parallel to currents of ideas, which in turn reflect the changing enterprise of learning as a whole, and can be most aptly exemplified by a glance at that characteristic British institution, the Royal Society of London for Improving Natural Knowledge. Although the unabridged title invokes the traditional concept of culture as improvement, it is deflected toward a fresh range of subject-matter. Accordingly, a charter member, John Evelyn, could write of "cultivating the sciences and advancing useful knowledge." Evelyn has survived as a man of letters; so has Samuel Pepys through his diary, though he belonged as a government official; and their fellow members, John Dryden and Abraham Cowley, were unabashedly poets. If we reexamine the Society's earliest rosters, we are likely to be struck by the large proportion of members who would not be retrospectively classified as scientists. Christopher Wren would not be, though he amply qualified as Astronomer Royal. Whereas Robert Boyle and Isaac Newton, who unquestionably would be, were theologians as well as experimentalists.

Bishop Sprat, in his contemporaneous *History of the Royal Society* (1667), testifies that its membership was to draw upon "all the professions"—plus, above all, non-professionals, "gentlemen free and unconfined." It would be their comprehensive purpose "to make faithful records of all the works of Nature or Art which can come within their reach." They were thereby expected to realize the well-rounded ideals of Renaissance Humanism, and in particular the proposals of Francis Bacon, for organizing and centralizing all the provinces of knowledge. But the very success of their specialized investigations was destined to exert a decentralizing force. Their *Philosophical Transactions* grew less and less philosophic, until in 1887 they were subdivided into a physico-mathematical and a strictly biological series. In the meantime, two other cultural organizations have separately and belatedly appeared to fill in their respective gaps: the Royal Academy of the Arts in 1786, the British Academy for the scholarly disciplines in 1902. The American Academy of Arts and Sciences should be congratulated for continuing to foster a meeting of minds across the broadest area. The American Philosophical Society has also retained its wide interdisciplinary scope. Our government-sponsored institutions divide into the National Academy of Science, on one hand, and the Academy-Institute of Arts and Letters on the other. France's immortal Academy is mainly literary, though it includes a few scientists and generals, while its surrounding Institute embraces four lesser academies, preponderantly humanistic: *Sciences, Sciences Morales et Politiques, Inscriptions et Belles-Lettres,* and *Beaux-Arts*.

The Royal Society, founded a generation after the Académie Française, never attempted to exercise a surveillance over artistic tastes; but it did commence with a comparable interest in, and a decisive influence on, the state of the language. This is a fundamental aspect of culture, though it resists legislation, and in our country it has been left to private entrepreneurs. Their latest contribution, the third edition of the Merriam-Webster *New International Dictionary*, has provoked a war of words involving a conflict between

Semantics of Culture

scientific and humanistic principles. The editors have viewed themselves as linguistic scientists, and construed their task as descriptive rather than prescriptive: a tabulation of living speech without regard for historical precedent or normative usage. In basing their canvass so largely on commonplace examples, where diction tends to be imprecise and vocabulary limited, they may have diminished the expressive capacity of the American English they expound. Their definitions of culture, which are generous enough to include "beauty culture," are illuminated by a single quotation from a twentieth-century historian. However, no dictionary could transfix a word which casts so many-sided a penumbra of signification, or chart the vicissitudes of an idea which has stimulated such thoughtful and forceful reactions on the part of such diverse witnesses. To scan their testimony is to step back a pace or two from history and from society, to pass in review the determining conditions of man's relation to them and theirs to him.

To step back a few paces farther would be to contemplate the drastic changes that underlie those conditions, to speculate upon contingencies where the imagination is hard put to keep up with advancing technology. Naturally we think of books as the principal medium of culture, and our thinking is framed by the five-hundred-year span between ourselves and the invention of printing. The manuscript culture that preceded it necessarily differed in intellectual structure, and functioned on a much narrower social base. Today book culture, with all that it opened up for the literate individual, seems to have reached—if not passed—its apogee. For the moment, thanks to the paperback explosion, its instruments are more widely and cheaply available than ever; and yet this facile plenitude adds to the problems of housing and handing on knowledge. The libraries of the future will not be designed to foster erudite browsing; their stores of televised microfilm will perforce be controlled through self-limiting catalogues. As for the introductory stages of learning, if their guide is to be the teaching machine, the consequences must be at once more uniform and more circumscribed. Culture is increasingly conceived as a hoard set aside by man, to be tapped at the dictates of occasion. Man himself becomes less and less a culture-bearer, more and more a codifier of programs and manipulator of electronics. Harbingers of audio-visual culture, such as Marshall McLuhan, promise us gains that will more than offset the incidental losses. Willingly we cede to them the mantle of prophecy.

JAMES S. ACKERMAN

On *Scientia*

IN THE Middle Ages, an "art" was a technique, and the seven liberal "arts" that constituted the core of education were not so much areas of knowledge as tools for getting and dispensing knowledge: the Quadrivium (arithmetic, music—because it taught proportion and harmony—geometry, astronomy) for penetrating into the structure of things, and the Trivium (grammar, rhetoric, logic) for representing the structure in words. Disciplines such as painting, architecture, and what we now call music were relegated to the inferior category of mechanical arts; they were considered merely sensuous and exclusively manual. To a medieval philosopher, our scientists trained, say, only in mathematics and astronomy, and our humanists only in language and logic, would appear to have no culture at all; they all would be half educated. But he would have been more puzzled by our curious concept of the "Arts" and "Sciences," because he would regard *scientia* as a higher learning to which the arts might lead a gifted mind. In his world, every trained man was an "artist," but only a chosen few were "scientists."

That medieval concept of *scientia* can be applied to education in our time, assuming that there are indeed two distinct categories of knowing that can be called Art and Science—but in the sense in which the Scholastics understood them, not in their current usage. Art, then, is to be read as "technique" (as in the word "artifact"), and *scientia* as something like "the structure of ideas" (or "images"). The concept of the image—a term embracing verbal, visual, and aural inventions—modifies the medieval definition by recognizing the more elevated function assigned since the Renaissance to certain "mechanical" arts such as painting and musical composition. So every discipline and form of expression—physics, anthropology, painting—has its technique—of the laboratory, the field, the studio—and its *scientia;* and every student and apprentice is trained as a technician with the hope that he may also join the company of creative formulators.

There were many arts in the medieval system, but only one *scientia;* that was not necessarily because the amount and the complexity of information was less than it is now, but rather because learning was ordered by a different concept of culture. Since the Middle Ages, the content and methods of learning have become progressively more complex and differentiated, and the number of disciplines has increased. The process began at the time when it became permissible once again to trust the evidence of the senses, expecially the eyes, as well as the analytic faculty of the intellect, and ever since that time artists and empirical scientists have been discovering new worlds. Those worlds were so diverse that only at the beginning could they be held together in a single mind. Leonardo da Vinci, the first modern empiricist, was also the last universal man. For him the techniques of painting and of natural history were identical—they all could be acquired by looking with bare eyes. One can be "universal" only in an environment where the same techniques are applicable in a number of different fields. As soon as the observations of natural scientists passed beyond the range of unaided vision (with telescopes, microscopes and other instruments), they stopped being essential, or accessible, to visual artists.

With the refinement of techniques there naturally came an accelerating increase in their number and intricacy, and consequently in the specialization of technicians. The trend of this evolution has been inevitable, and it has been undeservedly deplored by some "humanists" whose attack has missed its proper target. What warrants criticism is not the number or the intricacy of techniques, but the narrowness of technicians confined within a specialty. Since narrowness could occur as well in a culture with fewer specialties than ours, we could not hope to regain Leonardo's universality— even if it were thought possible and wise to try—just by reducing the amount of skill and information we have acquired or are now acquiring. If there are shortcomings in our culture, they are not the fault of our skills.

What the critics of specialization really mean is that techniques gain an exaggerated position in a culture insufficiently controlled by *scientia. Scientia* is the controlling form of every discipline, within which techniques are exercised and through which their development and change should be guided. In the natural sciences and humanities it would be a system of hypotheses and theories; in the arts, it would be what we call the principles of a style. But this is not the whole, for a "controlling form" implies something fixed, and no discipline can stay alive unless its system or style constantly is being refreshed by imaginative innovation. So *scientia* must be an evolving structure.

Although each discipline has its *scientia*, and disciplines have multiplied in number, the unity of the whole so apparent in the medieval period has not been fragmented. In every generation—today as in the past—one embracing structure of images has given form to the *scientia* of the vital disciplines of the time.

As Scholastic *scientia* had a characteristic form that was similar in Gothic architecture and Thomist theology, so the age of Italian Humanism was characterized by a particular structure of thought that made ancient texts and physical remains the guide not only to learning and art but to the form in which they were to be conveyed. It was not the copying of ancient texts, statues and buildings, nor references to Hercules and Venus that distinguished the *scientia* of Humanism—because mere content belongs in the category of technique—but rather the image that artists and scholars had of reality that made the ancient exemplar their most compelling model. That image they shared with the natural scientists of their time. There are pictures of lecturers on anatomy at Padua, standing in a pulpit and reading impressively out of their manuscript of Galen, while a handyman cuts up the corpse; those professors would not have dreamed of attempting to improve on Galen, because to them the ancient word was sacred. So it was for students of Ptolemy; opposition to the Copernican system came not just from reactionary theologians but from most of the learned Humanist astronomers. On this account, Humanism has been set down as a disastrous ambience for science, which is a mistaken notion. The work of the Humanists who discovered, edited and commented on ancient texts such as those of Aristotle or Lucretius was to become the springboard for theoretical activity. The empirical counter-reaction to Humanism represented by Leonardo, Vesalius (the first anatomist at Padua to be portrayed with messy hands), and Bacon would have exhausted itself soon enough without ancient models for formulating theory. It is an engaging commentary on Humanism that in the field of music, where no ancient sources survived, models were invented out of scattered literary references, and these inventions constituted an important part of the monodic movement that prepared for the development of opera.

On Scientia

In the Renaissance, ancient authority and empirical investigation were incompatible; the triumph of the seventeenth century was the creation of a *scientia* in which the two might be reconciled. In the figural arts the tired late Renaissance formulas were enlivened by a theory of generalization or idealization in the classic tradition, but based on close observation of nature. The same shift in direction is noticeable in Shakespeare's reinterpretation of his Italian forerunners. In the natural sciences the situation was similar; significant advances were now made by theoreticians who put generalized principles in the foreground without compromising the empirical foundation. In science the ancient theories themselves were abandoned, but the spirit of theorizing survived, and even the structure. Nobody was more classical in his *scientia* than Descartes; this classicism—and the symmetry and logic with which it was presented—puts him in many ways closer to Corneille and Poussin than to the Baconian observers of the time.

The danger of identifying the *scientia* of the nineteenth and twentieth centuries is shown by the way those who make the attempt usually confuse subject matter or tools with basic structures. Impressionist painting is compared to the study of the physics of light, or Cubism to relativity theory, because the object is viewed from several points of view simultaneously. A more recent cliché is the juxtaposition of abstract pictures with photographs taken with an electron microscope or in a cloud chamber; they often look quite similar, which proves, perhaps, that artists as well as other people look at *Scientific American* and science paperbacks. But that has little to do with community in the structure of thought, which is revealed at a more abstract level. For example, it is not just in the natural sciences that what once were described in common-sense terms as discrete bodies or objects have come to be described in terms of interactions—that, for instance, observers of the biochemical interaction of the human organism with the environment speak of the body as a process rather than an entity. Similarly, in twentieth-century abstract painting, the representation of distinct common-sense objects located in a measurable pictorial space has given way to the invention of complex interplays of colors, lines, planes, and shapes which eliminate the polarity of object and space. The scientist and the artist both are interested in relationship functions; they have been asking how the elements with which they deal behave with respect to one another rather than what they "really" are, or how they appear to be in the common-sense world.

JAMES S. ACKERMAN

This attitude is shared by twentieth-century philosophers, who, for all their differences, agree in discarding the absolutes of traditional philosophy in order to study people and ideas in action and interaction. The "ordinary language" philosophers analyze the implications in everyday statements—not asking, for example, "What is Beauty?" but rather "What do we mean when we say that such-and-such is beautiful?" The existentialist starts from the proposition that man is a being in whom existence precedes essence; he is, so to speak, defined by what he does. This common trait of our *scientia* is further revealed in the tendency of recent historical writing to examine the interaction of social, economic, and intellectual forces rather than the circumscribed units such as nations, reigns, or individuals favored in historical literature a century ago.

Another aspect of our *scientia* is a concern with the proposition that the nature or state of the observer affects the definition of the thing observed, a principle that has become as significant in modern physics as in psychology. The systematic study of perception, which has taught us how much our experience colors or alters what we see, has in turn affected disciplines such as the criticism of art by establishing essential ties between the observer and the thing observed. The breakdown of the barriers between observer and object has affected the arts themselves, as when the audience enters the arena of the actor in the theater, or, as more recently in only partially planned "Happenings," in which the viewer participates; or when sculpture becomes "environmental," sharing and invading the locus of everyday action; or, again, when the composer of a musical composition instructs the performer to select the order in which its passages are to be performed.

Some of these examples suggest that scholarship, when creative, partakes as much of *scientia* as do scientific theory and the fine arts. But, paradoxically, what scholars in the humanities and social sciences call "scientific method" is nothing more than the technical apparatus that the work of profound scholars has in common with pedantic Ph.D. theses. For many scholars, science is an enterprise of the laboratory in which the dominant feature is technical precision—a precision which scholars respect and strive to emulate. But this limited view of the scientific method helps to block any unitary view of our culture. We shall never come together in the laboratory or among the philological footnotes; only in the atmosphere of *scientia* shall we find the exceptional fraternity of creative processes that constitutes a cultural communications center.

On Scientia

The significant distinction in our culture, then, is not between the arts and the sciences, but between the limited technicians and the creators of images. In many respects the creators can communicate with one another more easily and certainly more profitably—even in radically different disciplines—than with technicians in their own fields. Thus communication on the level of images may demand some intelligence and wisdom, but it does not require encyclopedic knowledge; the most elementary introduction to principles in one discipline can stimulate invention in another. One may discover in an essay, a poem, even in a paragraph by someone in an unfamiliar field an image that gives shape to some inchoate concept that could not have been formulated otherwise. It is not even essential that the source of such inspiration be properly or fully understood in the terms established by experts in its own discipline; it is enough that it should inspire.

If *scientia* were exclusively within the province of those exceptionally endowed for creative production by heredity and disposition, we might profitably produce an army of technicians to serve that élite. But the fact that contact with *scientia* can enrich many of those unable to contribute significantly to it—that its light guides the evolution of techniques—demands a democratic education, and one better directed toward mutual understanding than are the present systems.

II

A useful product of these observations on the nature of culture would be to prompt discussions on the validity of assumptions underlying our educational systems, and particularly those of higher education. In a period when criticism from both the teaching profession and the public is bringing about rapid, if largely directionless, reforms in primary and secondary education, the universities have responded to no more purposeful forces than the pressures of increased enrollments and government subsidies; they have been evolving by drifting. To give meaning to the course of our higher learning is a task far beyond the scope of these observations; but because it is in the nature of educational institutions to change by evolution rather than by revolution, it may be useful to suggest means neither radical nor novel by which the pattern of our education could be gently rearranged into one more consistent with the cultural structure I have described. The suggestions that follow do not presume to resolve basic problems of education; they frame a curriculum within which the discussion of such problems might be encouraged.

Scientia is inaccessible except through mastery of technique. So today, as in medieval Europe, one must be grounded in the "arts," or at least in one of them. Starting with the technique in a particular discipline, students should proceed as far as their capacities admit toward a grasp of the *scientia* in their fields, and then on to a comparative study of other fields at whatever level they can manage. Since technique is the starting point, we may welcome an increase in the number of technicians—simply because it lessens the chances that potential creators may be lost.

Because education in a democratic society seeks to provide equal opportunity without assuming equal capacity, we should continue to educate in such a way that the path from every level of instruction to the next above remains open—that all students may have a view of the highest achievement in their field, and that the few who are willing and able to contribute to its *scientia* may encounter no barriers. This is especially important for training at lower levels, where technical indoctrination can be stifling if the ultimate purposes are unclear, as in the study of a language without an accompanying insight into the culture and land from which it springs.

Existing programs of higher education in the United States have tended to reverse what I believe to be the proper process by providing a broad general scope at the base—usually by means of "surveys" of the humanities and sciences—succeeded by progressively narrowing specialization at the advanced level and in the graduate schools. This design reflects a confusion of the scientific attitude with mere technique; at the same time, it represents a practical response to pressures of mass education at the college level and acquiescence in an inferior secondary education. But its weakness consists in underestimating the fact that students without the basic skills of any intellectual discipline are inhibited in their capacity to grasp intellectual constructions, although they may be adept at recording and re-presenting ideas.

This design reflects a confusion of the scientific attitude with mere technique; it tends to separate rather than to bring together the most intensively trained scholars. In offering panoramas of knowledge primarily to beginning students, it gives the colleges a responsibility that might be relinquished to the secondary schools and dissipates some of the potential capacity of college and university

On Scientia

faculties to aid more advanced students to synthesize their experiences in education.

A program more consistent with the pattern of culture proposed here would offer beginning students an intensive training in the basic methodology of cultural disciplines such as the historical, the philosophical-critical, the physical or biological sciences, together with the specifics of a particular specialty and such ancillary skills as languages or mathematics. The advanced student, having fulfilled most of the requirements in his special field, would be encouraged or required to attend courses in disciplines and subjects both allied to it and related to the *scientia* of our time—the latter being investigations of the abstract and concrete problems and conditions of contemporary culture. In studying and in writing for these high-level courses, the student would be as well equipped as possible to bring to his work skills and knowledge gained in his special field that enable him to confront with real perception challenging problems in other fields. It would be the purpose of the last years of his education to help him to coordinate the disparate strains of his training into an intellectual and ethical position.

These proposed changes are relevant chiefly to liberal arts programs in the universities. They also can be meaningful in other areas of education. Junior college curricula, which now constitute a weak reflection of the general education proffered in universities, do not provide their graduates either with a skill or with sufficient grasp of *scientia* to continue their education independently after graduation. If the universities were to adopt the new curricula, the junior colleges could offer two-year technical programs, graduates of which might choose skilled and semi-skilled employment in their fields or, if qualified, transfer to a university, where they would benefit from the summations that would become one of the purposes of the final years. Similarly, certain professional curricula in the universities such as engineering, pre-medicine, and education might benefit from deferring their general education requirements to the close of the college curriculum, where their students, if not specifically prepared for work in the humanities or the social or natural sciences, should be more mature and practiced in rigorous methods applicable in part to the study of other disciplines.

Such a simple reassembly cannot produce radical reforms, but a structure with its base at the bottom and its spire on top would appear more purposeful to both teachers and students. The increased awareness of purpose should reduce frustrations and make instruction and learning more economical, more exciting, and more effective.

In suggesting ways of introducing students to the *scientia* of our time, I have not accounted sufficiently for the evolutionary nature of culture. Because *scientia*, like technology, is perpetually in a state of becoming, an education that merely indoctrinated students in the structure of images at a given moment would be passive and conservative—the mirror or the servant of dominant intellectual forces. This education ought to be rather their critic and generator, and that is a demanding mission. The effort required to direct higher education into new paths always has imparted to its institutions inertial forces powerful enough to carry prevailing images far beyond their useful life span, to the point at which their obsolescence is evident to even the stuffiest academic minds.

Furthermore, the prevailing *scientia* not only may be hostile to images different from those it promotes, but consciously or unconsciously it may organize its education so that criticism is frustrated. This deficiency would explain some of the paradoxes of contemporary higher education, which, in being designed to promote empiricism and technological specialization, incidentally manages to stifle philosophical synthesis and ethical speculation. In proceeding from a broad survey at the base to a narrow parochialism at the apex, the university curriculum not only trains efficient specialists. It also protects obsolete scientism from being subjected to effective criticism by obstructing from the advanced student a commanding view of the topography of his culture.

At the root of these problems is the preoccupation of twentieth-century *scientia* with function and process, and with the nature of observation, which is a cause as well as a result of the insecurities of our time. It has brought extraordinary progress in science and scholarship, and radical changes in the arts, but it has not sought or promoted solutions to the major dilemmas of human existence and behavior, nor even provided the means of assessing the value of its own achievements. It is because of its concern with process that our *scientia* has exalted the technician and thus actually has blurred the distinction between technique and *scientia* that I am attempting to revive. The reaction of intellectuals to a *scientia* without values has been increasingly restive but—because the issues have been wrongly defined—quite undirected and often merely nostalgic. It

On Scientia

erupts occasionally in attacks on science and scientific method—attacks that ignore the underlying similarity in the attitudes of the scientist, the artist, and the humanist-scholar.

If our *scientia,* and the education that sustains it, deserves criticism, it is unlikely to receive it from without, since it encompasses all creative thought in our time. It will not give way to a competing system but will evolve, as *scientia* always has, by generating its own antitheses and responses. For this reason, I am convinced that the healing of present illnesses in our culture can be effected only by those who are committed to it and versed in it, as well as in its traditions, and not by those who reject our most distinguished and characteristic products—the work of the Wittgensteins, de Koonings, Beckets—on the grounds that they somehow lack the old humanistic values.

I should like to acknowledge my debt to the writings of Kenneth Boulding, Gerald Holton, Herbert Marcuse, Alexander Meiklejohn, and of the teacher who introduced me to the *scientia* of the past, Erwin Panofsky. The criticism of participants at the Academy Conference, particularly Talcott Parsons and Frederick Burkhardt, prompted significant changes in the argument.

EDMUND R. LEACH

Culture and Social Cohesion: An Anthropologist's View

MY PURPOSE is to show not only what culture is but also what it is not, to show how culture stands opposed to nature and how the adjective "social" mediates between the two. Some twelve years ago two very distinguished anthropologists devoted a large volume to the question of what the concept "culture" means to the various disciplines within the larger field of the social sciences.[1] They cited over four hundred different authors and at least one hundred thirty definitions. I shall not compete with such erudition, yet some formal definition is essential, since at the start we need a verbal formula to clear the ground.

The standard technical meaning of the word "culture" in the social sciences is that given by Tylor in the opening paragraph of his *Primitive Culture* (1871):

Culture, or civilization . . . is that complex whole which includes knowledge, belief, art, law, morals, custom, and any other capabilities of man as a member of society.

It is here assumed that in the stereotyped behaviours of any human being we may readily distinguish that which has been learned (cultural) from that which is instinctive (natural).

The principal variant of this definition is one which makes culture embrace human artifacts as well as human behaviours and beliefs. The emphasis in this case is upon the human heritage as a whole; thus, "Culture comprises inherited artifacts, goods, technical processes, ideas, habits, and values."[2] The artifacts, the behaviours and the beliefs are all plainly interdependent, but to avoid ambiguity I shall here use "culture" in Tylor's narrower sense, while distinguishing the material part of the cultural heritage as "the products of culture."

Both definitions are linked to a dogmatic belief that the specific peculiarity which distinguishes a human being from any other kind of living creature is his dependence upon learned behaviour; for man alone, instinctive endowment is not by itself sufficient to ensure survival. Actually, the gulf between man and the rest of nature is in this respect much less clearly marked than is sometimes supposed. Social insects, dolphins, birds, primates and sundry other creatures are all dependent to some degree upon learning, but, quite plainly, this faculty is of much greater significance to man than it is to any other creature.

Because man must learn in order to survive he is more dependent upon his seniors than are creatures with a more elaborate instinctive apparatus; correspondingly the lack of dependence upon instinct provides man with an unparalleled adaptability to circumstance. But while man is dependent upon culture, culture is dependent upon man. Culture can survive only where one human generation can transmit its accumulated knowledge to the next.

The mechanism for such transmission is the use of language, and a language of any kind, whether verbal or behavioral, entails a highly complex process of symbolic representation. This is the basis for such definitions as: "Culture is all behaviour mediated by symbols."[3]

Here again we cannot draw any sharp distinction between behaviour and things. Most of the information which is the heritage of a culture is stored in physical objects (for example, our books and computer tapes), but these objects can serve as a store of knowledge only when there are human beings who know how to decode the symbols which they contain. Every civilization has a task of information retrieval, of retaining access to information already accumulated in the past. *We* see this as a mechanical problem—how to keep track of vast accumulations of printed data—but the simplest pre-literate society has analogous difficulties. Travellers have often remarked of Australian aborigines that they seem to "read the desert like a book," and this is a very literal truth. Such knowledge is not carried in any man's head, it is in the environment. The environment is not a natural thing; it is a set of interrelated percepts, a product of culture. It yields food to the aborigine but none to the white traveller because the former perceives food where the latter sees only inedible insects.

The bewilderment of many "ordinary" men in the environment of modern science is very similar. The environment is meaningless because we do not understand the code which would give perceptual order to our mechanical desert. This is an important aspect of our general problem. We have modified our own environment to an exceptional degree with exceptional rapidity, so that very few of us can assimilate the stores of information that are embedded in its categories. The countryman is "lost" in the Great City; the factory worker feels alienated amid the automated marvels which provide his livelihood.

Thus culture is not an attribute of individuals, but of men in a particular society in a particular man-made environment. Conceptually we can distinguish the culture from the society and both from the environment, but each member of the triad is dependent upon the other two. This is just as true of simple societies where the material products of culture are slight as it is of societies like our own where they are enormously complex.

This reference to our own culture as opposed to that of the Australian aborigines suggests that cultures are distinct species of things, like cats and dogs, and this has been the prevailing tradition both in social science and political philosophy. Indeed, although culture is specifically defined as that which is *not* part of the genetic endowment, we repeatedly encounter authors who write as if cultural difference signified difference of "race." This fallacy provides the mythical justification for all varieties of national hostility and "inter-racial" conflict.

For more than two thousand years educated Europeans have presumed that the gulf between civilized man and the barbarian is absolute. For Aristotle there were the Greeks of the City States and there were the others (*ethnē*).[4] These others were slaves by nature; their inferiority was intrinsic and the forms of their society wholly devoid of interest. Because these others were only imperfect men, or perhaps not even men at all, they might be enslaved, exploited or exterminated without regard to moral justification. It is a long and gruesome story which trails on through the centuries: the Spanish in Mexico, the Dutch in Java, the British in Tasmania, the Americans on the Frontier, the Belgians in the Congo, the Italians in Ethiopia, Hitler and the Jews, with doubtless still more to come. But although the idiom of hostility is in terms of the "racial" (that is, *natural*) inferiority of the persecuted, the behaviour itself is strictly *cultural*. In all cases the exterminators have been, by their own reckoning, civilized men of a most superior sort, and such civilized men always conduct their mutual affairs according to strict and elegant rules. It is only when the inferior party is considered uncivilized that rules go by the board. But then, if my culture informs me that my neighbour is vermin and not man, I feel free to exterminate him as if he were a rat; indeed, it may be my duty to do so, as Hitler clearly felt.

If we are shocked by such matters it is we who are unusual; in the course of history it has been absolutely normal to distinguish "true men" (people like us) from "half men" (people who are not like us because of their colour, their religion, their economic condition). In our own contemporary culture the most dangerous disjunctions are still those which employ the myth of racial difference as a badge of discrimination.

The view that culture is a social heritage has often led to the misleading idea that culture exists independently of those who inherit it. Anthropologists who approach their data in this way conceive of culture as made up of a list of items each of which has a separate distribution across the face of the globe. The content of a culture is then the localized assemblage of such items, self-selected on a random basis as the consequence of historical accident. Many serious scholars have thought of culture in precisely this way. It is a thesis which conveniently reinforces the author's feeling that he is intellectually superior to the others whom he studies. For it is noticeable that the doctrine that the occurrence of a particular cultural feature is the outcome of non-rational accident is applied particularly to primitive and antique societies, seldom to our own. "We" act in a rational manner; it is only the "others" who are ignorant slaves to irrational custom. It is the Aristotelian dichotomy all over again.

But the alternative proposition, that all culture is rationally designed and functionally integrated, is not easy to sustain. This doctrine, too, has had its followers; it was propounded quite dogmatically by Malinowski in a series of writings published around 1930. The essence of the argument is quite simple. By Tylor's definition, culture is the sum of "the capabilities of man as a member of society," and it is plain nonsense to treat these capabilities as if they were free-floating entities which could wander about independently of either man or society. Items of culture and the products of culture are not just items and objects, they are complex usages; and it is the usage as a whole which should be our concern when we study culture. A Trobriand Island canoe is not just a material thing, it is a manner of use which entails knowledge of sailing techniques, of stability and buoyancy:

The canoe also has its sociology. Even when manned by a single person it is owned, produced, lent, or hired, and in this the group as well as the individual is invariably implicated. But usually the canoe has to be handled by a crew and this entails the complex sociology of ownership, of division of functions, of rights and obligation.[5]

For Malinowski the study of a culture meant the study of a total way of life. He was fascinated by the intricacy with which different facets of social existence interlock with one another, and he argued that the way to apprehend this totality is to keep constantly in mind that it is by means of culture that men preserve themselves alive. But his stress upon the mutual interdependence of different aspects of culture led him to represent the working of society as a delicately balanced piece of clockwork. Everything fits together perfectly, nothing is superfluous, and, by implication, everything is for the best in the best of all possible worlds. This hardly corresponds to our ordinary experience.

But if Malinowski's approach seems unduly idealistic, we need to recognize that the functionalist assumptions on which it is based represent a long standing and still persisting tradition in the social sciences. Durkheim held quite explicitly that cultural incoherence corresponds to a pathological condition of society, and he invented a special term *anomie* to represent the psychological condition which, in his view, such disjunction evoked. We need to be on our guard against any such *a priori* evaluation. Cultural disjunction may be uncomfortable; it is not necessarily evil.

The large-scale facts are not difficult to discover. It is quite feasible to map the continuities and discontinuities of the different aspects of culture. We can, for example, make a map of linguistic variation, another of the continuities of kinship, another of the continuities of political jurisdiction, another of religious cult, another of technical process, another of types of legal institution, another of styles in art, and so on indefinitely, sorting out as many or as few facets of the cultural whole as we choose. If the "integrated culture" thesis were valid, we should then expect that the discontinuities of these maps would coincide. As a general rule such is not the case.

This is an important discovery. If functional integration is not a normal attribute of primitive society, it is most unlikely to be a normal attribute of our own. We must dissociate ourselves from the widely held mythology which insists that the pursuit of concord is the only objective for the virtuous ruler.

The belief that concord and harmony are the basic requirements of the "good" society has had a long history and is very congenial to a certain type of conservative mind. But of course there are other possibilities. From Hegel onwards, a wide variety of European thinkers have held, not only that conflict and discord are normal, but that the continuous dialectic by which conflict is temporally mediated only to provoke immediately a new antithesis is the very essence of the social process. If this be so, then the features of incoherence and disjunction which are distinguishable in any cultural system are to be looked upon as the points of maximum growth. In this view a developing social system cannot possibly be fully integrated; there are always bound to be areas of innovation and areas of decay, both of which will seem out of place in the short-term contemporary context. Moreover, since the specific task of the scientist is to be constantly devising cultural innovations, the most obvious disjunctions in our own system are always likely to have the appearance of having been "caused by" science.

Very few social scientists can observe their own society with detachment; evaluations of symptoms of social change are especially likely to be prejudiced by political predisposition. The conservative-minded tend to equate all nonconformity with delinquency; for men of the Left non-conformity is the only virtue. In some ways the social scientist's own researches only make matters worse. A cohesive cultural situation is much easier to study than a disjunctive one; so the social scientist's field studies become biased towards the isolated, the conservative, and the traditional. This lends added force to the myth that our present circumstances of rapid change and cultural incoherence are thoroughly abnormal. They are not.

At this point I must draw attention to a difference between English and American academic categories. American anthropologists have tended to think that their main concern is with the history of particular cultural configurations, and some are still prepared to theorize on a grand scale about the processes of cultural evolution, a style which has been out of fashion in England for over sixty years. The code label for such pursuits is *cultural anthropology.* The equivalent specialist in England calls himself a *social anthropologist.* The latter claims that his field of interest is the sociology of social networks and small-scale social systems. He concerns himself with history only at an empirical level. If historical evidence is available he uses it, but he refuses to speculate. The word *culture* seldom appears in his vocabulary at all. But although the American cultural anthropologist and the British social anthropologist pose as quite different kinds of academic animal, they are commonly engaged on very much the same kind of problem. As Firth puts it:

If society is taken to be an organized set of individuals with a given way of life, culture is that way of life. If society is an aggregate of social relations then culture is the content of those relations. Society emphasises the human component, the aggregate of the people and the relations between them. Culture emphasises the component of accumulated resources, immaterial as well as material, which the people inherit, employ, transmute, add to and transmit.[6]

In the immediate practical context of any social investigation, the social and the cultural are two aspects of the same thing, and, although serious social scientists have argued otherwise,[7] I must insist most emphatically that the two frames can never usefully be considered in isolation from one another.

This is a most important point, for whatever the place of science in contemporary culture may be, we need to understand that contemporary culture has no separate existence from contemporary society. Science and the products of science do not "exist" in themselves; they exist only because they are given names and uses by members of society. I can best make this point by taking a bizarre example.

In terms of our original definition, "knowledge of radio communications" is an item of culture, a recent scientific innovation. In the form of transistor radio it has now penetrated into the furthest corners of the primitive world, a striking example of cultural "diffusion." Yet we delude ourselves if we suppose that we have here a free-moving isolate which exists quite independently of its social matrix. A colleague recently observed a pagan ritual in central Borneo. The procedures were exactly according to the book; the proper carvings had been made, the proper spells were being recited, the proper sacrifice was in train; but unexpectedly the whole procedure was accompanied by the sound of a jazz band from Radio Malaya. But the radio was not just a gratuitous addition, it had been incorporated; the magical voice of the magical machine had become an essential part of the ritual.

In an objective sense, a transistor radio is the same thing whether it is in a shop window in New York or in a Dayak longhouse in Borneo, but it is in an entirely different cultural category in the two situations. Failure to understand this fact has led to endless confusion. Anthropologists often write as if cultural items had "natural" and "unnatural" contexts; in its natural context a cultural detail has a concordant fit, in an unnatural context the same detail will promote "incoherence and disjunction." But this is fallacy. Cultural details are not concordant or discordant in any absolute sense; it all depends upon how they are used and how they are felt to be by the user. Two generations ago European travelers in West Africa held it to be a symptom of savage ignorance that empty gin bottles should be used to decorate a fetish shrine; today African visitors to New York are equally astonished to find common household utensils displayed as art treasures in the Museum of Primitive Art. An object becomes a cultural object only when it is given a name and place in a particular category, and the mere fact that similar looking objects turn up in different cultural situations does not in itself imply that there has been a "diffusion" of culture, or that things are out of place.

If the facts are looked at in this way it becomes evident that our problem should be reformulated. What is at issue is not "the place of science in contemporary culture," but "the place of scientists in contemporary society," and although the social frame and the cultural frame are closely interlocked it is the social that has priority. Culture has meaning only in its social context, it has no significance by itself. But what do we mean by social context?

This is a rather complicated matter. A society is not just a crowd of individuals, it is a set of persons occupying social positions. The way individuals behave towards one another is governed by their mutual recognition of status. This recognition depends upon culturally defined behaviours; all those who occupy a particular status in the system as a whole will wear much the same kind of clothes, live in the same kind of houses, maintain the same kind of life. We recognize what a man is (socially) by what he does (culturally). Nevertheless, the cultural behaviour derives its meaning from the social matrix; it has no autonomy.

This is most relevant for our understanding of the relation between science and contemporary culture. Just as we know that the cultural symbol "black dress with a veil" means "widow" only because our social system has a category "widow," so also the word "science" conveys meaning only because we have created in our social system a category of persons called "scientists." "Science" is the cultural insignia by which we recognize such people; science is what scientists do. If science seems entangled in the cohesions and disjunctions of contemporary culture, this is because of the way we treat our scientists, the role we expect them to play; it has nothing to do with science as such.

It will be seen that my recurrent emphasis is upon culture as a *communication system*. Granted this approach, language itself has a certain primacy as compared to any of the other polymorph aspects of culture. Whatever they may say, social scientists do not really study culture as a whole, they study language, or economics, or technology, or values, or social organization, or kinship systems, or religious organization. But of these specialisms economics and linguistics stand out as not only the most sophisticated but also the most basic, for production and communication are the two most fundamental necessities of human existence.

What, then, can we say of language as an index of social cohesion? Mutual intelligibility is a fundamental necessity for any cohesive social group. On the other hand, the maintenance of unintelligibility is a basic instrument by which interacting social groups manage to hold themselves apart. Differences of dialect, accent, and vocabulary are simultaneously both syncretic and diacritical.[8] Those who share an absolute identity of linguistic codes are able to feel that they share a social unity which excludes the outsiders who only partially understand and who are in turn only partially understood. In a society such as that of England, where social class is a cardinal feature of the social structure, the part played by language in group differentiation is extremely subtle. Although everyone "speaks English" there are one thousand and one different brands of English which embody the social categories into which the society is divided. Though barely aware of what he is doing, the individual will employ quite a different vocabulary and syntax according to the audience which he finds himself addressing. This is a normal characteristic of language use in most human societies. Incidentally, one of the most striking manifestations of science in contemporary society is the fact that each small group of technical experts feels impelled to create its own special jargon language which makes its esoteric activities quite unintelligible to everyone else. But let us be clear: the cultural incoherence does not create fissures in the social system, it reflects them.

What is true of spoken language is true also of "custom," for much that we call custom is simply a behavioral form of linguistic expression: social relations are expressed not only in the way individuals address (or fail to address) one another, but also in mutual behaviours, styles of dress, rights and obligations. Here again differences in the acceptable code serve as markers of major disjunction in the social system, but we need not think of such disjunction as a social evil. The "we group" with which an individual can feel himself to be fully identified is always quite small no matter what kind of society is under consideration, so that *every* social system is necessarily subdivided into solidary segments which are mutually opposed and in some respects actively hostile.

But what makes contemporary society seem especially complicated is the fact that any one individual may belong to a whole series of quite different "we groups" at the same time. Work and business, home and leisure, may draw the "I" into relation with quite distinct sets of people, each of which uses its own linguistic and behavioral codes. The psychological strain upon the individual who has to maintain this schizophrenic cultural existence must be considerable.

People adopt differences of symbolic behaviour in order to express differences of status which they already feel, but it is also true that the symbolic act itself reinforces the sense of difference and opposition. As the category distinction scientist/non-scientist becomes more sharply defined, there is a feedback into cultural behaviour; the scientist takes pride in the exclusive incomprehensibility of his activities, so that the group to which he belongs takes on for him many of the attributes of a religious sect.

This analogy is illuminating. We may note, for example, that the process of sect formation is dynamic; sect and counter-sect proliferate through dialectical disputes over points of dogma, but there is also a deep-rooted conservatism with which each particular sectarian group seeks to preserve the special tenets of its doctrine in unsullied purity from generation to generation. All culture has this dual characteristic: culture develops through the dialectical reinterpretation of symbol categories, yet at the same time the established culture of any particular group operates as an active force which seeks to impose on all new recruits the life-ways of existing members.

Sophisticated modern man is no exception. In my experience scientists are quite as preoccupied with problems of orthodoxy and heresy as the most bigotted theologian, and certainly they are quite as conservative. As Max Planck remarked, "A new scientific truth does not triumph by convincing its opponents and making them see the light but rather because its opponents eventually die, and a new generation grows up that is familiar with it."[9]

If we are to evaluate cultural discord on its merits, we must get right away from European political institutions in which the merits of concord are taken for granted, along with such slogans as Liberty, Equality, Fraternity. The most striking example of a society based on Un-freedom, Inequality and Non-fraternity is that of the Indian caste system. Even by negation it may provide us with some interesting hints concerning the social function of cultural disjunction.

The cultural sub-units of Indian society, the "we-groups," are the *jati* (sub-castes), which are in-marrying groups of kin. Very great stress is placed upon the principle of sub-caste endogamy and, as a consequence, "we" have no kinsfolk at all outside our own sub-caste group. Each sub-caste is further identified by a whole string of cultural badges: each has its own exclusive religious cult, its own peculiarities of linguistic usage, of dress, of food customs, and so on. But beyond that the members of each sub-caste are identified with a traditional occupation to which (in their own district) they have the exclusive right. Thus, although the sub-groups are sharply distinguished by cult usage and kinship, they are economically interdependent. Each sub-group, even the lowliest, has a vested interest in a sector of the total economic system.

It is a rigidly conservative structure. For anything comparable in Western society, one would have to imagine that every occupation was allocated as of right to the members of a particular trade union; that membership in such unions was by birth right only, and that a man could marry only the daughter of a member of his own union. Yet the history of India shows that such a system is quite workable; its principal defect (from our point of view) is that it is inflexible in the face of technical innovation. The Indian caste system begins to look out of date, not because it is morally wrong, but simply because it cannot adjust to the changing labour requirements which are a concomitant of industrialization.

How far is this Indian story relevant for our present discussion? It at least suggests where we might look for significant points of social and cultural disjunction. Consider, for example, the matter of group endogamy to which Indians attach so much importance. Of course, we have no such rule; there is no imminent threat that the practice of science will be reserved for the children of scientists. Yet if past history means anything, such a development is by no means improbable. I can speak only for England. Certainly in this country the groups which now hold the reins of real economic and political power, those whom we speak of as The Establishment, are quite astonishingly endogamous. The top hierarchy of the ruling Conservative party are all related to one another, not because of nepotism,

Culture and Social Cohesion

but because those in positions of authority all tend to be drawn from a narrowly defined social set which has been marrying within itself for generations. English marriages are not "arranged" in any overt way even among the aristocracy; it is simply that, at all social levels, the educational and recreational conventions are such that when boy meets girl, they are almost certainly of the same social class and very likely distant relatives. This is by no means an exclusively upper class phenomenon; some of the craft unions have the reputation for a high degree of endogamy. "It runs in the family, you know," and by that is meant that the craft is passed on not only from father to son but from father to son-in-law. It is a pattern which pervades the sects, not only the small (the Plymouth Brethren, the Quakers, the Unitarians), but also the large (the Catholics and the Jews). All are strongly endogamous and, in a country the size of England, such group endogamy has a very striking dual effect; on the one hand it creates a real sense of social solidarity among the in-group, on the other it stimulates a sense of separation and hostility vis-a-vis "the rest." "Scientists" have not yet existed long enough as a self-defined category to develop this characteristic. That they may do so in the future seems to me distinctly probable. Anyone who thinks that such a prognosis is absurd should reflect for a moment on the implications of the class-conscious snobberies latent in certain behaviours of the "scientists" themselves. Note for example the anxiety with which it is asserted that "pure science" is somehow a superior activity to "applied science" and how the expression "a mere technologist" can become virtually a term of abuse. There have been precise precedents for this: the English nineteenth-century ruling class deigned to intermarry with "the professions" but not with those engaged in "trade," a distinction of an extremely subtle kind! Will the new élite isolate themselves behind similar social barriers?

According to our Indian model, kin group endogamy coupled with cult membership provides a focus for social disjunction, but the interdependence of specialized labour units is a source of overall social unity. Is that the way we are going? It could be so. One could certainly envisage groups of technical specialists acquiring such a vested interest in their secret knowledge that they formed themselves into a caste hierarchy. But that is not how things look at present. One of the classical propositions of theoretical sociology[10] was that the intricate division of labour in industrialized society must lead to a structure of organic interdependence between occupational specialists. But Durkheim's specialists were professional craftsmen, and it is questionable whether his argument applies at all in the modern age of conveyor-belt production lines and computer-controlled technology. In the automation age, tasks in industry are becoming *less*, not more specialized. The division of labour is tending toward a two-tiered hierarchy, an elite of "scientists" narrowly specialized in particular forms of expertise, and a vast mass of machine minders who can readily switch from one job to another. Comparative sociology can offer no precedents for such a pattern. It seems uncomfortably reminiscent of classical slavery.

Two particular characteristics of contemporary Western culture are unique. Together they lend themselves to a deeply pessimistic prognosis, which runs something like this: On the one hand, there is the growth of major conurbations by virtue of which huge populations come to spend virtually their entire existence in a city environment,[11] on the other hand, the phenomenal growth of the communication system in all its aspects from supersonic jet aircraft and six-lane highways to television and computer technology. We know very little about how these cultural products of the age of science are fitted into the total social experience of ordinary men and women. But certainly there are many who feel alienated to an unprecedented degree. The Great City can be felt as a lonely and hostile place. There is so much of everything so densely aggregated that it cannot be experienced at all. The solidary local community, which in the past has everywhere been the real unit through which culture has been transmitted, is now squeezed out of existence. And so also with the intensification of communication, which can be felt as a confused din rather than as an aid to relationship. Many people have come to feel that they live in a world where they cannot hear anything because everyone is talking at once.

In industry the marvels of technology are simply a barrier to understanding. An increasing gulf tends to develop between the small minority of highly skilled experts who actually design the processes and the automated machines and the workmen who, despite their high wages, are reduced to the status of machine minders rather than craftsmen. The factory hand has become an appendage of the intricate communication system rather than a part of it.

In such circumstances the ordinary man's occupation is felt to be quite alien to himself, "work" is just a way of earning a livelihood, not a way of living, and in that case occupational groups cease to have any social meaning. Society seems to be in danger of becoming fragmented into its most miniscule element, the solitary human being.

What kind of reality should we attach to this pessimistic image of the lonely worker in the lonely crowd? In an empirical sense there is no uniformity among workers any more than there is uniformity among scientists, but the concepts "scientist" and "worker" are stereotypes of the mass communication system, so that when, as now, I write a public essay for a public audience, I have no choice but to allocate living human beings in all their variety to cardboard categories such as these. "The scientists" are a category of much the same kind as "the Upper Class." They are not people who are necessarily inter-related, but they share common values and common cultural attributes, and in this special sense it seems to me quite fair to say that "the scientists" are becoming a cohesive élite whose only common characteristic is the possession of secret knowledge and an unwillingness to communicate with others. But we do not have to go on from here to think of science as a kind of Frankenstein monster which must necessarily dominate all our lives.

Let me remind you of two points in this essay which may seem far removed from the discussion of science in contemporary culture: first, my thesis that the learning of an Australian aborigine is stored "out there" in the patterned facts of the environment just as our learning is stored "out there" in the patterned symbols of printed books and computer tape; and secondly, my story of the transistor radio in the jungle which becomes a new kind of thing when it is assimilated into a new kind of milieu. This is the optimistic lesson which the anthropologist can offer. Man is not the servant of his environment; he can make of things and persons what he will, for these things have not only been produced "out there" by human action, they are also categories which have been created as figments of the human imagination.

Our pessimism arises because we tend to forget that what the imagination has created is indeed no more than a figment, a concept. We become slaves to science because we begin to think of science as a reality existing outside ourselves.

The human reality is individual human beings living together in organized groups, that is, "in relationship." It is by means of culturally defined behaviours that relationship is expressed. But relationship is not *only* a matter of the ties between man and man, it also entails ties between man and his environment. What this environment is, is not discoverable objectively; it is a matter of perception. The relation between a society and its environment can be understood only when we see how the environment is organized in terms of the verbal categories of those who use it. What science means for our society is discoverable only when we know what "the scientist" does, or is thought to do. If, as I suspect, this highly emotive word means very different things to many different kinds of people, then this may well denote a cultural disjunction which reflects a very serious kind of social incoherence. But do not let us imagine that even in the best of worlds this kind of difficulty would disappear.

Notes and References

1. A. L. Kroeber and Clyde Kluckhohn, *Culture: A Critical Review of Concepts and Definitions,* Papers of the Peabody Museum, Harvard University, Vol. 47, No. 1 (1952), Cambridge, Mass.

2. B. Malinowski, "Culture," in *Encyclopædia of the Social Sciences,* Vol. 4, p. 621, New York, 1931.

3. R. Bain, "A Definition of Culture," *Sociology and Social Research,* Vol. 27, pp. 87-94, 1942.
It deserves note that Kroeber and Kluckhohn, *op. cit.*, p. 155, would like to confine the word "culture" to the patterning of behaviour rather than behaviour itself. This seems to me quite out of line with general usage.

4. For Aristotle *"ethnos"* meant a "non-Greek"; cf. Aristotle, *Politics,* 1324 *b* 10.

5. Malinowski, *op. cit.*, p. 5.

6. R. Firth, *Elements of Social Organization,* London, 1951, pp. 27-28.

7. Kroeber and Kluckhohn, *op. cit.*, pp. 180-190.

8. S. F. Nadel, *The Foundations of Social Anthropology,* London, 1951, p. 157.

9. M. Planck, *Scientific Autobiography and Other Papers* (trans.), Gaynor: New York, 1949, pp. 33-34.

10. E. Durkheim, *De la division du travail social,* Paris, 1893.

11. "The Future Metropolis," *Dædalus,* Winter, 1961.

TALCOTT PARSONS

Unity and Diversity in the Modern Intellectual Disciplines: The Role of the Social Sciences

THIS ESSAY will discuss the intellectual disciplines as one major aspect of contemporary culture. Roughly, I conceive their scope as comparable to that of the German term *Wissenschaft*. Perhaps their best criterion is general recognition in this country as main subjects for teaching and research in the central university faculties of Arts and Sciences. Thus, for most purposes, the "applied" fields that predominate in professional schools are excluded,* as are the creative and performing arts. Typically, the included disciplines are also organized in professional associations, both national and international, though the networks of such associations are extremely complex.

I will particularly address the problem of understanding the unity and diversity exhibited by these disciplines: the principles on which they are organized, the principles from which distinctions among them derive, and the principles they hold sufficiently in common that their common placement in typical "pure discipline" faculties is justified. That the intellectual disciplines can be treated as belonging together requires an explanation salient to problems of both the conjunction of cultural disciplines and the social organization of the university system. When, in so many respects, our society steadily becomes more specialized, why do our universities not specialize in one field, the humanities, the natural sciences, or the social sciences, leaving the other two for other universities? Why do such technical schools as the Massachusetts Institute of Technology tend to "round out" by strengthening their humanities and social sciences instead of specializing in the natural sciences with increas-

* There are, however, some difficult borderline problems, such as the status of law as an intellectual discipline.

ing rigor? Similarly, the Brookings Institution, originally conceived as a graduate school of the social sciences, did not long survive on that specialized basis except as a research organization.

When conceived broadly enough, all the disciplines seem to share certain normative elements, that is, standards, or values and norms that derive from their common grounding in man's quest for knowledge. Whether the subject materials are natural phenomena, human behavior, or documents of the cultural heritage, in language or in stone, it is agreed that assertions about them should be solidly grounded in objective evidence accessible, if at all possible, to the relevant scholarly public. Similarly, inferences from factual statements should follow standard canons of logic, concepts should be precise and clear, and different statements claiming objective grounding should be logically consistent with each other. In social terms, scholars' assertions and evidence should be public and exposed to the criticism of professional peers. These standards apply no less to the humanistic disciplines than to the sciences. It is not necessarily required that a poet be logically consistent. But a scholarly critic of poetry must face the negative criticism of colleagues if his statements *about* his subject are not consistent.

These common standards of the intellectual disciplines, in which commitment to specific convictions other than procedural beliefs in their own importance and their own methodological standards is inherently tentative, suggest that a convenient distinction separates them from structures in which *commitment* takes precedence over further investigation, which necessarily places questions of how and why particular bases of commitment should be accepted above action on the bases of commitment.

Four basic areas of the latter type of commitment may be distinguished. Where empirical scientific knowledge is the primary focus, members of the applied professions must act with what knowledge is immediately available. Thus a surgeon responsible for a patient with cancer will operate to remove the malignant tissue to the best of his ability, *not* stopping for further investigation into the causes of even this particular cancer except insofar as he can improve his knowledge of the particular case within the available time. There seems to be a parallel line between humanistic scholarship and the "creative" arts. Like the good applied scientist, the good artist is certainly concerned with knowledge of the traditions and history of his art and with "theories" about it, but in the actual process of creation he is a practitioner, not an historical scholar or theorist. He must act upon his commitments and convictions, not primarily consider on what bases they are justified or not.

In the field of religious activity, the central concern is faith, which is a matter of commitment, not of posing a problem for investigation. The religious believer, including the clergyman, is not in the first instance a theologian or philosopher, but a practitioner, no matter how important the theological traditions of his faith may be. Finally, the distinction between investigator and practitioner has a special application, which will be more fully discussed presently, to the relation between moral culture or "values" and social action. The responsible social activist, whether high official or ordinary citizen, defender of the *status quo* or revolutionist, is not as such a moral philosopher or social scientist, but once again a practitioner.

Contrary to much received opinion, I shall base my discussion on the fact that the proper classification of disciplines now seems to be broadly *tripartite* rather than dichotomous; we have the humanities, the natural sciences, and the social sciences. The last are the latest comers and are considerably more prominent in the United States than in Great Britain, or, indeed, France. The relatively late emergence of the social sciences as a "third force" seems to be a particularly important phenomenon—a deserving focus for the following discussion.

The Philosophical Background

The modern form of the intellectual disciplines originated during the Renaissance. In that early phase, they were, variously, *secular* studies not rigidly bound to *specific* religious premises like the theological-philosophical and literary-artistic endeavors of the Middle Ages. Stimulated by their encounter with texts long since lost to them, the humanists of the West eagerly undertook to recapture the civilization of the past, its religion, philosophy, art, science, even its social organization. Beyond this, it served as a point of departure not only for new and independent creation of their own in imitation of the ancients, but for such use of the riches of antiquity as Aquinas' theological appropriation of Aristotelian philosophy.

The humanities were thus the oldest and generally most prestigeful of the intellectual disciplines. With important components of theology, philosophy, and, eventually, mathematics, they comprised the core of higher learning throughout the Western world for a very long time, maintaining a virtual monopoly which was not really broken before the middle of the nineteenth century. They thereby constituted the principal common culture of the educated classes of Europe, with history, philosophy, language, and literature gradually assuming more prominent places within the same basic framework.

The natural sciences developed notably only in the late Renaissance, after the humanistic studies had been deeply absorbed. But despite the great achievements of such figures as Galileo and Newton—and the impact of their ideas on philosophy—the natural sciences did not effectually rival the humanities in higher education and the culture of the most influential social classes until well into the nineteenth century. Thus President Charles Eliot of Harvard, the most eminent modernizer of the American university system, was "only" a chemist, and his appointment was viewed very much askance because of the relatively low repute of scientists even at that late day.

It is often said that a most distinctive feature of modern Western philosophy has been its concern with the epistemological problem, the grounding of the validity of cognitive enterprises. The great seventeenth century synthesis certainly established a frame of reference that gave primacy to the problem in Descartes' sharp formulation of a subject-object dichotomy. This tended toward a metaphysical dualism of the knowing mind and the known external world.

Interestingly, such conceptions as Hobbes's "passions" and power or Locke's "sensations" and the association of ideas contained the germs of many outstanding later developments in psychology and the social sciences. Yet their prototype of the external world was the physical world as understood by the new physical science.* Thus, during its first stage, modern philosophy, as "philosophy of knowledge," concentrated on knowledge of the physical world. This comprised only part of philosophy, which was also concerned, above all, with metaphysics and its relation to theology. But with reference to empirical knowledge, the internal world of "experience," the subjective side of Descartes' dichotomy, was generally understood to be only a "position of the observer" for studying physical objects, not a category of objects for study.

* This is extremely clear, for instance, in Hobbes's deliberate construction of his social science on the model of "geometry." See the opening chapters of Thomas Hobbes, *Leviathan*, Blackwell, Oxford, 1946.

The Role of the Social Sciences

It is curious—and would merit investigation in terms of the sociology and psychology of knowledge—that the priority given to knowledge of the physical world in the development of modern philosophy reverses the priorities applying to the development of the human individual's knowledge of his own environment and, it seems, the formation of empirical knowledge in early cultural evolution.

Since Freud, it has been known that the child's first structured orientation to his world occurs in the field of his *social* relationships. The "objects" involved in Freud's fundamental concept of object relations are "social" objects: persons in roles, particularly parents, and the collectivities of which they are parts and into which the child is socialized. This orientation includes an empirical cognitive component which is the foundation on which a child builds his later capacity for the scientific understanding of the empirical world. What is often interpreted as the child's "magical" thinking about the physical world probably evidences a lack of capacity to differentiate between physical and social objects.*

Similar things appear true of cultural evolution more generally, though, coming under the general principle that ontogeny repeats phylogeny only very broadly; the parallels are far from exact. Perhaps the best single reference on the problem is the old article by Durkheim and Mauss on the forms of primitive classification.** This emphasizes, with special but not exclusive reference to the Australian aborigines, the priority of the social aspect of primitive categorization of the world, notably in the conception of spatial relations in terms of the arrangement of social units in the camp.

The Two Principal Conceptions of the Intellectual Disciplines

That these problems are crucial in an underlying sense is perhaps evidenced by the fact that the great British empiricist philosophers who most sharply crystallized the basic problems of epistemology were also greatly interested in human behavior and social phenomena—especially Hobbes and Locke in the seventeenth cen-

---

* On this aspect of Freud, see my article, "Social Structure and the Development of Personality," reprinted as Chapter 4 of my volume, *Social Structure and Personality*. Free Press, 1964.

** Emile Durkheim and Marcel Mauss, *Primitive Classification,* The University of Chicago Press, 1963; French edition, 1903.

tury and Hume in the eighteenth. Hume's essays, for example, contain outstanding insights into many fields of social analysis.*

This concern with both the physical and social worlds was the source of one of the most important movements from which modern social science has derived. It seems best to call the movement "utilitarian" in a sense close to Halévy's term, "philosophical radicalism,"** applying to the early nineteenth century. From it grew, first and perhaps with the most solid grounding, the main outline of the science of economics, in the line running from Locke to Adam Smith to Ricardo and his successors. It is no accident that economics could be relatively easily related to a viewpoint particularly concerned with the physical world. As a practical field economics is the sphere of social action most directly concerned with articulating the social and physical worlds, especially regarding technology's place in physical production and the psychological significance of physical goods in consumption contexts. The fact that money, the generalized medium of economic transaction, is quantified in a linear continuum having a logical pattern identical with that of the principal variables of classical mechanics is particularly significant in this connection.

Social science's other principal point of emergence from a utilitarian base was in psychology. Here the problem involved bridging the gap between concepts of the sheer givenness of the consumption wants of individuals, a cardinal reference point for economic theory, and the problem of explaining the genesis of wants or motives.*** Insofar as handling this problem went beyond just postulating the association of inherently discrete elements (e.g., in the "association" psychology of James Mill), this frame of reference contained very strong pressures to "reduce" its psychological phenomena to more or less physical terms and lead directly into the heredity-environment dichotomy which came to dominate its biological thought. This has broadly produced the dichotomy between the "instinct" psychology of the Anglo-American tradition and "behaviorism," with its environmentalist emphasis and, hence, concern

---

* Just to give examples, cf. "Of Superstition and Enthusiasm," which is a kind of charter for the sociology of religion, and the essays on commerce, money, trade, public credit, interest, and taxes, which are landmarks in economics. David Hume: *Essays and Treatises*, vol. I, Cadell, London, 1793.

** Halévy, *The Growth of Philosophical Radicalism*, Beacon Paperbacks, 1960.

*** James Olds, *The Growth and Structure of Motives*, The Free Press, 1954.

The Role of the Social Sciences

with the mechanisms of learning. The crucial point for present purposes is that the differences between the social and physical aspects of the actor's environment were not considered problematical for the purposes of this type of psychology.

Like perhaps all great intellectual movements, utilitarianism had its "revolutionary underground" subverting the neat, orderly schemes of the main trend. The greatest of its representatives were probably Hobbes, one of its chief founders, and Malthus. Both were deeply concerned with the problem of the grounding of elementary social order, something which Locke took for granted.* The problems they posed were destined to play in various ways a critical part in breaking the closed system which gave the physical world, as conceived by early modern science, essential priority in the whole theory of possible empirical knowledge.

It will be remembered that this basically epistemological phase of modern philosophy took its departure from the Cartesian dichotomy of knowing subject and known object, and the attempt to relate them to each other. The empiricist-utilitarian phase of the movement seems to have retained a relatively simple version of this frame of reference, essentially treating its "subjective" side *only* as a point of reference and then concerning itself with objects treatable as involved *only* on the objective side. For the physical world this seemed quite appropriate, but it presented difficulties for the study of human behavior. It seems that the economists' insistence on the *givenness* of wants, involving *de facto* assumptions of their randomness, was in the first instance a way of avoiding the apparently hopeless complications of considering the knowing, wanting subject as also belonging to the objective category and requiring analysis on its merits. The complications derived from the fact that the Cartesian dichotomy had then to be conceived as being not singly but doubly salient. There were, concretely, no longer only knowing subjects on the one hand and known or observed objects on the other hand, but there were also entities in both positions at the same time. Insofar as they were both, how could specific structured properties of their different aspects relate to each other? It does not seem too harsh to say that the history of utilitarian thought has involved an elaborate evasion of this problem. The favorite device has been to hold, implicitly if not explicitly, that the subject-as-object in fact has no determinate structure. Insofar as it exists em-

* Talcott Parsons, *The Structure of Social Action*, McGraw-Hill, New York, 1937.

pirically at all, it consists only of given wants which, so far as they do not reflect physical realities, may safely be treated as random.

Kant, Hegel, and German Idealism

The alternative treatment of the problem was embarked upon, with all its enormous hazards, by the idealistic movement. The first step was taken by Kant. He focused in the first instance on the skeptical consequences which Hume drew from the conception of an uncontrolled impact of sense impressions from all phases of the action situation impinging on a knowing subject as equally valid "experience." Kant's answer was that order could be grounded in the field of what he called empirical knowledge only by a sharp *restriction* of the conception of empirical knowledge to what he called the field of phenomena, which in effect meant the physical world in the sense of the relevance of Newtonian theory. This world could be ordered in terms of the combination of the forms of intuition, namely Euclidean space and linear time, and the categories of the Understanding—among which causality appeared with special prominence.

This realm constituted only a small part of the legitimate concerns of human interest. Kant, however, threw everything else into one basket. To the realm of phenomenal determinism, he contrasted the realm of freedom. To that of theoretical understanding, he contrasted that of *Practical* Reason. In this connection, one of his principal concerns was with the status of theology, which he radically denied could be a rational, theoretical discipline. Thus the realms of theoretical understanding and practical commitment were radically dissociated, the latter having radical precedence for all realms of human concern other than natural science.

Important as this was in setting the whole frame of reference for the modern intellectual world, it was very substantially modified in its subsequent development. The next major step was introduced by Kant's successor, Hegel, and consisted in a highly ambitious attempt to order the subjective side of the dichotomy in terms of the conception of *objectiver Geist,* or spirit, as it can sometimes be translated. The important concept here is in the objective element—i.e., that what are now often called cultural patterns, namely ideas, norms, or, more diffusely, "orientations," are treatable as *objects* of observation and rigorous analysis rather than merely as ways of locating the ultimate reference point for knowledge of phenomenal objects in Kant's sense.

Although he reintroduced the conception that the world of *Geist* belonged to that of objects, Hegel did not simply assimilate it to the physical world, but rather formulated its characteristics in a special way of the greatest importance for the future. "Ideal" objects were considered authentically objects, but they were to be treated conceptually in exclusively "historical" terms. The conception historical contained two primary components. One was that the historical object stood in a developmental sequence cognizance of which was essential to knowledge of it. The other asserted the object's uniqueness and, hence, in certain respects, its incomparability with other empirical entities.

Hegel himself built this into a grand scheme of the philosophy of history, interpreted as a process of the "unfolding" of the world spirit (*Weltgeist*) through the agency of human action. This had the greatest importance as one of the principal early versions of the general idea of evolution, antedating Darwin by nearly half a century. It also integrated the ideas of conflict and progress through the conception of the dialectic process in the famous formula of thesis-antithesis-synthesis.

Two themes involved in the aftermath, however, especially concern us. The first is the insistence that the field of human "subjective" concerns, of meanings, must be conceptualized in ideographic as distinguished from generalized and analytical terms. Secondly, the implications of the dissociation between the realms of the physical (and in Kant's sense phenomenal) and of the "ideal" were pressed so radically that a certain duality of determinisms tended to emerge in the contention that each "realm" functioned according to its own unique necessities and in the failure to consider clearly how the "realms" interacted with each other. The dialectic conception of the ultimate unity of conflict and integration was a third major theme which, however, may be considered secondary.

A complex set of variations on the theme of Cartesian dualism seems to have developed. We have not stressed the common philosophical concern with the difference between mind and matter, but rather the problems close to the issues of the development of social science. The social terms of the utilitarian tradition evidently emerged from what, contrary to Kant's view, were the inherently open boundaries of the physical world as conceived by early modern science and philosophy. The utilitarian tendency was to assimilate analysis of human behavior as closely to that of physical objects as seemed feasible. The case of the logical structure of early economic theory is paradigmatic. The consequence was the extension into the behavioral realm of conceptions of the scientific treatment of a world of objects in a way which left the status of knowing subjects highly equivocal in this context.

The Kantian statement cut off this tendency to extension sharply. It radically shifted the problem to the field of the noumenal, which we can equate with essentially humanistic concerns, in German terminology, of *Geist*. Here the crucial questions concerned whether and in what sense the idea of science, conceived roughly as a compromise between the Western emphasis on physical science and the broader German conception of *Wissenschaft* (roughly equivalent to discipline in English), could find an application in the intellectual world of the idealistic movement. That it did so must be interpreted in terms of the operation of the imperatives of intellectual discipline, the general values of integrity in intellectual objectivity and generality, in the subject-matters of subjectively meaningful human concerns. Another process of "extension," parallel to the utilitarian extension of the paradigm of physical science, occurred here.

The sharpness of the Kantian dichotomy could not be expected to endure without modification. One reason lay in the fact that each of the two great traditions issued in an extremism having a profound bearing on the future structure of the intellectual disciplines. On the utilitarian side, it took the form of the pervasive physicalist reductionism that tended to hold that only the natural sciences, on the model of classical mechanics, could yield valid empirical knowledge in any sense. On the idealistic side, there was a corresponding radicalism that in a sense considered Hegel too "rationalistic" in attempting to formulate laws of the development of the *Weltgeist*. In the Germany of the later nineteenth century, Hegelianism thus gave way to radical "historicism," the conception of the universe as comprised of discrete, empirically observable "historical individuals" which were, however, in principle incomparable. The sharpest formulation of the philosophical position of historicism in this sense was probably in the work of Wilhelm Dilthey.[*]

The emergence of this radically empirical trend was associated

[*] Wilhelm Dilthey, *Einleitung in die Geisteswissenschaften* (Duncker und Humblat, Leipzig, 1883).

The Role of the Social Sciences

with a major intellectual movement in Germany, namely, the rise of the "historical schools" in a whole range of disciplines concerning human affairs, not only in history itself, but also in law, economics, and the cultural fields. This in turn involved a great deal of meticulous and detailed scholarship. The pull of this scholarship, as contrasted with the tendency to generalize, seems to have been responsible for a major division which appeared within this tradition and formed an exceedingly important background for the work, among others, of Max Weber.

This was the division between the atomistic and holistic trends within historicism. The first tended to break down the phenomena into minimum units and treat each as maximally independent of all others. The second tended to treat whole civilizations or epochs of history as unified entities. For the latter, the untranslatable German word *Gestalt* seems to be the best single characterization.

Very clearly, this entire mode of thinking tended to assimilate the whole sphere of human concerns to the model of the humanities. Indeed, it carried this emphasis to an extreme comparable in certain respects to the extremism of physical reductionism. The attempt to relate the two main conceptions of knowledge to each other systematically was perhaps carried farthest by Heinrich Rickert, who discussed the basic distinction between the problems of knowledge in the natural sciences and those in the *Kulturwissenschaften.*[*] Contrary to the generalizing, analytical characteristics of conceptualization in the former, the latter were characterized by emphasizing the individuality of each phenomenon and therefore its inherent incomparability with others.

Movements Toward Synthesis

The two patterns of extremism, physical reductionism and historicist uniqueness and ultimate givenness, could not completely dominate the field for long, however prominently their theses still reverberate. Three main movements toward a synthesis soon appeared and have played an important part in the intellectual history of the last century.

The first of these can hardly be called a movement at all. Yet it has certainly contributed importantly to the present definition of the situation. On the Western, more "empiricist" side, it has in-

[*] Heinrich Rickert, *Über die Grenzen der Naturwissenschaftlichen Begriffsbildung*, 5th edition, J. C. B. Mohr, Tübingen, 1929.

volved a combination of biological and "humanistic" emphases. Its essential keynote is a concern with the phenomena of organization —and the fact that this emphasis directs attention to patterns of relationship rather than to units in the sense of the individual particle. The trend sketched above which united physics and classical economics generally gave primary consideration to units, that is, the wants of individuals were the particles of the economic system. Biology, however, with its concern for organization and structure, tends to emphasize "forms" or patterns, in the first instance as anatomical traits. Seen in this context, the emergence of Darwinism was a culmination rather than an origin—these emphases were "in the air."

From this viewpoint, "human biology," the concern with organizational traits, can move very readily from anatomy and physiology to the behavioral and cultural levels. Indeed, there is a long tradition connecting "natural history" with an historical approach to the study of human artifacts and "ways of doing things," viewed in terms of their meanings and functions, and social institutions.

This seems to be the origin of the predominantly Anglo-American discipline of anthropology. Its self-definition, the "science of man," was conceived in a biological frame of reference as comparable to branches of biology, such as ornithology or ichthyology, which studied other sectors of the organic world. In this respect, there was nothing unusual in the specialization on humanity, except that biologically it was very limited in time and variety, there being only one human species. Such study, however, inevitably led into the human traits which were separable from man's genetically organic constitution, which anthropologists have designated generically as his "culture." Anthropology then had to define its concern as the "environmental" side of the human equation, with reference to distinctively human behavioral phenomena, if "culture" could be considered to characterize these.

Within this definition, however, the anthropological concern was with "traits," not with particles. This was a radically different focus from that of the utilitarian economists, because traits were elements in the organization of human relationships, not properties of the individual human being. There was a much less direct correspondence with the logical structure of the physical theory of the day. In fact, the crucial point for present purposes is that this background of anthropology permitted a direct convergence with the trait particularism of the German historical tradition. This convergence was most directly mediated by Franz Boas, the most influential figure in American anthropology in the first part of this century. It is significant both that Boas was a biologist before becoming an anthropologist and that he was German. In the light of this connection, it is not surprising that anthropology also developed the alternative position within ideographic historicism in the idea of a total "culture" as a unified *Gestalt*. This occurred most prominently in the work of Ruth Benedict, whose book title, *Patterns of Culture*, gave a classic expression to this viewpoint.

The second, largely contemporaneous, though somewhat earlier, synthesis was developed by Karl Marx. It involved building a bridge between the pre-historicist Hegelian works and the utilitarian aspect of the empiricist tradition.

All the emphasis in Marxian theory on "materialism" refers primarily to a contrast with "ideal" in the Hegelian sense, not to matter in the more primitive Cartesian sense. The theory does not seriously treat the physical world at all, and has had severe difficulties in the biological sphere. It is primarily an attempt to redress the imbalance created by Hegelianism in its idealistic emphasis by "setting Hegel on his head," as Marx said. The significant thing here is that Marx went rather directly to theory developed from a utilitarian base, namely, classical economics in a modified Ricardian form. As we have noted, this conceptual scheme had special connections with the physical sphere, but clearly was not itself a part of physical science—and it wholly by-passed the biological level.

The crucial Marxian concept here is "material interests." These are clearly economic in the utilitarian sense, which includes the assumption of the *unproblematical* character of individuals' wants. The concept attempts to introduce determinism into the system by postulating that, in the situation of the individual in a market economy, basically only *one* line of action is open.* For the "Capitalist," this is maximization of profit. For the "worker," it is staving off disaster by the acceptance of employment on the available terms.

Any serious student of modern industrial societies recognizes the tremendous oversimplification inherent in this scheme—no Western society has ever been that deterministic in precisely such narrow terms. Marx and, by and large, his followers have met this problem primarily by supplementing the economic element, which

* Michel Crozier, *The Bureaucratic Phenomenon*, University of Chicago Press, 1964.

had the virtue of its special articulation with the physical sphere, with one which we would call political today. That is, Marx interpreted the structure of the situation in which interests in the economic sense were defined and pursued in terms of a socially structured conflict—which he construed as class conflict. This, however, involved the use of coercive sanctions by those occupying positions of superior power, the individual capitalist vis-à-vis his workers at the level of the firm, the capitalist class conceived as basically controlling the state at the macro-social level. The Hegelian dialectic of ideas was thus translated into a dialectic of interests which were both economic and political; the two categories were not clearly differentiated from each other.

It may be said that Marx took over Hegel's conception of the pattern of historical development, but replaced the *Weltgeist* with a modified version of Ricardo, and the periphery* of Ricardian theory in the broad utilitarian tradition. The content of this scheme was formulated in terms of human interests in "want-satisfaction" or goal-attainment, mainly at the individual level. But the paradigm of the Hegelian historical process, activated by dialectic conflict and moving through a series of stages, gave it a quite different meaning. This aspect is crucially significant because Marxian theory has never taken, with all its materialism, many steps toward giving human social behavior a generalized analytical treatment, but, on the basis of certain broad assumptions about "human nature," has relativized all problems to particular systems and historical stages of their development. For Marxians, Ricardian economic theory has been *only* the theory of capitalist economics and not an early stage of a general economic theory applicable, with others and with appropriate qualifications, to socialist societies.

Thus the Marxian synthesis, though certainly a genuine one, was incomplete in not breaking with the basic assumptions of the idealistic tradition in three respects. First, though it formulated, with heavy borrowing from utilitarian sources, the conception of material interests and gave it priority in analyzing the causal historical process, it remained historical in the ideographic sense and did not extend the conception of generalized analytical theory from the natural sphere to that of human behavior. In this respect it represents a retrogressive step relative to the great traditions of English

---

* In these respects, Marx was more Hobbesian and Malthusian than Lockean in stressing the potentials for disorder and conflict.

economics from Ricardo through J. S. Mill and Marshall to Keynes.

Secondly, though repudiating the specifically Hegelian conception of the determination of human behavior by the unfolding *Geist*, Marxism retained the "ideal"—"real" dichotomy of "factors," so that explanation was couched in either-or terms rather than terms of interdependence. Since Hegel's ideal factors could not explain "history," Marx tended to propound an explanation totally in terms of material factors as the only alternative. The logical resemblance of this dilemma to that between heredity and environment in biology is too patent to need further discussion.

Third and most basically, Marxian theory, by accepting, largely implicitly, the utilitarian formula of the givenness of wants, tended to cut itself off from the most important problems leading toward a synthesis of the two sides of the Kantian dichotomy. The basic question is why, having freedom of choice, people in fact opt for one, not some other, personal goal and means of attaining it. The "ideal" component is postulated as given in Marxian theory, in a sense directly comparable to that in which the wants of individuals were assumed to be given in utilitarian theory. In other words, this is the area of an intellectual "neutrality pact," which in the nature of the subject-matter is suspect of inherent instability.

The period including the turn of the last century and the early decades of this century saw extraordinary ferment in all the fields of this discussion. A critically important development was the philosophical criticism of older views concerning the status of physical theory, strongly influenced by internal developments within physics itself. This was classically stated by Whitehead, who attributed a new level of abstraction to this type of theory, the ignoring of which involved the fallacy of misplaced concreteness.[*] This was clearly a more radical conception of the relativity of references to the physical world than that formulated by Kant. It demonstrated the validity of considering the same concrete empirical phenomena from the viewpoint of various different modes of cognitive interest, not just that of understanding in the Kantian sense.

A second major trend of the period developed interests in organizational conceptions in the biological sphere at the more physiological level, as well as at the more anatomical level. This extended the conception of organization involved in the original

---

[*] A. N. Whitehead, *Science and the Modern World*, the Macmillan Company, 1925.

emergence of anthropology to dynamic levels. Perhaps the most eminent figure here is W. B. Cannon,* the physiologist. With *homeostasis,* he conceived of a spontaneous built-in control within the organism which maintained an equilibrium state within boundaries; this concept referred more to a "pattern of functioning" like that of behavior than to an "inert" anatomical structure.

Still later, this trend of thinking established contact with that of cybernetics and information theory, which originated in the physical field of engineering more than in physics itself, but which has nevertheless grounded conceptions of an organized system maintained by integrative control mechanisms much more solidly in the *general* theory of science. This trend in the fields closest to the physical sciences has been most important to the development of a new status for the social disciplines. However, its primary references have been outside the latter field.

Another substantive field tending to bridge the traditional gap between the humanities and the natural sciences in a way directly involving the social sciences has been the science of linguistics. Language has been the citadel of humanistic studies. Indeed, German humanists in general have tended to call themselves "philologists." This is understandable, since language has been the primary medium of symbolic process and cultural communication. However, increasingly language has been subjected to analytical rather than merely historical study. Also, this trend has connected very directly with theoretical developments in the natural science field, notably information theory. Linguistics has also had important contact with the social sciences. First there was the older French work of de Saussure and Meillet. In American anthropology in particular, Edward Sapir and Benjamin Whorf have treated linguistic evidence as a main keynote of the idea of cultural relativity. More recently, Claude Levi-Strauss has been attempting to develop general social theory from linguistic models. It is perhaps not too much to say that linguistics is becoming a discipline that is concurrently a natural science, a branch of the humanities, and a social science.

A very significant methodological convergence should be added to these substantive convergences. First, logic itself is a general resource of all intellectual disciplines—as it has become refined technically, its general relevance has become increasingly evident. Sec-

* W. B. Cannon, *The Wisdom of the Body.* A comparable view with reference to genetics is stated by H. S. Jennings, *The Biological Basis of Human Nature.*

ondly, logic has tended to merge increasingly with mathematics as a preeminent tool of analysis. Then statistics, from having been an empirical art, has increasingly gained mathematical foundations and extended its range of application, even into the humanistic disciplines, particularly via linguistic studies. The recent rapid development of computer techniques is a latest phase involving an application of a complex combination of these elements. The essential point is that these technical innovations cut clean across traditional divisions between disciplines. Their recent invasion of the humanities is the clearest sign that the latter cannot be regarded as inherently isolated from their "scientific" sister disciplines.

After this digression, however, we may return to the more specifically social and behavioral reference. Somewhat antedating most of the movements just sketched has been a third major synthetic development, following the anthropological and the Marxian. This, the emergence of the modern phase of sociological theory, may be considered synthesis of a higher order than either of the other two because it has included the principal components of the other syntheses and because it has avoided the extremism of the either-or dichotomies which have plagued the other syntheses, namely, heredity-environment in the one case and ideal-material in the other.

Max Weber and Emile Durkheim

Two great figures were mainly responsible for this development, namely Max Weber, starting in Germany from a critique of the idealist-historicist tradition, and Emile Durkheim, developing in France a corresponding critique of the utilitarian tradition.[*] These two converged very significantly on a common, though broad, conceptual scheme. Let us start with Weber.

Because of the relation to the humanistic tradition, it may be illuminating to note that Weber began his intellectual career in jurisprudence under the aegis of the historical school then dominant in

---

[*] See Talcott Parsons, *The Structure of Social Action*, McGraw-Hill, New York, 1937, and H. Stuart Hughes, *Consciousness and Society*, Knopf, New York, 1958, for more detailed analyses of the theoretical positions surveyed in the following. Vilfredo Pareto in sociology, Freud in psychology and the American development of social psychology, related to Pragmatism and involving James, Dewey, C. H. Cooley, G. H. Mead and W. I. Thomas, also belong in this context.

Germany. This is significant because, in a very important sense, the law stands squarely between the two poles of the Hegelian-Marxian spectrum so far as human behavior is concerned. Though, as noted above, legal norms, as rules and institutions, are essentially cultural in structure, they are relational patterns. As such, they are the first-line mechanisms regulating the pursuit of the type of interests which predominate in Marxian theory. Furthermore, so far as a society is concerned, law has a reference to the system as a whole, to the "public" interest, which is not shared with the "self-interest" of businesses or political "interest groups." It may also be noted that the Marxian attitude toward law has been exceedingly ambiguous. By grounding the conception of capitalistic interest in the concrete structure of the family firm, certain property institutions, and market structures regulated by institutions of contract, Marxians have generally tended to *include* basic legal institutions within the famous material factors, the relations of production. At other times, however, they have treated law as a component of the "superstructure," and thus as "determined by," rather than as a *part of*, the relations of production. The historicist pattern of thinking facilitates this ambiguity by denying the legitimacy of the abstract analytical procedures required to straighten out the problem.

From his juristic start, Weber embarked on an ambitious study of the "material" base underlying and interacting with legal institutions, mostly through various historical studies in economic organization after the genre of the historical school of economics of the time. He did so reacting against the "formalism" of much of the jurisprudence of the time, notably Rudolf Stammler's work. In his excursions into economic history, Weber did not, however, abandon the basic idea that legal norms *control* action in pursuit of interests, both economic and political.* Here he was very much concerned with Marxian ideas, but the retention of this fundamental position is a prime index of his refusal to become a Marxist.

A major reorientation in Weber's thought occurred after he had recovered from an incapacitating mental illness in about 1904, and was expressed in writings on a new front. Substantively the first important new work was the famous essay on the *Protestant Ethic and the Spirit of Capitalism*.** This dealt directly with an "ideal

* Max Weber, *Max Weber on Law in Economy and Society*, Harvard University Press, 1954.
** Max Weber, *The Protestant Ethic and the Spirit of Capitalism*, C. Scribner's Sons, New York, 1930; German original, 1905.

factor" in reference to its significance for a specific process of historical development, indeed, the one Marxian theory had spotlighted. It was undoubtedly meant to challenge the Marxian view, but *not* in the sense of "setting Hegel back on his feet." Rather, it put the problem in a frame of reference neither Hegelian nor Marxian nor historicist in Dilthey's sense.

The crucial point is that Weber's analysis, the core of which is the Protestant Ethic thesis, bridged the theoretical gap between "want" in the economic-psychological sense and "cultural patterns" in the idealistic senses. To put it simply and radically, Weber's solution was that, once cultural patterns of meaning have been internalized in the personality of an individual, they define the situation for the structuring of motives. Therefore questions of how action (including the acceptance of the goals toward which it is oriented) makes sense must be answered by reference to the meaning-system defining the situation of action. Weber then postulated, not given wants, but given cultural definitions of the situation (the human condition) which make commitment to the satisfaction of certain classes of wants intelligible. These meaning-systems, however, were the very subject-matter of humanistic-cultural study.

Did this, however, constitute only a step along a line of regression which merely put the discreteness of cultural patterns, within which particular wants became meaningful, in the place of the givenness of discrete wants of individuals? At the very least, the discrimination of two levels in the want system, the concrete, satisfaction-oriented want itself and the cultural grounding of its meaning, would be a gain. But Weber's analysis went a step farther. He treated these as independently variable factors in the determination of action, which, in their mutual inter-relations and in relation to other factors, could be treated as interdependent in a system. This view basically broke through the ideal-material dichotomy of idealistic thinking about human action. The answer, analogous to that of modern biology regarding the heredity-environment problem, is that *both* sets of factors are crucial, standing in complex relations of interdependence with each other.

Before Weber, the "cement" which had been holding the parts of the dichotomy in their rigid relationship was the postulate of *historical* connection in its Hegelian-Marxian version. Thus, either the ideal constellation or that of material interests constituted a *Gestalt*, which either existed or did not, as a totality. A second focus of Weber's break with the tradition was salient there. He assumed as a matter of principle that the components of such a *Gestalt* should be treated as independently variable. He set out to analyze certain of these relations by the *comparative* method, which in terms of the logic of science is the nearest empirical equivalent to the experimental method that is accessible to this subject-matter.

In treating the problem of Protestantism's role in the development of capitalism, any historicist, idealist, or Marxist would have treated the problem entirely as one of the sequences in Western history from the Reformation, and its immediate antecedents, to the Industrial Revolution. But Weber, in adopting the comparative method, studied the negative cases especially. Along with the question of why modern "capitalism" developed in Europe, Weber investigated its *non*-development in other advanced civilizations. He completed extensive monographs on China and India in this connection.* Again, the substantive question, how far he progressed toward the empirical demonstration of his case, is not our concern here. The point is that his *method* involved an *analytical* isolation of classes of variables by comparing cases in which they demonstrably varied independently of each other.** In the subject matter of cultural *Gestalten* this was a very new departure.

Concurrently, in a series of essays which, in the first instance, were polemically oriented, Weber attempted a principled grounding of this new orientation in the conception of empirical knowledge as such, but particularly in the context of the social sciences.*** As noted he anticipated writers like Whitehead in establishing that analytical abstraction was essential even to physical science. By no means does its theory, for example, in the case of classical mechanics, simply "reflect" the reality of the external world. It is selective and hence in important degrees evaluative in its concern for empirical problems and facts. Thus it is partly determined by the interests

* Max Weber, *The Religion of China*, The Free Press, Glencoe, 1951; *The Religion of India*, The Free Press, Glencoe, 1958; the original German editions of both, posthumous.

** Here it should be noted that the comprehensive survey of religious structures recently translated as *The Sociology of Religion*, Beacon Press, Boston, 1962 (originally published as *Religionssoziologie* in *Wirtschaft und Gesellschaft*, 1922), unparalleled at the time in the analytical qualities of its approach, was written as a relatively independent section of a larger work on the relationships between the economy and other aspects of social structure.

*** Max Weber, *Gesammelte Aufsätze zur Wissenschaftslehre*, 2nd edition, Johannes Winckelmann, editor, Mohr, Tubingen, 1951. Selections from this work have been translated and edited by Edward A. Shils and Henry K. Finch, *The Methodology of the Social Sciences*, The Free Press, Glencoe, 1949.

and values of the scientist, among which possibilities of controlling natural events figure prominently, but by no means exclusively. This dependence on the evaluative concerns of the investigator (which Weber called *Wertbeziehung*) had to be matched, in whatever field, natural, social, or humanistic, by a favorable evaluative orientation to problems of the empirical disciplines centering about the canons of intellectual discipline, above all for objectivity in empirical observation and for logical, clear, and precise theoretical statement and inference. This is the focus of Weber's famous doctrine of the "value-freedom" of social science (*Wertfreiheit*). It does not mean, as so many have erroneously believed, that the scientist or scholar should be free of *any* values, but rather that in his professional role, he must be free to give the discipline's values priority over others, notably in Weber's mind over political commitments. In contemporary terminology, I believe he meant that the values of the intellectual disciplines must be *differentiated* from other types of values constitutive of the culture. Only on such a basis can science and scholarship be institutionalized.

As a matter of course, however, Weber also insisted on the central importance of the "empathic" understanding (*Verstehen*) of motives and patterns of meaning as this had been emphasized in the humanistic and idealistic tradition, namely, the "subjective" side of the Cartesian dichotomy. These entities, however, were now also given the full status of objects, as regards both their own internal structure and the relevance to them of analytical abstraction and abstract generalized conceptualization. In certain senses the utilitarians had prepared the way for this, but had shied away from its full consequences. They had preferred to limit this whole realm to the status of givenness under a set of restrictive assumptions, and to follow the problems of variability only in the other direction.

The *Verstehen* conception, however, was crucial to the new position because the impact of the "ideal" factors as *variables* was to be systematically studied precisely in the definite, specific structures of cultural patterns, including legal norms, and motives. Both the utilitarian and the behavioristic positions simply foreclosed this possibility with bland philosophical assumptions.

On the background of these three essential doctrines of social science methodology, Weber thus culminated his argument by asserting that the social disciplines required generalized analytical concepts and propositions. Indeed, when Weber wrote, such theory-building had already advanced considerably in economics and parts of psychology. He, however, stated this requirement very sharply and clearly while discussing the idealist and humanistic tradition. Weber's own attempts at formulation in this field primarily took the form of ideal types. Though legitimate, they have certain limitations and constitute only one of a number of the necessary theoretical components of the social sciences.

Weber thus broke cleanly with the dogma that cultural and historical materials were subject only to ideographic conceptualization as forming unique historical individuals. His most important contention was that the more advanced analytical methods of the natural sciences must be adopted in the realm of the cultural disciplines—which meant primarily the humanities, but the bridge between the natural sciences and humanities was constituted by the new social disciplines. In Weber's case, above all, economics could not be allowed to remain caught between the imperatives of a "Western" analytical definition of its scope and a German "historical" one. Indeed, it can be said that the main rationale of Weber's venture into sociology was that he saw this as the only way out of the dilemma, the only path to a synthesis of the best in the two traditions of economics that could relate both to the essentials of the "cultural" sciences.

While Weber's innovation in defining social science came from the Idealist-Marxist tradition, that of Durkheim was primarily significant in taking its substantive departure from a critique of the utilitarian position, but doing so in such a way as to converge very directly with Weber. It is significant that Durkheim tackled the same basic set of substantive problems as did Weber, namely the interpretation of the changes in Western society which have variously been called capitalism and industrialism. His focus, however, was not directed at the "wants" category, but the social relations involved, the contractual system. He chose Herbert Spencer's conception of a system of contractual relations as his principal critical target[*] and showed conclusively that such a system of "pursuit of individual self-interest" could not be understood as a stable social system without the establishment of an institutional structure, the position of which was not a simple function of the interests of the participating individuals. This structure he found above all embodied in the legal order, in the institution of the contract, the sub-

[*] Emile Durkheim: *The Division of Labor in Society*, The Free Press, Glencoe, 1949. French original, 1893. Pt. I, Chapter VII.

The Role of the Social Sciences

stance of which was not a matter of agreement among contracting parties.

It is interesting that here Durkheim took up a central theme of the great tradition of economics, namely the division of labor. His main attempt was to show that, empirically correct and important as the insights of the economists had been, they still could not adequately *account* for the phenomena they described. This required what Durkheim called a factor of "organic solidarity" which could have no place within the conceptual scheme of the utilitarian tradition.

Durkheim's critique of the utilitarian interpretation of the modern economic order, however, did not as such supply a theoretical alternative. In working this out—it was very incomplete in his first main work on the Division of Labor—he went back to the Cartesian frame of reference which underlay the whole development with which this paper has been concerned, and modified it in a highly original and ingenious way. Stating our point in more contemporary terms, Durkheim put himself in the position of an actor who was a member of modern society, and, taking that actor's point of view, considered his relation to the society considered as his social environment (*milieu social*). In doing so he treated this social environment as an object, at the same time considering the actor as subject in strict Cartesian terms. His departure from Descartes lay in his locating his problem with reference to a classification of objects—the facts his actor was concerned with were *social* facts, not those of the physical environment. These were facts about *society*, which Durkheim asserted to be a "reality *sui generis*,"* not reducible to terms of physical, biological, or psychological constituents; in this view Durkheim followed Auguste Comte who in turn built on the tradition of Rousseau.

The Cartesian formula of a set of cognitively knowable facts about a category of objects, however, fell far short of providing a solution of the problem of an alternative theoretical frame of reference to the utilitarian for the analysis of a social system. The direction taken was to try to clarify the conception of the social milieu by taking account of the fact that this overall object was composed of entities which were at the same time *both* subjects and objects in the Cartesian sense. But if this were done the "subject" could no

---

* Durkheim: *The Rules of Sociological Method* (French original, 1895).

longer be conceived as having *only* cognitive functions—he had to be an "actor" in the full sense. Correlatively, the object was at *one* level an object of cognition like any other, but, when the meaning of its special, *sui generis* properties was looked into, it became clear that this included subentities which, though "objects" to an outside observer—for example, the legal norms of a contractual system—were *norms* to the individual members of the system. Durkheim as a student of law, though not fully professional, was quite clear that norms were a special category of phenomena. They "constrained" action, as he himself put it, not by their givenness as in the case of the stone kicked in Dr. Johnson's famous example, but because they defined *desirable* courses of action. Undesired consequences of their nonobservance took the form, not of automatic physical events, like pain in the foot from kicking a stone, but of sanctions imposed by human decision, like punishment for a criminal act.

There is thus not just one subcategory of social facts, maximally similar to physical facts, but the category must be differentiated. There is sheer empirical givenness, but there is also normative requirement of expectation of the part of others, including "official agencies" in the social system. Moreover, on the subjective side, a further differentiation is also required. Of course the Cartesian subject is to Durkheim not only a "knower" but, more broadly, an actor. But this broadening makes way not merely, as in the utilitarian case, for "wants" which are treated as unstructured so far as the social system is concerned. The very norms which appeared on the object side of the Cartesian equation as indispensable social facts, also appear on the subject side, as norms or rules which "constrain"—again Durkheim's own term—by *moral* authority, and not by their mere givenness without normative status nor by their demandedness by other members of the system, as backed up by sanctions.

Indeed this inclusion of the normative component in the "structure" of the subject or actor, and note a normative component which is common to many actors, is Durkheim's path to the generalization of his analysis from the actor of reference to the level of the social system, and to the solution of the problem of order which was his empirical point of departure. Durkheim's later work increasingly stressed the cultural character of this normative component of social systems and its link with other components of the culture such as religious beliefs and the symbols involved in rituals. The exploration of these relations provided the main theoretical subject matter for

The Role of the Social Sciences

his last major work, the *Elementary Forms of the Religious Life*.*
In this direction he converged strikingly with Weber. This convergence lay not only in their common solid basis for a social science approach to problems in the area of culture and notably religion, but in the fact that they clarified, in directly comparable ways, the *relations* between the normative components in social systems and the factors of "interest" which had played the principal part in the utilitarian tradition on the one hand, the Marxian, on the other. The solution is familiar, but this fact makes it none the less important that it be clearly grounded. It is that norms—which for present rough purposes may be said to include what are ordinarily called values—"control" the operation of interests—economic, political, and psychological— in social systems, *both* at the more obvious societal levels of their incorporation in legal systems and in authority, and at the less obvious level of their internalization in the personalities of individuals, as in Weber's religiously grounded economic ethic and Durkheim's constraint by moral authority. This control, however, is correlative with a crucial independent significance of the various interest levels as factors which condition possibilities of success in the organization of social relations. It is not a matter of the determinative predominance *either* of wants or of the "activities" or objective conditions of their satisfaction. Nor is it a matter of *either* ideal or material factors as the Hegel-Marx dichotomy would have it predominating. The relations are far more complex than either the internal alternatives of the utilitarian or the idealistic camp made allowance for. They involve partial independence combined with mutual interdependence in a sense familiar for the relation of variables in systems throughout science. Beyond that, they involve systems of control—in the cybernetic sense—and of conditions which modify the meanings both of independence and of interdependence in the most general senses.

Durkheim was considerably more advanced than Weber, in a technical theoretical sense, in his analysis of the *internalization* of normative elements of the cultural and social systems in the structure of the personality of the individual. In this very basic insight it is notable that Durkheim converged not only with Weber—and certain other movements coming from the idealistic tradition such as those connected with the name of Georg Simmel—but also with two

* French original, 1912.

others from the utilitarian-positivistic side, namely Freud and in the broadest sense the Pragmatist movement in the United States. It has been noted that there was direct continuity between British empiricism in philosophy, utilitarianism, and the emergence of the Darwinian movement in biology. As a physician, Freud belonged, above all, in this tradition, indeed his earlier research was in the field of pharmacology. The main trend, then, of his earlier work in the field of psychopathology seemed to indicate the immense importance of biologically given instinctual needs relative to the "veneer" of rational factors in behavior. Both the history and the structure of Freud's theoretical work in this field are enormously complex, and to the end of his long career this note seemed to be very prominent.

There was, however, another, which, though clearly visible as early as the *Three Contributions to Sexual Theory* (1906), only emerged into centrality in his late work—a centrality which some would even now contest. There has, however, been a central theme of unmistakable significance in our context, that of *object-relations*. This, in the light of the above discussion, has unmistakable Cartesian-Durkheimian overtones. Freud of course put cognitive aspects of the relation far down on his priority list. But he shared with Durkheim the conviction of the importance of *social* objects—in his case the human *persons* particularly significant in the early life history of an individual, but by inference also the collectivities, such as the family, in which he came to be included.

In any case, Freud's later schema for the analysis of personality converged strikingly with Durkheim. The concept of the *superego* was the entering wedge. It essentially referred to the internalization of normative cultural content, in this case with special reference to the forms operating at the Oedipal stage of child development. This, however, has not only led to inevitable generalization to the normative structure important at all stages of the life cycle, but to the other sectors of the personality, notably what Freud called the *ego*, but also even including the *id*.* Internalized normative culture, not just the given wants of individuals, was thus for Freud not only an essential, but, on the whole, the controlling component of the human personality. It was of course learned by the individual in the course of his "socialization" in the family and later.

* On this aspect of Freud's work see my article, "Social Structure and the Development of Personality," printed as Chapter 4 of the collection *Social Structure and Personality*, Free Press, 1963.

The Role of the Social Sciences

The Pragmatist movement in this country built still another partially independent bridge between these traditions. William James did much to break up Cartesian rigidities with respect to the concept of the self, above all recognizing such plural meanings as the "I" and the "Me." The development from James which is most important here is not the one most prominent in philosophy, via Dewey, but rather the "social psychology" centering on the names of Charles Horton Cooley and George Herbert Mead.* Cooley came to the insight that there was in the early development of the personality such an intimate relation between the self and the significant others of its environment that they could be assumed to be equally immediately given and inseparable—he coined the expressive term of the "looking-glass self," which reflects others' views of it as well as its own immediate experience. Mead further developed this line of thought on the level of symbolic processes, and added the important conception of the "generalized other" which is another version of the internalized normative culture we have found in Durkheim and Freud. In addition Mead showed how this conception should be linked with the conception of the same acting units, human persons as objects of orientation to each other and of course to an external scientific observer who can analyze as well as interpret social action.

It is thus perhaps clear that modern social science has been characterized by a complex convergence of a number of intellectual currents which have come together in a broadly common frame of reference which clearly defines not a middle ground between the two earlier principal categories of disciplines, but a third distinctive type, which in certain respects constitutes a synthesis of components drawn from both. Its most distinctive characteristic is the conception that human action is always interactive in reference except in limiting cases, and that in this capacity every unit in it is *both* a knowing and acting subject and an object of knowledge and orientation.

Conclusion

In outlining this intellectual history, I have attempted to trace a principal path by which the intellectual disciplines, institutionalized in the central faculties of American universities, acquired the foun-

---

* Charles Horton Cooley, *Human Nature and the Social Order*, Schocken Books, Inc., New York, 1964.

George Herbert Mead, *Mind, Self, and Society*, The University of Chicago Press, 1934.

dation of a basic unity which is nevertheless compatible with their inherent diversity. In a sense it was natural that, as modern intellectual culture emerged, the humanities and sciences should hold radically different patterns of orientation, and that the social disciplines should be substantially less well crystallized.

The growth of knowledge itself, accompanied by generalization and sophistication on both sides, exerted pressure for firmer methodological and, eventually, philosophical groundings. Indeed, this pressure may well have been an important factor in the emphasis modern philosophy has placed on epistemological concerns.

In the movement emerging from philosophical empiricism, which included the physical sciences, utilitarianism, and eventually Darwinian biology, these problems were not generally brought into sharp focus. The social disciplines developed slowly on the basis of a rather empirical, common-sense view of the task of history, utilitarian theorizing in economics and psychology, and the extension of Darwinian biology into the behavioral fields.

This history clearly illustrates the difficulty of drawing sharp boundaries to the domain of natural science within this frame of reference. One mode of extension into the social field, of which classical economics is the type case, could be stabilized only by a "walling off" against further extension by assuming the givenness of wants and their purely individual character. The development of biological thinking, however, presented still greater difficulties, since it introduced, particularly in its extension through anthropology to the human behavioral field, the especially important conceptions of organization and relational pattern. This, in its environmental reference, eventuated in the concept of culture, which, on a utilitarian background, was a truly revolutionary concept. This too tended to be "walled off" through the trait atomist doctrine of the so-called "historical" school of British-American anthropology.

The relevant intellectual history on the background of empiricism and utilitarianism involved a gradually increasing strain in the direction of giving a more independent status to the human cultural-behavioral fields, but attended by a continuing anxiety that doing so would imply abandoning the attempt to be scientific. Kant introduced a clean break in these respects, explicitly confining science to the field of physical phenomena—only this limited area was accessible to the methods of "pure reason." Problems of how the areas of human behavior excluded from science could be treated as objects of observation and analysis thereby became acute. The idealistic

The Role of the Social Sciences

movement, especially with Hegel, solved this by focusing on the conception of *Geist* as itself objectively observable through a rather different kind of "understanding" than the Kantian, namely, that conveyed by later uses of the German term *Verstehen*. The problem here was the obverse of the one posed for the utilitarian tradition, namely, not how to treat human motives or wants as independent of their conditioning substratum in the physical world or the organism, but how to relate the imperatives of ideal patterns to the exigencies of the real world in a way accounting for the realistically effective qualities of such entities in actual behavior. This orientation went through two stages: the Hegelian grand philosophy of history and the historicist particularism which keynoted the conception of the isolated historical individual.

Beginning with this orientation, Marx developed the first major bridge toward the phenomenal world, to use Kant's term. By setting Hegel on his head, he conceived of a dialectic of "material interests" which directly matched Hegel's dialectic of the *Geist* in form. This venture directly complemented the anthropological introduction of cultural pattern as a discrete elementary particle in the human field. Each intellectual movement had, in a peculiar sense, undercut the ground of the other. The anthropologists, from a naturalistic base, had come to see the "essence" of the human behavioral world in cultural-humanistic terms, whereas the Marxians, from an idealistic base, had located its essence in the interest formulated by the utilitarians. In each case, the dominant category was the one which had figured most prominently in the history of the other tradition.

Surely this was an intellectual impasse. It is in this setting that I place the movement of which the Weber-Durkheim convergence may be regarded as the core. Its most important feature was its capacity to synthesize the two great sets of intermediate categories, wants or interests on the one side and organization and relational pattern on the other side. Culture, as well as the organism and the physical world, had become inherently involved in the human behavioral sphere. This concurrently becomes the subject of an autonomous set of intellectual disciplines, neither humanities nor natural sciences. They are cultural in that they study the cultural productions of human experience, but they are at the same time analytical, oriented to empirical understanding in the sense of science.

This chapter of intellectual history has been sketchily analyzed to help make intelligible the *three*-fold structure of the intellectual disciplines in modern academic organization. It is my contention that neither the implicit empiricist-utilitarian monistic structure, in which basically all such disciplines were conceived as monolithic, nor the idealistic dualism is tenable as a frame of reference for the modern level of sophistication in this area. The social sciences must be treated as a fully autonomous category. They are not natural sciences in the sense of excluding the categories of subjective meaning, that is, they must consider knowing subjects as objects. Nor are they humanistic-cultural in the sense that the individuality of particular meanings must take complete precedence over analytical generality and such categories as causality. The emergence of sociological theorizing in the sense outlined crystallized this synthesis more sharply than any other intellectual event of recent times.

On this basis it has at last become clear that the analytical and historical components of knowledge are just that—components, not concrete classes. First, this means specifically that generalized analytical methods have become crucial, not only to economics and behavioristic psychology, but also to the social disciplines extending much farther into the "humanistic" range such as sociology, anthropology, law, political science, and certain aspects of history itself. Conversely, however, historical perspectives have been extended far into the normal domains of natural science. Perhaps the original crystallization of this perspective lay in "natural history's" exceedingly important role in biology. A particularly important extension of this conception went toward paleontology as the historical perspective on the whole process of organic evolution. This in turn is most intimately related to the historical aspect of geology, the "story" of the planet earth. Extension to still further ranges has become very prominent in recent times, through the historical aspect of astronomy, the history of planets, suns, and indeed galaxies.

Finally, all three sets of disciplines have their practical aspects as knowledge applied to the implementation of human values and interests, not only as fields of knowledge for its own sake. The concept of "practical reason" is not confined to any one branch of learning, but is relevant to all of them. There is, however, the essential proviso that it is exceedingly important not to confuse the two references.* Increasingly, this distinction seems to be becoming institu-

---

* The fields of engineering technology and somatic medicine, as applications of natural science knowledge, and of economic policy and of the use of psychological testing in personnel selection, as applications of social science are relatively obvious. Sometimes, however, humanists make a virtue of their claim that the humanities are completely free of any taint of practicality—that

tionalized in the distinction between arts and sciences faculties and the applied "professional" faculties. Equally, the underlying premises of all the intellectual disciplines require grounding at levels which are not problematic simply for the development of the individual sets of disciplines. Thus the philosophy of science is not itself a science in the sense of physics or chemistry. All the members of the triad of intellectual disciplines look both downward to the fields applying their "pure" patterns of knowledge and upward to the grounding of their premises in the more ultimate problems of the meaning of the human condition. No basic distinction can be drawn among them on either of these two accounts.

---

they are fields of the pursuit of learning solely for its own sake. This claim may be doubted on one ground in particular. This is that for a considerable period in European history a humanistic education constituted the principal basis of the common culture of the elite classes of European Society—and indeed still does to a considerable extent. We may suggest that the "use" of the humanistic disciplines in giving its principal cultural character to the elite of a great civilization was just as much a "social" application as any of engineering or medicine. Far from being simply the erudite scholar whose studies had no relevance beyond his own esoteric self-gratification, the typical humanist has been par excellence the educator of men of understanding and character.

HARVEY BROOKS

Scientific Concepts and Cultural Change

THERE ARE many difficulties of communication between the subgroups within our culture—for example, between the natural sciences, social sciences, and humanities. But there are also ways in which they are becoming increasingly united, and most of this essay will be an effort to trace a few common themes and viewpoints derived from science which I see as increasingly pervading our culture as a whole.

Perhaps one of the most important is the common allegiance of scholarship to the ideal of objective research, to the possibility of arriving by successive approximations at an objective description of reality. Whether it be concerned with the structure of a distant galaxy or the sources of the art of the nineteenth century poet, there exists a common respect for evidence and a willingness to follow evidence wherever it leads regardless of the preconceptions or desires of the scholar. This is, of course, only an ideal; but failure to conform to this ideal, if detected, damns a scholar whether he be a scientist or a humanist. In a sense the whole apparatus of academic scholarship is an attempt to bring scientific method into the pursuit of knowledge through progressive refinements in the uncovering and use of evidence.

A characteristic of scholarship, as of science, is that it prefers to tackle well-defined, finite problems that appear to be soluble with the methods and evidence available. This often means eschewing the more fundamental, the more "metaphysical" issues, in the belief that the cumulative result of solving many smaller and more manageable problems will ultimately throw more light on the larger issues than would a frontal attack. One of the paradoxes of modern science has been that the greater its success in a pragmatic sense, the more modest its aims have tended to become in an intellectual sense. The goals and claims of modern quantum theory are far more modest than those of Laplace, who believed that he could predict the entire course of the universe, in principle, given its initial conditions. The aim of science has changed from the "explanation" of reality to the "description" of reality—description with the greatest logical and aesthetic economy. The claims to universality of nineteenth century physics have been replaced by a greater awareness of what still remains to be discovered about the world, even "in principle." The day of global theories of the social structure or of individual psychology seems to have passed. Experience has taught us that real insight has often been achieved only after we were prepared to renounce our claim that our theories were universal. The whole trend of modern scholarship has been towards greater conservatism in deciding what can be legitimately inferred from given evidence; we are more hesitant to extrapolate beyond the immediate circumstances to which the evidence applies. We are quicker to recognize the possibility of unrevealed complexities or unidentified variables and parameters. Even in artistic criticism we tend to recognize greater diversity in the influences playing on an artist, greater ambiguity in his motives or artistic intentions. Art, scholarship, and science are united in looking further behind the face of common-sense reality, in finding subtleties and nuances. It is, of course, this search for subtlety which has made communication between disciplines more difficult, because to the casual observer each discipline appears to be working in an area beyond common sense.

The admission of finite aims in scholarship has been connected with an increasingly sophisticated view of the scope and limitations of evidence in all fields. But the emphasis on finite and limited aims in scholarly inquiry has also been paralleled by the extension of scientific and scholarly attitudes to practical affairs. One sees a close analogy between the preoccupation of science with manageable problems and the decline of ideology and growth of professional expertise in politics and business. One of the most striking developments of the post-war world has been the increasing irrelevance of political ideology, even in the Soviet Union, to actual political decisions. One sees the influence of the new mood in the increasing bureaucratization and professionalization of government and industry and in the growth of "scientific" approaches to management and administration. The day of the intuitive entrepreneur or the charismatic statesman, seems to be waning. In a recent volume of *Dædalus* on "A New Europe?" the recurring theme is the increasing relegation of questions which used to be matters of political debate to professional cadres of technicians and experts which function almost independently of the democratic political process. In most of the western world the first instinct of statesmanship is to turn intransigent problems over to "experts" or to "study groups." There appears to be an almost naive faith that if big problems can be broken down sufficiently and be dealt with by experts and technicians, the big problems will tend to disappear or at least lose much of their urgency. Although the continuing discourse of experts seems wasteful, "Parkinsonian," the fact remains that it has worked surprisingly well in government, just as it has in science and scholarship. The progress which is achieved, while slower, seems more solid, more irreversible, more capable of enlisting a wide consensus. Much of the history of social progress in the twentieth century can be described in terms of the transfer of wider and wider areas of public policy from politics to expertise. I do not believe it is too fanciful to draw a parallel between this and the scientific spirit of tackling soluble problems.

The trend towards the acceptance of expertise has been especially striking in Europe where both ideology and the apolitical professional bureaucracy have been stronger than in the United States. But even in this country there has been increasing public acceptance of expert analysis and guidance in such areas of government as fiscal policy and economic growth. In the realm of affairs, as in the realm of knowledge, the search for global solutions or global generalizations has been replaced by the search for manageable apolitical reformulations of problems. The general has been replaced by the specific. Concern with the theoretical goals and principles of action has been replaced by attempts at objectively predicting and analyzing the specific consequences of specific alternative actions or policies. Often the problems of political choice have become buried in debates among experts over highly technical alternatives.

It remains to be seen to what degree this new reign of the bureaucrat and the expert reflects the influence of science and scientific modes of thinking and to what degree it represents a temporary cyclic phenomenon resulting from unprecedented economic growth and the absence of major social crises. However, the modes of thought which are characteristic of science have penetrated much deeper into scholarship and practical affairs than the hand-wringing of some scientists would tend to suggest, and the general adoption of these modes of thought does not appear to have relegated genuine human values to the scrap heap to the degree which some of the humanists would have us believe. Indeed it has brought us closer to a realization of many of the human values which we regard as desirable.

On the other hand, it must be recognized, that some of this reliance on expertise has moved us in directions in which we would not have gone had we been more aware of the unspoken and unrecognized assumptions underlying some of our "technical" solutions. For example, economic growth and technology have come to be accepted as valuable in themselves. The assembly line has brought more and more goods to more and more people, but it has also introduced monotony into work and a sometimes depressing standardization into our products. The technology of production tends to accept as its goals values which technology alone is well adapted to achieving without balanced consideration of other, equally important goals.[1] The very definition of gross national product connotes measurement of economic progress in purely quantitative terms without reference to changes in the quality of the social and physical environment or improvement and deterioration in the quality and variety of the products available. The inclination to tackle the soluble problems first often extrapolates to the view that the more intractable problems are less important.

In the preceding paragraphs I have argued that both scholarship and practical affairs have increasingly adopted the spirit and mode of thought of the natural sciences. An interesting question is to what extent the actual concepts and ideas of science have entered into other disciplines and into our culture generally. There are, of course, some very obvious ways in which this has occurred. Scarcely any other scientific theory, for example, has influenced literature and art so much as Freud's psychoanalytical theory. Though some of Freud's ideas might be said to contain dogmatic elements which are essentially non-scientific or even anti-scientific in spirit, nevertheless, psychoanalysis is based on largely empirical observation and professes to test itself against objective evidence. It is clearly a scientific theory which, though extensively elaborated and modified, is still basically valid in its description of the irrational and subconscious elements in human motivation and behavior. It has completely altered our view of human nature, and this changed viewpoint is reflected almost universally, though in varying degrees, in modern literature and art, as well as in the interpretation of history and political behavior. The orderly Lockean world embodied in the American Constitution, in which each man acts rationally in his own self-interest, can no longer be accepted in quite the undiluted way that the Founding Fathers believed in it. There is ample evidence of neurotic and irrational behavior on the part of whole communities and social systems, often in opposition to their own self-interest. Even organized religion has largely accepted and adapted many of the principles of psychoanalysis, while rejecting some of the world views which have been extrapolated from it.

A more problematic example is the parallel between the increasingly abstract and insubstantial picture of the physical universe which modern physics has given us and the popularity of abstract and non-representational forms of art and poetry. In each case the representation of reality is increasingly removed from the picture which is immediately presented to us by our senses. As the appreciation of modern physics requires more and more prior education, so the appreciation of modern art and music requires a more educated—some would say a more thoroughly conditioned—aesthetic taste. In physics the sharp distinction which used to be made between the object and its relations to other objects has been replaced by the idea that the object (or elementary particle) is nothing but the nexus of the various relations in which it participates. In physics, as in art and literature, form has tended to achieve a status higher than substance.

It is difficult to tell how much psychological reality there is to this parallel. It is not sufficient to reply that a physical picture is still a definite model which can be related by a series of clear and logical steps to the world which we see and that no such close correspondence exists between abstract art and the sensible world. For physical models depend to a larger degree on taste than is generally appreciated. While correspondence with the real world exists, this probably is not sufficient by itself to constitute a unique determinant of a model. Yet the successful model is one that has evolved through so many small steps that it would take a bold imagination indeed to construct another one which would fit the same accumulation of interconnected facts or observations. What is regarded as acceptable evidence for a model of reality, even in physics, is strongly dependent on the scientific environment of the time. Evidence which favors theories already generally accepted is much less critically scrutinized than evidence that appears to run counter to them. One always makes every effort to fit new evidence to existing concepts before accepting radical modifications; if a theory is well established the contradictory evidence is usually questioned long before the theory, and usually rightly so. Established theories depend on many more bits of accumulated evidence than is often appreciated, even by the scientist himself. Once a principle becomes generally accepted the scientific community generally forgets much of the detailed evidence that led to it, and it takes a real jolt to lead people to reconsider the evidence. In fact, scientific theories are seldom fully displaced; rather they are fitted into the framework of a more comprehensive theory, as Newtonian mechanics was fitted into the formulations of relativity and quantum mechanics. This, in itself, suggests that there are many theories or models which will fit given facts.

All of this points to the fact that a scientific theory is the product of a long evolutionary process which is not strictly logical or even retraceable. The mode of presentation of science, especially to the non-scientist, usually suppresses or conceals the process by which the results were originally arrived at, just as the artist does not reveal the elements which went into his creation. Thus it seems possible that there is some common or universal element in the modern mentality which makes quantum theory acceptable to the physicist, abstract art to the artist, metaphysical poetry to the poet, atonal music to the musician, or abstract spaces to the mathematician. The attack on these aspects of modern culture by totalitarians of both the right and the left perhaps lends further credence to these common threads. It is interesting to observe that children with previously untrained tastes have little trouble in appreciating and enjoying modern art or music and that the younger generation of physicists has no trouble in absorbing the ideas of quantum mechanics quite intuitively with none of the sense of paradox which still troubles some of the older generation. It is probable that the main elements of taste, whether it be scientific or aesthetic, are formed quite early in our experience and are strongly conditioned by the cultural climate. Science, as one of the most dynamic of contemporary intellectual trends, is undoubtedly a strong factor in creating this cultural climate, but it would be rash to ascribe causal connections. It would be interesting to know whether some psychologist, by studying current tastes in art or poetry, could predict what *kinds* of theories were likely to be acceptable in elementary particle physics, or perhaps vice versa!

Another obvious but superficial way in which scientific ideas enter our culture is through some of the dominant "themes" of science. One such theme, for example, is evolution and natural selection, and the derived philosophical concept of progress. Today we take the idea of evolution so much for granted that we are inclined to forget that until the nineteenth century it was generally believed that the present state of society and man was the result of degeneration from some antecedent golden age or hypothetical ideal "state of nature." The Puritan Revolution in England and the French Revolution had ideologies which appealed to a hypothetical prehistoric past for their model of an ideal society. Only with Marx did revolution present itself as a forward movement into a more "advanced," previously non-existent state of human society.

In the nineteenth century the idea of evolution and particularly the concepts of natural selection, competition between species, and the "survival of the fittest" were seized upon as an explanation of and justification for the contemporary laissez-faire capitalist society. State intervention in the competitive economic process was regarded as an almost immoral interference with the "balance of nature" in human society. In the United States and Britain the first science of sociology was built upon an interpretation of the ideas of natural selection. A whole generation of future American businessmen was educated in the ideas of men like Sumner. This sociology stressed the dangers of permitting organized society to tamper with the inexorable laws of social evolution.

In the early part of the twentieth century Darwin's ideas lost some of their original influence, but now, in the second half, they have regained much of their influence in biology and have tended to be reinforced by recent discoveries in biochemical genetics. However, it is interesting to note that a subtle change of emphasis has crept into the interpretation of natural selection. The modern evolutionary biologist tends to stress the concept of the "ecological niche" and the fact that natural selection, when looked at more carefully, leads to a kind of cooperation among species, a cooperation which results from finer and finer differentiation of function and of adaptation to the environment.[2] Indeed, biologists stress the fact that natural selection generally leads not to the complete domination of one species, but rather to a finer and finer branching of species, a sort of division of labor which tends ultimately to minimize competition. Is it too much to suggest a parallel here between the changing scientific interpretations of biological

Scientific Concepts and Cultural Change

evolution and changing attitudes towards cooperative action in human societies? Is there any connection between the modern view of ecology and the progressive division of labor and specialization of function which are characteristic of modern economic organization? Certainly the analogies with biological evolution have been extremely suggestive in the development of modern cultural anthropology.

Another theme which is involved here is that of dynamic equilibrium or balance, also fruitful in the study of chemical equilibrium. When dynamic equilibrium exists, a complex system can be apparently static from the macroscopic viewpoint even though rapid changes are taking place in its elementary components. All that is necessary is that the rates of changes in opposite directions balance. This is the kind of equilibrium that is envisioned as occurring in an ecological system or in a social or economic system. It would, perhaps, be wrong to suggest any causal or genetic relation between the growth of such ideas of chemical theory and their application to social or biological systems. The fact is, however, that the concepts arose at similar periods in scientific development and helped to establish a kind of climate of taste in scientific theories which undoubtedly facilitated intuitive transfer from one discipline to another. One finds the images and vocabulary of chemical equilibrium theory constantly recurring in descriptions of social and economic phenomena.

Two of the germinal ideas of twentieth-century physics have been "relativity" and "uncertainty." Philosophers generally recognize that both of these themes have had an important influence on their attitudes, but the physical scientist finds it more difficult to connect the philosophical view with its role in physics. At least the connection is not so self-evident as it is in the case of evolution or of psychoanalysis. Indeed, both relativity and uncertainty are words which have rather precise operational meanings in physics, but which have been given all sorts of wishful or anthropomorphic interpretations in philosophy. Indeed, scientific popularizers have themselves been especially guilty of this type of questionable semantic extrapolation.[3] The situation has been aggravated by the tendency of physicists to use words from everyday discourse to denote very subtle and precise technical concepts. The popularizer and the layman then use the technical and the everyday term interchangeably to draw conclusions bearing little relation to the original concept.

Let us consider relativity first. The basic idea of relativity is that all the laws of mechanics and electromagnetism are the same, independent of the state of uniform motion in which the observer happens to be moving. Relativity is "relative" in the sense that there is no "absolute" motion, no fixed reference point in the universe that has greater claim to validity than any other. On the other hand, the elimination of absolute motion is achieved only at the price of introducing an absolute velocity which is the same in all reference systems, namely, the velocity of light. Thus it may be legitimately questioned whether "relativity" or "absolutism" is the correct name for the theory. Nevertheless, the first terminology was the one that caught the popular and speculative imagination and provided the basis of a revolution in viewpoint which affected many areas of knowledge. Not long after relativity was absorbed into physics, the anthropologists were stressing the extraordinary diversity of human customs and ethical norms and were arguing that moral standards had to be viewed not in an absolute sense but relative to the particular culture in which they were found. The judgments of history became less moralistic; the actions of individuals tended to be viewed in the context of the ethical norms of their time. The realistic novel or drama in which human behavior was depicted without moral judgment became fashionable. Yet if these things have little to do with "relativity" in the sense that Einstein intended, the very fact that the word caught fire so easily suggests there does exist a kind of common taste in such matters and that this taste forms part of the intellectual climate of the time.

The other key idea of physics is "uncertainty," as embodied in the Heisenberg Uncertainty Principle. The philosophical interpretation of this principle has been the subject of interminable debate by both scientists and laymen. On one extreme, people have viewed the uncertainty principle as repealing the laws of causality and reintroducing "free will" into the physical as well as the mental universe. Most working physicists tend to take a somewhat more pedestrian view of the principle. They interpret it as being the result of an attempt to describe the state of the universe in terms of an inappropriate and outmoded concept, namely that of the point mass or "particle," a concept derived by analogy with macroscopic, i.e. common sense, physics. Nevertheless, regardless of the exact interpretation, the uncertainty principle does imply that the idealized classical determinism of Laplace is impossible. The laws

Scientific Concepts and Cultural Change

of quantum theory are deterministic or "causal" in the sense that the state of the universe at any time is determined by its "state" at some previous time. The lack of determinism in the Laplacian sense comes from the impossibility of specifying the "state" at any time in terms of any set of operations which will not themselves change its state and thus spoil the assumptions. What is wrong in the old determinism is the idea that the universe can be uniquely and unequivocally distinguished from the observing system, which is a part of it. In this sense the uncertainty principle can be seen as merely a further extension of the concept of relativity.[4] Interpreted in this light, we find the same idea cropping up in many fields of knowledge. The social scientist is increasingly conscious that the measurements that he can make on any social system affect the future behavior of the system. A good example is public opinion polls, which, if made public, affect the attitude of the public on the very matters the polls are supposed to measure "objectively." Another example is educational tests, which not only measure human ability, but tend to change the cultural and educational norms which are accepted and sought. This aspect of the uncertainty principle in the social sciences is, in quantitative terms, a matter of some debate, but it is an important factor in social measurement, which has to be dealt with just as in physics. In many social situations the mere fact that the subjects know they are being observed or tested affects their behavior in ways which are difficult to discount in advance. Even in a subject like history a sort of analog of the uncertainty principle is found. It lies basically in the fact that the historian knows what happened afterwards and therefore can never really describe the "initial conditions" of his system in a way which is independent of his own perspective. In seeking to discern the underlying causes of events he inevitably tends to stress those factors which demonstrably influenced events in the way they actually came out, minimizing factors or tendencies which did not develop even though the relative strengths of the two tendencies may have been very evenly balanced at that time. The modern historian, of course, tends to be very aware of this uncertainty principle and to allow for it as much as possible. Again, while there is probably little intellectual connection between these various attitudes in the different disciplines, there is a general intellectual climate which stresses the interaction between the observer and the system being observed, whether it be in history, physics, or politics.

There are a number of themes in science having a somewhat more direct and traceable intellectual connection between different disciplines. Here I should like to mention three, namely, energy, feedback, and information. Each of these is a highly technical concept in physics or engineering; however, each also has broad and increasing ramifications in other disciplines. Of these, the oldest and most loosely used is probably energy. This concept is closely associated with that of "transformation." That is, the reason energy is a useful concept is that it has many different forms or manifestations which may be transformed into each other. In physics it is probably the most general and unifying concept we have. All physical entities or phenomena, including "matter" or "mass," are forms or manifestations of energy. Though it may be transformed, its quantity is "invariant," and this is what makes it important. The concept of energy has, of course, been important in biology almost as long as in physics. Living matter functions by transforming energy, and much of the early science of physiology was concerned with studying the transformations of energy in living systems. But the term "energy" has also found its way into many other fields of knowledge, where it is used often more metaphorically than with precise significance. Nevertheless, even in its metaphorical use it tends to partake of some of the characteristic properties of physical energy; namely, it is subject to transformation into different forms, and in the process of transformation the total energy is in some sense preserved. One speaks of psychic energies, historical energies, social energies. In these senses energy is not really measurable, nor is it directly related to physical energy. Nevertheless, like physical energy it can be released in the form of enormous physical, mental, or social activity; and, when it is, we tend to think of it as somehow "potential" in the pre-existing situation. The term "tension" denotes a state of high potential energy, like a coiled spring; and a high state of tension, whether social or psychological, is usually followed by a "release" or conversion into kinetic energy or activity of some variety. Thus the language of energy derived from physics has proved a very useful metaphor in dealing with all sorts of social and psychological phenomena. Here the intellectual connection is more clear than in the case of relativity or uncertainty, but it is more metaphorical than logical.

The concept of feedback is one of the most fundamental ideas of modern engineering. It underlies the whole technology of auto-

Scientific Concepts and Cultural Change

matic control and automation. The original concept was quite restricted in application. It arose in connection with the design of electronic amplifiers in which a part of the output was fed back into the input in order to control the faithfulness with which the amplifier would reproduce in the output the form of the input signal.[5] An amplifier with what is called negative feedback reproduces the time behavior of the input more faithfully than the same amplifier without feedback, the more so the greater the feedback.

The concepts and methods of analysis originally developed for amplifiers were rapidly applied to control systems, where they had a far more fundamental influence. In recent years the feedback concept has been extended still further to embrace the idea of "information feedback," which is important in biological and social phenomena as well as in the engineering of physical systems. The idea has been stated by Forrester[6] in the following way:

"An information feedback system exists whenever the environment leads to a decision that results in action which affects the environment and thereby influences future decisions."

At first this may seem unrelated to amplifiers and control systems, but if we identify "environment" with "input" and "decision" with "output" we can readily see how the more general definition includes amplifiers and control systems as a special case. In the case of the amplifier the decision is completely and uniquely determined by the environment, but the concept of information feedback applies equally well when the decision is a discrete rather than a continuous function and when it is related to the environment only in a probabilistic sense.

In this more general use of the words environment and decision we can see many examples of the information feedback concept in biology and the social sciences. For example, the process of natural selection in evolution is itself a type of feedback. The selection process—the particular population which survives in each generation—is the decision, and this is fed back into the genetic constitution of the next generation; in this way the characteristics of the population adjust to the environment over successive generations.

The muscular activities of animals also illustrate information feedback. In this case, the environment, which must be considered as including both the external environment and the relation of the body to it, influences the decision through perception. The work of the muscles is the analog of the amplifier or controller, and the perception of the organism provides the feedback loop. The process of learning may be readily regarded as an information feedback system. Indeed the theory behind the teaching machine is essentially designed to establish a tighter feedback, through the process of "reinforcement," which helps the student to decide whether he has learned correctly. Much of the concern with the techniques of teaching is related to improvement of the feedback loop in the learning process.

The consideration of such processes as learning or cultural evolution as feedback systems would be merely a convenient metaphor, like energy, were it not for the fact that information feedback systems have certain general properties which tend to be independent of their particular embodiment. The two most important properties are those of stability and response. There exists a whole theory of the stability of feedback systems, which depends on the amplification or "gain" of the system and the time delays which occur throughout the whole decision-environment-decision loop. High gain and large time lags tend to produce instability which will cause the system as a whole to "hunt," that is, the state of the system oscillates in a more or less uncontrolled way about the position of adjustment to the environment. The term "response" relates to the closeness and rapidity with which the system in question will adjust to a changing environment; this is analagous to the closeness with which the time behavior of the output of a feedback amplifier will reproduce the time behavior of the input.

The mathematics of the stability of linear amplifiers and control systems—that is, physical systems in which the output or "decision" is directly proportional to input or "environment"—is highly elaborated and well understood. Real feedback systems, however, are often non-linear, probabilistic in nature, and discrete rather than continuous. The mathematics for dealing with such systems is not very well developed, and for this reason it has not, until recently, proved very profitable to look at biological or social systems from the standpoint of information feedback. However, the advent of the high speed digital computer has speeded up the processes of ordinary arithmetical calculation by a factor of more than a million and has brought much more complicated and pathological (from the mathematical standpoint) systems within the purview of calculation. The usefulness of the computer lies in the fact that the behavior of feedback systems depends on only certain of their abstract properties; these properties, in turn, can be readily modeled or "simulated" on a computer. Thus we are enabled to study the dynamics of the model in great detail and, if necessary, at a speed much greater than that of the real life situation.

It is now being recognized that many types of unstable behavior that occur in biological and social systems are, in fact, examples of unstable feedback systems, the instability usually arising from unacceptable time lags in the transmission of information through the system. A case which is by now fairly well documented is that of inventory policy in a business.[7] In times of high demand a business may tend to build up inventory in anticipation of future demand, and this further increases demand; but there is a lag between orders and production as well as between the measurement of demand and the decision to increase inventory. This can have the effect of introducing a highly fluctuating factory output in a situation in which the external demand is actually rather steady. Forrester[8] has given an analysis which suggests strongly that exactly this model may account for the notorious instability of production and employment in the textile industry.

It seems highly likely that the business cycle in the economy as a whole represents a form of feedback instability to which many individual elements of decision making contribute through their time lags. In fact all forms of social decision making tend to contain an inherent time lag arising from the fact that anticipations of the future are simply linear extrapolations of past trends. Thus one can even discern a similar tendency in history for political and social attitudes towards public issues to be those appropriate to the experience of the recent or distant past rather than to the actual situation which is faced. For example, the philosophies of laissez-faire economics were conditioned by the mercantile and pre-industrial era in which the principal problem was the inhibiting effects of state interference in the economy. Or, to take a more recent example, early post-war American economic policy was based on the fear of a major depression similar to what followed the first war, while much of present public thinking is based on the fear of inflation of the type which followed World War II. Such lags in social attitudes probably contribute to many of the cyclic phenomena which are often attributed to history. Of course, the examples given above are somewhat crude oversimplifications, but the basic idea is one which may have quantitative as well as suggestive or metaphorical value.

Another possible example is the cycle in moral attitudes. Attitudes towards moral values, because of the long time they take to diffuse throughout society, tend to lag behind the actual social conditions for which they were most appropriate. Thus, for example, Victorian attitudes towards sex arose partly as a reaction to the extreme laxity which existed in previous times, and conversely modern liberal attitudes towards sex are to some extent a response to the social and psychological effects of Victorian repression. Such attitudes tend to go in cycles because their inherent time lag produces unstable feedback in the social system. Such lags are especially important in the dynamic or "high gain" cultures characteristic of the West.

The problem of stability in feedback theory is relevant to situations in which the environment without considering feedback is more or less constant. When an unstable feedback situation exists, the system "hunts" about the stable situation of adjustment to the environment. The other important concept, however, is that of the response of the system to environmental changes imposed from without, or, in amplifier terminology, the faithfulness and speed with which the output follows the input. This introduces the idea of "optimization" in control systems. An optimized system is one which responds to its environment in the best way as defined by some quantitative criterion. Of course, the optimal configuration of the control system will be dependent on the properties of the environment to which it is expected to respond or adapt. We can imagine an environment which is subject to short-term and long-term changes and a feedback system which is optimized for the short-term changes occurring during a certain period. If the nature of the short-term changes also varies slowly in time, then the feedback system will not remain optimum. We could then imagine a feedback system whose properties change with time in such a way as to keep the response optimal as the short-term changes in the environment occur. The continuing optimization can itself be described as a form of information feedback. For example, we can imagine a man learning a game requiring great physical skill. When he has learned it, his muscular and nervous system may be thought of as a feedback system which has been optimized for that particular game. If he then engages in a new game, his muscles and nerves will have to be optimized all over again for the new game, and the process of learning is itself a form of information feedback. In this way we arrive at the concept of a whole hierarchy of feedback systems—of systems within systems, each operating on a different time scale and each higher system in the hierarchy consti-

Scientific Concepts and Cultural Change

tuting the learning process for the next lower system in the hierarchy. In the technical literature these hierarchies are referred to as adaptive control. Adaptive control systems appear to "learn" by experience and thus come one step closer to simulating the behavior of living systems. In fact we may imagine that biological and social systems are information feedback systems with many more superimposed hierarchies than we are accustomed to dealing with in physical control systems.

The other key idea from engineering which has had an important impact on social and biological theory is that of information, and the closely associated concept of noise. The idea that information was a concept that could be defined in precise mathematical terms was recognized by Leo Szilard in 1929.[9] Szilard was the first to point out the connection between the quantity of information we have about the physical world and the physical concept of the entropy of a system. However, Szilard's ideas lay fallow until twenty years later when they were rediscovered by Shannon[10] and precisely formulated in their modern form—the form which has revolutionized modern communications. There is a very close relation between information and probability. In fact, the amount of information in an image or a message is closely connected with its deviations from a purely random pattern. The concept of information is basic to the quantitative study of language and has provided one of the cornerstones of a new science known as mathematical linguistics. It is also generally recognized that the transmission of genetic properties from generation to generation is essentially a communication of information. This has led to the idea of the "genetic code" which contains all the information necessary to reproduce the individual. So far the attention of biologists has mostly been focused on the elementary code, that is, on the relationship between the structure of the DNA molecule and the genetic information which it carries. The possibility of precise definition of the quantity of information in a system, however, opens up the possibility of considering evolution from the standpoint of a system of information transmission.[11]—a type of study which is still in its infancy. A remarkable consequence of information concepts is the realization that the information embodied in the biological constitution of the human race is essentially contained in the total quantity of DNA in the human germ cells—at most a few grams in the whole world. One suspects that it may be possible to apply information concepts similarly to the study of cultural evolution and to the transmission of culture from generation to generation.

One cannot talk about information without considering noise, which is the random background on which all information must ultimately be recognized. By its very nature noise is the absence of information. When an attempt is made to transmit a definite piece of information in the presence of noise, the noise destroys a definite amount of the information in the transmission process. No transmission system is completely faithful. Noise is, in the first instance, a physical concept; but, as in the case of information and feedback, the concept may be extended in a somewhat vague way to social and biological systems. For example, in evolutionary theory the "noise" is the random variations in the genetic constitution produced by cosmic radiation and other external influences on the genetic material. In the transmission of cultural information, the "information" communicated by a piece of literature or a work of art depends not only upon the intrinsic information content of the work but also on the experience and education of the recipient. Unless the artist and the recipient have had the same experience, the communication is always less than faithful.

In the foregoing I have tried to suggest how a number of important themes from the physical and biological sciences have found their way into our general culture, or have the potential for doing so. In the case of the concepts of feedback and information, the ideas appear to have an essentially quantitative and operational significance for social and cultural dynamics, although their application is still in its infancy. The most frequent case is that in which a scientific concept has served as a metaphor for the description of social and political behavior. This has occurred, for example, in the case of the concepts of relativity, uncertainty, and energy. In other cases, such as evolution and psychoanalysis, the concept has entered even more deeply into our cultural attitudes.

REFERENCES

1. Lewis Mumford, "Authoritarian and Democratic Technics," *Technology and Culture*, 5 (1964), 1.

2. Ernst Mayr, *Animal Species and Evolution* (Cambridge: Harvard Belknap Press, 1963).

Scientific Concepts and Cultural Change

3. L. S. Stebbing, *Philosophy and the Physicists* (New York: Dover Publications, Inc., 1958).

4. P. W. Bridgman, *The Logic of Modern Physics* (first edition, New York: Macmillan, 1927). Although written as a philosophical interpretation of relativity before the discovery of quantum mechanics in its modern form, this work is extraordinarily prescient with respect to the philosophical ideas underlying quantum theory.

5. H. S. Black, U. S. Patent No. 2,102,671 (1934); cf. also, H. W. Bode, *Network Analysis and Feedback Amplifier Design* (New York: van Nostrand, 1945).

6. J. W. Forrester, *Industrial Dynamics* (Cambridge and New York: M.I.T. Press and John Wiley, 1961).

7. *Ibid.*

8. *Ibid.*

9. L. Szilard, Z. Phys. 53 (1929), 840; cf. also, L. Brillouin, *Science and Information Theory* (New York: Academic Press, 1956).

10. C. E. Shannon and W. Weaver, *The Mathematical Theory of Information* (Urbana: University of Illinois Press, 1949).

11. W. Bossert, private communication.

GERALD HOLTON

The Thematic Imagination in Science

I

MY THESIS will be that the dichotomy between scientific and humanistic scholarship, which is undoubted and real at many levels, becomes far less impressive if one looks carefully at the construction of scientific theories. This will become evident first at the place where explicit and implicit decisions are most telling—namely in the formation, testing, and acceptance or rejection of hypotheses.

Current opinion on the way scientific theories are constructed is by no means unanimous. We may, nevertheless, take the account given not too long ago by the physicist Friedrich Dessauer as a quite typical contemporary presentation of the so-called hypothetico-deductive, or inductive, method of science. His scheme[1] reflects both general professional and popular understanding.

There are, he reports, five steps. (1) Tentatively, propose as a hypothesis a provisional statement obtained by induction from experience and previously established knowledge of the field. An example, drawn from experimental work in physics, might be this: the observed large loss of sound energy when ultrasonic waves pass through a liquid such as water is possibly due to a structural rearrangement of the molecules as the sound wave passes by them. (2) Now, refine and structure the hypothesis—for example, by making a mathematical or physical analogon showing the way sound energy may be absorbed by clumps of molecules. (3) Next, draw logical conclusions or predictions from the structured hypothesis which have promise of experimental check—for example, if

This article is reprinted, with some revisions, by permission from Harry Woolf (ed.), *Science as a Cultural Force* (Baltimore: Johns Hopkins Press, 1964).

more and more pressure is applied to the sample of water, it should be more and more difficult for the associated molecular groups to absorb sound so strikingly. (4) Then check the predicted consequences (deduced from the analogon) against experience, by free observation or experimental arrangement. (5) If the deduced consequences are found to correspond to the "observed facts" within expected limits—and not only these consequences, but all different ones that can be drawn (for example, behavior at constant pressure but changing temperature, or similar effects in other liquids)—then, a warrant is available for the decision that "the result obtained is postulated as universally valid." Thus, the hypothesis, or initial statement, is found to be "established" scientifically.

But, popular opinion continues, until the facts support such a position any hypothetical statement is to be held scrupulously with open-minded skepticism. The scientist, Dessauer reports, "does not take a dogmatic view of his assumption, he makes no claim for it, he does not herald it abroad, but keeps the question open and submits his opinion to the decision of nature itself, prepared to accept this decision without reserve." This, he concludes, is "the inductive method, the fundamental method of the entire modern era, the source of all our knowledge of nature and power over nature."

We note that this account fits in well with a widespread characterization of a supposed main difference between scientists and humanists: the former, it is often said, do not pre-empt fundamental decisions on esthetic or intuitive grounds; they do not make a priori commitments, and only let themselves be guided by the facts and the careful process of induction. It is, therefore, not surprising that in this, as in most such discussions, nothing was said about the *source* of the original induction, or about the criteria of *preselection* which are inevitably at work in scientific decisions. Attention to these would seem to be as unimportant or fruitless as a discussion, say, of the "reality" of the final result. To paraphrase Newton's disclaimer in the General Scholium of the *Principia,* to us it is enough that, for example, sound absorption in water does really exist and act according to the laws which we have explained, and abundantly serves to account for the pressure and temperature dependence of absorption in a great variety of liquids, even of the sea.

This account of scientific procedure is not wrong; it has its use, for example, in broadly characterizing certain features of science as a public institution. But if we try to understand the actions and decisions of an actual contributor to science, the categories and steps listed above are deficient because they leave out an essential point: to a smaller or larger degree, the process of building up an actual scientific theory requires explicit or implicit decisions, such as the adoption of certain hypotheses and criteria of preselection that are not at all scientifically "valid" in the sense previously given and usually accepted.[2]

II

To illustrate this point as concretely as possible, let us look at a case for which it has long been thought the last word had been said. As is well known, Book III of Newton's *Principia,* which was supposed to use the principles and mathematical apparatus developed in Books I and II to "demonstrate the frame of the System of the World," opens with a section that is as short as it is initially surprising: the four rules of reasoning in philosophy, the Regulae Philosophandi. At any rate, they appear so in the third edition, of 1726, known to us usually through Motte's translation of 1729. These are, of course, well-known rules, and I need remind you of them only briefly. They can be paraphrased as follows:

I. Nature is essentially simple; therefore, we should not introduce more hypotheses than are sufficient and necessary for the explanation of observed facts. This is a hypothesis, or rule, of simplicity and *verae causae*.

II. Hence, as far as possible, similar effects must be assigned to the same cause. This is a principle of uniformity of nature.

III. Properties common to all those bodies within reach of our experiments are to be assumed (even if only tentatively) as pertaining to all bodies in general. This is a reformulation of the first two hypotheses, and is needed for forming universals.

IV. Propositions in science obtained by wide induction are to be regarded as exactly or approximately true until phenomena or experiments show that they may be corrected or are liable to exceptions. This principle states that propositions induced on the basis of experiment should not be confuted merely by proposing contrary hypotheses.

It has been justly said that these epistemological rules are by no means a "model of logical coherence."[3] They grew in a complex

The Thematic Imagination in Science

way, starting from only two rules (I and II) in the first edition of the *Principia* (1687) where they were still called Hypotheses I and II. As Newton, with growing dislike for controversy, came to make the corrections for the third edition, he added the polemical rule IV which is a counterattack on the hypotheses-laden missiles from the Cartesians and Leibnizians.

But it turns out that Newton at one time was on the verge of going further. It was discovered only recently in a study of Newton's manuscripts by Koyré[4] that Newton had written a lengthy *Fifth Rule;* and then had suppressed it. The significant parts of it for our purpose are the first and last sentences of this rule, and the likely reasons that it had to be suppressed.

"Rule V. Whatever is not derived from things themselves, whether by the external senses or by internal cogitation, is to be taken for hypotheses. . . . And what neither can be demonstrated from the phenomena nor follows from them by argument based on induction, I hold as hypotheses."

To us, even as to Newton's contemporaries, disciples, and defenders, the sense in which Newton uses here the word "hypothesis" in the suppressed rule is clearly pejorative. It was after all Newton himself who, in 1704, had written as the first sentence of the *Opticks*, "My design in this Book is not to explain the Properties of Light by Hypotheses, but to propose them, and prove them by Reason and Experiment." And in this and other ways, he had begun to sound the declaration "hypotheses non fingo" in the second, 1713 edition of the *Principia*. We are apt to remember this slogan rather than the fact that in Newton's work from beginning to end, and even in the last edition of the *Principia* itself, one can readily find explicit hypotheses as well as disguised ones. And we are apt to overlook that rules against hypotheses are themselves methodological hypotheses of considerable complexity.

But, then, is it not strange that Newton after all *did* suppress this fifth rule which the Newtonians after him, his modern, empiricist disciples, from Cotes to Dessauer, would accept readily? To understand why Newton may have done this is of importance if we want to understand the cost of having so long been the philosophical heirs of the victorious side in that seventeenth-century quarrel concerning what science should be like.

The answer has, I think, several elements, but one is surely an ancient one: that disciples are usually eager to improve on the master, and that the leader of a movement sometimes discovers he cannot or does not wish to go quite as fast to the Promised Land as those around him. (Thus, it was not Cortes but the men he had left in charge of Mexico who, as soon as his back was turned, tried to press the victory too fast to a conclusion, and began to slaughter the Aztecs, with disastrous consequences.)

Here it is significant that Newton had only said, in one draft of his *General Scholium:* "I avoid hypotheses"; and in the final version, "I do not feign hypotheses," that is, I make no false hypotheses. But his spokesman and friend, Samuel Clarke, translated him to read: "And hypotheses I *make* not"; and Andrew Motte rendered it as the famous "I frame no hypotheses." In this, as in several other places, Newton's protagonists went much further than he did, and seemed to ask for a Baconian sense of certainty in science which Newton knew did not exist.

Newton had indeed exposed and rejected certain hypotheses as detrimental; he knew how to tolerate others as being at least harmless; and he, like everyone else, knew how to put to use those that are verifiable or falsifiable. But the fact is that Newton also found one class of hypotheses to be impossible to avoid in his pursuit of natural philosophy—a class that shared with Cartesian hypotheses the characteristic of neither being demonstrable from the phenomena nor following from them by an argument based on induction, to use the language in Newton's suppressed *Fifth Rule* itself. The existence, nay, the necessity, at certain stages, of entertaining such unverifiable and unfalsifiable, and yet not quite arbitrary, hypotheses —that is an embarrassing conception which did not and does not fit into a purely positivistically oriented philosophy of science. For the decision whether to entertain such hypotheses is coupled neither to observable facts nor to logical argument.

In Newton's case, two obvious examples of his use of this class of hypotheses—to which I refer as "thematic" propositions or thematic hypotheses, for reasons to be discussed later—appear in his theory of matter and his theory of gravitation. On the latter, A. R. Hall and M. B. Hall, in their recent book *Selections from the Unpublished Scientific Papers of Sir Isaac Newton* (Cambridge, 1961), have printed the first manuscript draft of the *General Scholium* (written in January, 1712/13) in which Newton very plainly confesses his inability to couple the hypothesis of gravitational forces with observed phenomena: "I have not yet disclosed the cause of gravity, nor have I undertaken to explain it, since I could not understand it from the phenomena. For it does not arise from

The Thematic Imagination in Science

the centrifugal force of any vortex, since it does not tend to the axis of a vortex but to the center of a planet." And speaking of Newton's inability to arrive at the cause of gravity from phenomena, the Halls add: "In one obvious sense, this is true, and in that sense it knocks the bottom out of the aethereal hypothesis. In another sense it is false: Newton knew that God was the cause of gravity, as he was the cause of all natural forces. . . ."[5]

Exactly so—for this indeed was Newton's central presupposition in the theory of gravitation. The Halls continue, "That this statement could be both true and false was Newton's dilemma: In spite of his confident expectation, physics and metaphysics (or rather theology) did not smoothly combine. In the end, mechanism and Newton's conception of God could not be reconciled . . . Forced to choose, Newton preferred God to Leibniz."

That Newton could not bring himself to announce this hypothesis in the *Principia* is not strange since the grounds of the hypothesis are so foreign to the avowed purpose of this book on the *Mathematical Principles of Natural Philosophy*. And also, a thematic hypothesis becomes more persuasive the longer the period of unsuccessful attempts to use other hypotheses, namely, those that *are* coupled to phenomena. The thematic hypothesis is often an impotency proposition, in the sense that the search for alternatives has proved to be vain. The point when one is forced to rely on thematic hypotheses is exactly when one has to say, with Newton: "I could not understand it from the phenomena."

So when we approach the physics of a man like Newton, and even when we try to interpret his epistemological position, we must look beyond the explicit and obvious component of it, the basically operationist and relativistic physics of observable events. What made his work meaningful to Newton was surely that in his physics he was concerned with a God-penetrated, real world: God himself is standing behind the scenes, like a puppeteer, moving the unseen strings of the marionettes that merely act out the thoughts in His great sensorium. And this is a proposition which Newton tried to avoid having to state openly, where his friends and enemies would see it, though this reluctance accounts for some of the strange tension which pervades the *Principia* and his other writing. Reading Newton, one is struck by the fact that below the surface the major problems which haunted him were very closely related. They are: (a) the cause of gravity, whose existence only he had "established from phenomena"; (b) the existence of other forces, for example, short-range forces to explain cohesion, chemical phenomena, and so forth; (c) the nature of space and time, what he called the "sensory" of God; (d) and last, but not least, the proofs for the existence of the Deity (namely, by showing that there can be no other final causes for demonstrated forces and motions than the Deity—that, therefore, the Deity not only has properties, but also "dominion").

In Newton's physics, the hypothesized "sensory" of God is the cut-off point beyond which it was unnecessary and inappropriate to ask further questions. And this is an important function of a thematic hypothesis, which by its very nature is not subject to verification or falsification. For unlike the usual class of hypothesis—which, to use Aristotle's formula, is a statement that may be "believed by the learner" but ultimately is "a matter of proof"—the thematic hypothesis is precisely built as a bridge over the gap of ignorance. Thus, as scientists, we cannot and need not ask *why it is* that we believe, with Descartes, in an "inescapably believable" proposition; or why it is that we can perceive correspondences between certain observations and the predictions that follow from a model; or nowadays, for that matter, with Niels Bohr, why we can "build up an understanding of the regularities of nature upon the consideration of pure number."

III

We have indeed left the recipe for a step-by-step construction of scientific theory far behind. Let us now turn from the specific example and attempt to discern in a schematic way what the analysis of scientific theories in terms of themata adds to the more conventional kind of analysis.

Regardless of what scientific statements they believe to be "meaningless," all philosophies of science agree that two types of proposition are *not* meaningless, namely statements concerning empirical matters of "fact" (which ultimately boil down to meter readings), and statements concerning the calculus of logic and mathematics (which ultimately boil down to tautologies).

There are clearly difficulties here that we might well discuss. For example, the empirical matters of fact of modern science are not simply "observed," but are nowadays more and more obtainable only by way of a detour of technology (to use a term of W. Heisenberg) and a detour of theory. But in the main we can distinguish between these two types of "meaningful" statements quite well. Let

The Thematic Imagination in Science

us call them respectively *empirical* and *analytical* statements, and think of them as if they were arrayed respectively on orthogonal x- and y-axes; thereby we can represent these two "dimensions" of usual scientific discourse by a frank analogy, and generate terminology which will be useful as long as we do not forget that all analogy has its limits.

Now we may use the x-y plane to analyze the concepts of science (such as force), and the propositions of science, e.g., a hypothesis (such as "X-rays are made of high energy photons") or a general scientific law (such as the law of universal gravitation). The *concepts* are analogous to points in the x-y plane, having x and y co-ordinates. The *propositions* are analogous to line elements in the same plane, having projected components along x and y axes.

To illustrate, consider a concept such as force. It has empirical, x-dimension meaning because forces can be qualitatively discovered and, indeed, quantitatively measured, by, say, the observable deflection of solid bodies. And it has analytical, y-dimension meaning because forces obey the mathematics of vector calculus (namely, the parallelogram law of composition of forces), rather than, for example, the mathematics of scalar quantities.

Now consider a proposition (a hypothesis, or a law): the law of universal gravitation has an empirical dimension or x component—for example, the observation in the Cavendish experiment where massive objects are "seen" to "attract" and where this mutual effect is measured. And the law of universal gravitation has an analytical or y component, the vector-calculus rules for the manipulation of forces in Euclidean space.

An interpolation is here in order, to avoid the impression that there is some absolute meaning intended for the x- or y-components. Indeed, it is preferable to use the term "heuristic-analytic" for the y dimension, on grounds which I can at least indicate by noting that there exist in principle infinitely many possible logical and mathematical systems, including mutually contradictory ones, from which we choose those that suit our purposes. On the x axis we do not appear to have this degree of freedom to make "arbitrary" decisions on heuristic grounds. At least at first glance, we seem constrained to deal with the phenomena of our natural world as they present themselves to us, rather than with many mutually contradictory worlds of phenomena from which we might be free to select those to which we wish to pay attention. However, one can at least imagine worlds that are quite differently constructed, where on the one hand an infinitely large pool of phenomena contains "contradictory" sets (for example, stones that sometimes fall and sometimes rise, in some random sequence), but where on the other hand our logical and mathematical tools are severely restricted—say, only to Aristotelian syllogisms and elementary arithmetic. Then we would be forced to select from all possible observables those which can be represented and discussed in terms of scalar quantities, and we would have to exclude forces, acceleration, momenta, etc. In that case, the x-dimension could be named the dimension of heuristic-empirical statements.

Now, to some extent we *are* in this situation even now in our "real" world. We get a hint of it when we think of the great number of phenomena that are thought to be important today, but that were unknown yesterday;[6] or if we think of the continual change in the allegory (for example, the allegory of motion itself), from the Aristotelian conception which equated motion and change of any kind, to the modern, much attenuated idea of motion as the rate of change of distance or displacement with respect to time, or quantifiable local motion.

We realize the same point also when we think of all the "phenomena" which at any time are simply not admitted into science—for example, heat and sound in Galileo's physics, or most types of single-event occurrences that do not promise experimental control or repetition in modern physical science. In short, we are always surrounded on all sides by far more "phenomena" than we can use, and which we decide—and must decide—to discard at any particular stage of science.

The choice of allowable *analytical* systems is in principle also very large. Thus, any point, on any object, could for purposes of kinematical description be regarded as the center of the world. But the choice, in practice, is quite restricted. Indeed, the reason that science, until the late nineteenth century, was so sure of the uniqueness of the given world is to be sought in the fact that the analytical systems then available were so simple and had so long remained without fundamental qualitative changes and alternatives. Thus Newton could say in the preface of the *Principia* that geometry itself is "founded in mechanical practice and is nothing but that part of universal mechanics which accurately proposes and demonstrates the art of measuring." This impression helped to reinforce the feeling that the world, found and analyzed by science in terms of then current x and y components, existed in a unique, a

The Thematic Imagination in Science

priori way. In mathematics one calls such a situation, where the potential plurality of solutions shrinks to one or a very few, a "degenerate" case. It is only after the discovery of non-Euclidean mathematics that one begins to see the essential arbitrariness of the y-dimension elements in which our scientific statements are couched, and that one becomes open to the suggestion that there is also an arbitrariness in the decisions about what x-dimension elements to select. This recognition is perhaps at the heart of the current agnosticism concerning the old question as to the "reality" of the world described in the x-y plane.

But whether they are arbitrary or not, the x-y axes have, since the seventeenth and eighteenth centuries, more and more defined the total allowable content of science, and even of sound scholarship generally. Hume, in a famous passage, expressed eloquently that only what can be resolved along x- and y-axes is worthy of discussion:

If we take in our hands any volume; of divinity, or school metaphysics, for instance: Let us ask, Does it contain any abstract reasoning concerning quantity or number? No. Does it contain any experimental reasoning concerning matter of fact or criteria? No. Commit it then to the flames. For it can contain nothing but sophistry and illusion.

If we now leave the x-y, or *contingent*,[7] plane, we are going off into an undeniably dangerous direction. For it must be confessed at once that the tough-minded thinkers who attempt to live entirely in the x-y plane are more often than not quite justified in their doubts about the claims of the more tender-minded people (to use a characterization made by William James). The region below or above this plane, if it exists at all, might well be a muddy or maudlin realm, even if the names of those who have sometimes gone in this direction are distinguished. As Dijksterhuis has said:

Intuitive apprehension of the inner workings of nature, though fascinating indeed, tend to be unfruitful. Whether they actually contain a germ of truth can only be found out by empirical verification; imagination, which constitutes an indispensable element of science, can never even so be viewed without suspicion.[8]

And yet, the need for going beyond the x-y plane in understanding science and, indeed, in doing science, has been consistently voiced since long before Copernicus, who said that the ultimate restriction on the choice of scientific hypotheses is not only that they must agree with observation but also "that they must be consistent with certain preconceptions called 'axioms of physics,' such that every celestial motion is circular, every celestial motion is uniform, and so forth."[9] And if we look carefully, we can find even among the most hard-headed modern philosophers and scientists a tendency to admit the necessity and existence of a non-contingent dimension in scientific work. Thus Bertrand Russell speaks of cases "where the premises of sciences turn out to be a set of pre-suppositions neither empirical nor logically necessary"[10]; and in a remarkable passage, Karl R. Popper confesses very plainly to the impossibility of making a science out of only strictly verifiable and justifiable elements:

Science is not a system of certain, or well-established, statements; nor is it a system which steadily advances towards a state of finality . . . *We do not know: we can only guess.* And our guesses are guided by the unscientific . . . faith in laws, in regularities which we can uncover—discover. Like Bacon, we might describe our own contemporary science—"the method of reasoning which men now ordinarily apply to nature"—as consisting of "anticipations, rash and premature" and as "prejudices."[11]

One could cite and analyze similar opinions by a number of other scientists and philosophers. In general, however, there has been no systematic development of the point. But it is exactly here that we should discern the existence of a door at the end of the corridor through which the philosophy of science has recently been traveling. To supplement contingency analysis, I suggest a discipline that may be called thematic analysis of science (by analogy with thematic analyses that have for so long been used to great advantage in scholarship outside science). In addition to the empirical or phenomenic (x) dimension and the heuristic-analytic (y) dimension, we can define a third, or z-axis. This third dimension is the dimension of fundamental presuppositions, notions, terms, methodological judgments and decisions—in short, of themata or themes —which are themselves neither directly evolved from, nor resolvable into, objective observation on the one hand or logical, mathematical, and other formal analytic ratiocination on the other hand. With the addition of the thematic dimension, we generalize the plane in which concepts and statements were previously analyzed. It is now a three-dimensional "space"—using the terms always in full awareness of the limits of analogy—which may be called *proposition space*. A concept (such as force) or a proposition (such as the law of universal gravitation) is to be considered, respectively, as a point or as a configuration (line) in this threefold space. Its

The Thematic Imagination in Science

resolution and projection is in principle possible on each of the three axes.

To illustrate: the phenomenic and analytic-heuristic components of the physical concept force (its projections in the x-y plane) have been mentioned. We now look at the thematic component, and see that throughout history there has existed in science a "principle of potency." It is not difficult to trace this from Aristotle's ἐνέργεια, through the neo-Platonic *anima motrix,* and the active *vis* that still is to be found in Newton's *Principia,* to the mid-nineteenth century when "Kraft" is still used in the sense of energy (Mayer, Helmholtz). In view of the obstinate preoccupation of the human mind with the theme of the potent, active—I would almost say masculine—principle, before and quite apart from any science of dynamics (and also with its opposite, the passive, persisting principle on which it acts), it is difficult to imagine any science in which there would not exist a conception of force (and of its opposite, inertia).

It would also be difficult to understand certain conflicts. Scholastic physics defined "force" by a projection in the phenomenic dimension that concentrated on the observation of continuing terrestrial motions against a constantly acting obstacle; Galilean-Newtonian physics defined "force" quite differently, namely, by a projection in the phenomenic dimension that concentrated on a thought experiment such as that of an object being accelerated on a friction-free horizontal plane. The projections above the analytic dimension differed also in the two forms of physics (i.e., attention to magnitudes versus vector properties of forces). On these two axes, the concepts of force are entirely different. Nevertheless, the natural philosophers in the two camps in the early seventeenth century thought they were speaking about the same thing, and the reason was that they shared the need or desire to incorporate into their physics the same thematic conception of *anima,* or *vis,* or *Kraft*—in short, of force.

A second example of thematic analysis might be the way one would consider not a concept but a general scientific proposition. Consider the clear thematic element in the powerful laws of conservation of physics, for example the law of conservation of momentum, as formulated for the first time in useful form by Descartes. In Descartes' physics, as Dijksterhuis wrote:

All changes taking place in nature consist in motions of . . . three kinds of particles. The primary cause of these motions resides in God's *con-*

cursus ordinarius, the continuous act of conservation. He so directs the motion that the total *quantitas motus* (momentum), i.e., the sum of all the products of mass and and velocity, remain constant.[12]

"This relation Σ mv = const., constitutes the supreme natural law...."[13] This law, Descartes shows, springs from the invariability of God, in virtue of which, now that He has wished the world to be in motion, the variation must be as invariable as possible.

Since then, we have learned to change the *analytic* content of the conservation law—again, from a scalar to a more complex calculus—and we have extended the phenomenic applicability of this law from impact between palpable bodies to other events (for example, scattering of photons). But we have always tried to cling to this and to other conservation laws, even at a time when the observations seem to make it very difficult to do so. Poincaré clearly saw this role of themata in a passage in *Science and Hypothesis:* "The principle of the conservation of energy simply signifies that there is a *something* which remains constant. Whatever fresh notions of the world may be given us by future experiments, we are certain beforehand that there is something which remains constant, and which may be called *energy*"[14]—(to which we now add: even when we used to call it only mass). The *thema* of conservation has remained a guide, even when the language has had to change. We now do not say the law springs from the "invariability of God"; but with that curious mixture of arrogance and humility which scientists have learned to put in place of theological terminology, we say instead that the law of conservation is the physical expression of the elements of constancy by which Nature makes herself understood by us.

The strong hold that certain themes have on the mind of the scientist helps to explain his commitment to some point of view that may in fact run exactly counter to all accepted doctrine and to the clear evidence of the senses. Of this no one has spoken more eloquently and memorably than Galileo when he commented on the fact that to accept the idea of a moving earth one must overcome the strong impression that one can "see" that the sun is really moving:

Nor can I sufficiently admire the eminence of those men's intelligence [Galileo's Salviati says in the Third Day of the *Dialogue Concerning the Two Principal Systems*], who have received and held it [the Copernican system] to be true, and with the sprightliness of their judgments have done such violence to their own senses that they have been able to prefer that which their reason dictated to them to that which sensible experience represented most manifestly to the contrary . . . I cannot find any bounds for my admiration how reason was able, in Aristarchus and Copernicus, to commit such rape upon their senses as, in spite of them, to make itself master of their belief.

Among the themata which permeate Galileo's work and which helped reason to "commit such rape upon their senses," we can readily discern the then widely current thema of the once-given real world which God supervises from the center of His temple; the thema of mathematical nature; and the thema that the behavior of things is the consequence of their geometrical shapes (for which reason Copernicus said the earth rotates "because" it is spherical, and Gilbert, following the lead, is said to have gone so far as to prove experimentally, at least to his own satisfaction, that a carefully mounted magnetized sphere keeps up a constant rotation). Thus too, Sigmund Freud in *Moses and Monotheism,* after surveying the overwhelmingly unfavorable evidence standing against the central thesis in his book, would say in effect, "But one must not be misled by the evidence."

IV

While developing the position that themata have as legitimate and necessary a place in the pursuit and understanding of science as have observational experience and logical construction, I should make clear that we need not decide now also on the *source* of themata. Our first aim is simply to see their role in science, and to describe some of them, as a folklorist might when he catalogues the traditions and practices of a people. It is not necessary to go further and to make an association of themata with any of the following conceptions: Platonic, Keplerian, or Jungian archetypes or images; myths (in the nonderogatory sense, so rarely used in the English language); synthetic a priori knowledge; intuitive apprehension or Galileo's "reason"; a realistic or absolutistic or, for that matter, any other philosophy of science. To show whether any such associations do or do not exist is a task for another time.

I also do not want to imply that the occurrence of themata is characteristic only of science in the last centuries. On the contrary, we see the thematic component at work from the very beginning, in the sources of cosmogonic ideas later found in Hesiod's *Theogony* and in *Genesis.* Indeed, nowhere can one see the persistence of great questions and the obstinacy of certain pre-selected patterns for defining and solving problems better than in cosmologic speculations. The ancient Milesian cosmologic assumptions presented a three-step scheme: At the beginning, in F. M. Cornford's words, there was

a primal Unit, a state of indistinction or fusion in which factors that will later become distinct are merged together. (2) Out of this Unity there emerge, by separation, parts of opposite things . . . This separating out finally leads to the disposition of the great elemental masses constituting the world-order, and the formation of the heavenly bodies. (3) The Opposites interact or reunite, in meteoric phenomena, or in the production of individual living things . . .[15]

Now the significant thing to notice is that when we move these conceptions from the animistic to the physical level, this formula of cosmogony recurs point for point, in our day, in the evolutionist camps of modern cosmology. That recent theory of the way the world started proposes a progression of the universe from a mixture of radiation and neutrons at time $t = 0$; through the subsequent stages of differentiation by expansion and neutron decay; and finally to the building up of heavier elements by thermonuclear fusion processes, preparing the ground for the later formation of molecules. And even the ancient main *opposition* to the evolutionary cosmology itself, namely, the tradition of Parmenides, has its equivalent today in the "steady-state" theory of cosmology.

So the questions persist (for example, concerning the possibility of some "fundamental stuff," of evolution, of structure, of spatial and temporal infinities). And the choices among alternative problem solutions also persist. These thematic continuities indicate the obverse side of the iconoclastic role of science; for science, since its dawn, has also had its more general themata-creating and themata-using function. J. Clerk Maxwell expressed this well a century ago in an address on the subject of molecular mechanics:

The mind of man has perplexed itself with many hard questions. Is space infinite, and in what sense? Is the material world infinite in extent, and are all places within that extent equally full of matter? Do atoms exist, or is matter infinitely divisible?
The discussion of questions of this kind has been going on ever since man began to reason, and to each of us, as soon as we obtain the use of our faculties, the same old questions arise as fresh as ever. They form as essential a part of science of the nineteenth century of our era, as of that of the fifth century before it.[16]

We may add that thematic questions do not get solved and disposed of. Nineteenth-century atomism triumphs over the ether

The Thematic Imagination in Science

vortices of Kelvin—but then field theories rise which deal with matter particles again as singularities, now in a twentieth-century-type continuum. The modern version of the cosmological theory based on the thema of a life cycle (Beginning, Evolution, and End) may seem to triumph on experimental grounds over the rival theory based on a thema of Continuous Existence, and throw it out the window—but we can be sure that this thema will come in again through the back door. For contrary to the physical theories in which they find embodiment in x-y terms, themata are not proved or disproved. Rather, they rise and fall and rise again with the tides of contemporaneous usefulness or intellectual fashion. And occasionally a great theme disappears from view, or a new theme develops and struggles to establish itself—at least for a time.

Maxwell's is an unusual concession, but it is not difficult to understand why scientists speak only rarely in such terms. One must not lose sight of the obvious fact that science itself has grown strong because its practitioners have seen how to project their discourse into the x-y plane. This is the plane of public science,[17] of fairly clear conscious formulations. Here a measure of public agreement is in principle easy to obtain, so that scientists can fruitfully cooperate or disagree with one another, can build on the work of their predecessors, and can teach more or less unambiguously the current content and problems of the field. All fields which claim or pretend to be scientific try similarly to project their concepts, statements, and problems into the x-y plane, to emphasize the phenomenic and analytic-heuristic aspects.

But it is clear that while there can be automatic factories run by means of programmed computers and the feedback from sensing elements, there can be no automatic laboratory. The essence of the automaton is its success in the x-y plane at the expense of the z-direction (hence automata do not make qualitatively new findings). And the essence of the genial contributor to science is often exactly the opposite—sensitivity in the z-direction even at the expense of success in the x-y plane. For while the z-dimension is never absent even in the most exact of the sciences as pursued by actual persons, it is a direction in which most of us must move *without* explicit or conscious formulation and without training; it is the direction in which the subject matter and the media for communication are entirely different from those invented specifically for discussion of matters in the x-y plane with which the scientist after long training can feel at home.

Therefore it is difficult to find people who are bilingual in this sense. I am not surprised that for most contemporary scientists any discussion which tries to move self-consciously away from the x-y plane is out of bounds. However, it is significant that even in our time the men of genius—such as Einstein, Bohr, Pauli, Born, Schrödinger, Heisenberg—have felt it to be necessary and important to try just that. For the others, for the major body of scientists, the plane of discourse has been progressively tilted or projected from x-y-z space into the x-y plane. (Perhaps prompted by this example, the same thing is happening more and more in other fields of scholarship.) The themata actually used in science are now largely left implicit rather than explicit. But they are no less important. To understand fully the role a hypothesis or a law has in the development of science we need to see it also as an exemplification of persistent motifs, for example the thema of "constancy" or of "conservation"; of quantification; of atomistic discreteness; of inherently probabilistic behavior; or—to return to our example from Newton —of the interpenetration of the worlds of theology and of physics. Indeed, in this way we can make a useful differentiation that to my knowledge has not been noted before, namely that Newton's *public, experimental,* and *mathematical* philosophy is science carried on in the x-y plane, whereas Newton's more covert and more general *natural* philosophy is science in the x-y-z proposition space.[18]

V

I have spoken mostly of the physical sciences. I might, with equal or greater advantage, have dealt with the newer sciences, which do not have a highly developed corpus either of phenomena or of logical calculi and rational structures. In those cases, the z-elements are not only still relatively more prominent but also are discussed with much greater freedom—possibly because at its early stage a field of study still bears the overwhelming imprint of one or a few men of genius. It is they who, I believe, are particularly "themata-prone," and who have the necessary courage (or folly?) to make decisions on thematic grounds.

This was certainly the case in early mechanics and chemistry, and again with relativity and the new quantum mechanics. I suspect that an analogous situation has held in early modern psychology and sociology. Moreover, in those fields, as in the natural sciences during a stage of transformation, the significance and impact of themata are indicated by the fact that they force upon people notions that are usually regarded as paradoxical, ridiculous, or outrageous. I am thinking here of the "absurdities" of Copernicus' moving earth, Bruno's infinite worlds, Galileo's inertial motion of bodies on a horizontal plane, Newton's gravitational action without a palpable medium of communication, Darwin's descent of man from lower creatures, Einstein's twin paradox and maximum speed for signals, Freud's conception of sexuality of children, or Heisenberg's indeterminacy conception. The wide interest and intensity of such debates, among both scientists and enraged or intrigued laymen, is an indication of the strength with which themata—and frequently conflicting ones—are always active in our consciousness.

And the thematic component is most obvious when a science *is* young, and therefore has not yet elaborated the complex hierarchical structure of hypotheses which Braithwaite has pointed out to be the mark of an advanced science. As a result, the chain leading from observational "facts" to the most general hypotheses—those with a large thematic component—is not long, as in, say, modern physics or chemistry, but is fairly short. A physical scientist is used to having his most general and most thematic hypotheses safely out of sight, behind the clouds of a majestic Olympus; and so he is apt to smile when he sees that the altar of other gods stands on such short legs. When for example a chemist interprets a half-dozen clicks on a Geiger counter as the existence of a new chemical element at the end of the Periodic Table, he implicitly (and, if challenged, explicitly) runs up on a ladder of hierarchically connected hypotheses, each of which has *some* demonstrable phenomenic and heuristic-analytic component, until at the top he comes up to the general thematic hypotheses—which he is, by agreement of this fraternity, exempt from going into—namely, the thematic hypotheses of atomicity, of constancy, of the transformability of qualities, of the ordering role of integers. In contrast, the early psychoanalysts, for example, tried to go by a relatively untortuous route from the detail of observed behavior to the generality of powerful principles. Freud himself once warned of the "bad habit of psychoanalysis . . . to take trivia as evidence when they also admit of another, less deep explanatory scheme."[19]

I do not, of course, say this to condemn a science, but on the contrary to point out a difference between it and the physical sciences which I hope may help to explain the attitude of "hard" scientists to fields outside their own (or even of psychologists of one school to those of another). At the same time, it may help to elucidate why disciplines such as psychology (and certainly history) are so constructed that they are wrong to imitate the habit in the modern physical sciences to depress or project the discussion forcibly to the x-y plane. When the thematic component is as strong and as explicitly needed as it is in these fields, the criteria of verification should be able to remain explicitly in three-dimensional proposition space. To cite an instance, I am by no means impressed with the "Conclusion" at the end of R. G. Collingwood's influential book, *Essay on Philosophical Method:*

> The natural scientist, beginning with the assumption that nature is rational, has not allowed himself to be turned from that assumption by any of the difficulties into which it has led him; and it is because he has regarded that assumption as not only legitimate but obligatory that he has won the respect of the whole world. If the scientist is obliged to assume that nature is rational, and that any failure to make sense of it is a failure to understand it, the corresponding assumption is obligatory for the historian, and this not least when he is the historian of thought.[20]

This is a statement of the most dangerous kind, not because it is easy to show that it is wrong, but because it is so difficult to do so.

VI

Much could, and should, be said about other problems in the thematic analysis of science, such as the mechanisms by which themata change; or the way in which the choice of a thematic hypothesis governs what we are to look for in the x-y plane and what we do with the findings; or the remarkably small number of different themata that, over time, seem to have played the important roles in the development of science.

But for the purposes of this volume, it should be clear that the most significant fact, implied in the examples given, is that most and perhaps all of these themata are not restricted merely to uses in scientific context, but seem to come from the less specialized ground of our general imaginative capacity. This view leads us at once beyond the usual antithetical juxtaposition between science and the humanities. For the laments on the separation between science and the other components of our culture depend on the oversimplification that science is done only in the contingent plane, whereas scholarly or artistic work involves basic decisions of a different kind, with predominantly esthetic, qualitative, mythic

The Thematic Imagination in Science

elements. In my view this dichotomy is much attenuated, if not eliminated, if we see that in science, too, the contingent plane is not enough, and never has been.

It is surely unnecessary to warn that despite the appearance and reappearance of the same thematic elements in science and outside, we shall not make the mistake of thinking that science and non-science are at bottom somehow the same activity. There are differences which we should treasure. As Whitehead once said about the necessity to tolerate, no, to *welcome* national differences: "Men require of their neighbors something sufficiently akin to be understood, something sufficiently *different* to provoke attention, and something great enough to command admiration." It is in the same sense that we should be prepared to understand both the separateness that gives identity to the study of each field, as well as the kinship that does exist between them.

To return, therefore, to Newton's *Fifth Rule* of reasoning: he surely must have known that he could not publish it and remain true to his own work and that of most major innovators. As Newton's suppressed rule stands, it ends, you will recall, with the words: "Those things which neither can be demonstrated from the phenomena nor follow from them by an argument of induction, I hold as hypotheses." To be justified in publishing this rule Newton would have had to add something—perhaps this sentence: And such hypotheses, namely thematic hypotheses, have a place in natural philosophy as they do in all creative work.

REFERENCES

1. F. Dessauer, *Eranos-Jahrbuch* XIV (Zürich: Rhein-Verlag, 1946), 282 ff.

2. Some of these problems were first considered in my George Sarton Memorial Lecture, presented on December 28, 1962, before the meeting of the American Association for the Advancement of Science; others in a lecture of November 11, 1963, to the American Philosophical Society. See also my article "Über die Hypothesen, welche der Naturwissenschaft zu Grunde liegen," *Eranos-Jahrbuch* XXXI (Zürich: Rhein-Verlag, 1963), pp. 351-425.

3. Cf. Alexandre Koyré, "Etudes Newtoniennes I.—Les regulae philosophandi," *Archives Internationales d'Histoire des Sciences*, **13** (1960), p. 6. This article and Koyré's "L'Hypothèse et l'experience chez Newton," *Bull. Soc. Française de Philos.*, **50**, 2 (1956), pp. 60-97, are perhaps the best introduction to the large literature on this subject.

4. Koyré, "Etudes Newtoniennes I," *loc. cit.*

5. Or perhaps more precisely, in Newton's thought, as A. Koyré said, the cause of gravity is the action of the "Spirit of God." *From the Closed World to the Infinite Universe* (New York: Harper and Brothers, 1958), p. 234.

6. Or, conversely, observables that were once considered important, as in chemistry, where the fundamental attention to the appearance and color of the flame in violent chemical reactions was given up together with the phlogiston theory.

7. One may call the x-y plane the *contingent* plane because the meanings of concepts and statements in it are contingent on their having both empirical and analytical relevance. Contingency analysis is thus the study of the relevance of concepts and propositions in x- and y-dimensions. It is a term equivalent to operational analysis in its wider sense.

8. Dijksterhuis, *The Mechanization of the World Picture* (Oxford: Clarendon Press, 1961), p. 304.

9. Quoted from E. Rosen, *Three Copernican Treatises* (New York: Dover Publications, Inc., 1959), p. 29.

10. Russell, *Human Knowledge* (London: G. Allen & Unwin, 1948), Part 6, Ch. 2.

11. Popper, *The Logic of Scientific Discovery* (New York: Basic Books, Inc., 1959), pp. 279-80.

12. Dijksterhuis, *The Mechanization of the World Picture*, p. 410.

13. Descartes, *Principia Philosophiae* II, c. 36; *Oeuvres* VIII, 62-65.

14. Henri Poincaré, *Science and Hypothesis* (1952 reprint, New York: Dover Publications, Inc.), p. 166. Emphasis in original.

15. F. M. Cornford, *Principium Sapientiae* (London: Cambridge University Press, 1952), Ch. XI.

16. Quoted in C. C. Gillispie, *The Edge of Objectivity* (Princeton, New Jersey: Princeton University Press, 1960), p. 477.

17. For the distinction between public and private science, see G. Holton, "On the Duality and Growth of Science," *American Scientist*, 41 (1953), pp. 89-99.

18. As Newton writes in the General Scholium, "hypotheses, whether metaphysical or physical, whether of occult qualities or mechanical, have no place in *experimental* philosophy." But in the previous paragraph, at the end of a long passage on the properties of the Deity and His evidences through observable nature, Newton writes: "And thus much concerning God; to discourse of whom from the appearance of things, does certainly belong to *Natural* Philosophy." (Emphasis added.)

19. Sigmund Freud, "Ein religiöses Erlebnis," *Imago* XIV (1928), 9.

20. R. G. Collingwood, *Essay on Philosophical Method* (Oxford: Clarendon Press, 1933), pp. 225-26.

DON K. PRICE

The Established Dissenters

THE CELEBRATED conflict between science and the humanities is real enough that it takes up a lot of the time of those who prepare academic budgets or give out foundation grants. But in the American political system, it is a phony war.

The literary and the artistic branches of the humanities have never been in the thick of the political battle at all; they have never contended for the role of determining the values that guide policy decisions, or of supplying a systematic basis for political thought. The branch of the humanities that once undertook to do so was theology, the medieval "Queen of the Sciences." If science has had any rivals for the honor of providing the intellectual basis for government action, they have been law and moral philosophy, the branches of learning that were subordinate to theology, or closely allied to it, during the formative centuries of the European political tradition.

And if today there is hardly a real political battle between these rival fields of learning it is partly because, in academic politics, science has won a crushing victory; partly because, having won that fight, science seems to have no desire to occupy the political throne from which theology has been driven; and partly because theology shows no disposition whatever to regain its old uncomfortable seat of power, from which it once proclaimed the basic values by which government was to be guided.

Science, although it has become an establishment supported more or less on its own terms by society, is not moving toward the status of an Established Church, not becoming the citadel of a new orthodoxy. In the American (and generally, in the Western)

This essay is from the author's new book, *The Scientific Estate* (Cambridge, Mass.: The Belknap Press of Harvard University Press, 1965).

political system, scientists behave more like dissenters than like hierarchs. And this seems to be almost equally true whether a scientist in theory asserts the unlimited competence of science or whether he defers to traditional values.

In theory, indeed, there seems to be a wide range of opinion within the scientific community. The eminent scientists (and their professional allies among the engineers and physicians) who hold important positions of influence in government, and in the institutional structure by which government and science are now so closely connected, seem to retain rather conventional views. As Insiders, they are likely to accept the subordination of science to the value systems established by the nation's political tradition and interpreted by the authority of its government, and they can get along without much confidence that they are on the road to Utopia. The Outsiders, on the other hand—the scientists who prefer to appear as independent critics of present policy—are less willing to accept the validity of the traditional political ethos, or the necessity for science to be subordinated to a system of organized authority based on traditional values.

Obviously this is an impressionistic caricature of two wings of opinion, but it seems to me to identify roughly the difference of attitude between, say, the President's Science Advisory Committee and the members of the Council for a Livable World, and perhaps even many of the contributors to *The Bulletin of the Atomic Scientists*—even though the two attitudes are mixed in most scientists and in most of the rest of us.

The Insiders' view was typified by the Special Assistant to the President for Science and Technology when he told the National Academy of Sciences at its Centennial Celebration that 90 per cent of the federal expenditures for research and development should be undertaken only after administrators and legislators had decided that the individual projects were needed. The role of the expert in such decisions was to give advice, and to pass on means, not ends.[1]

The Outsiders, on the other hand, are comparatively unwilling to fit into a system the ends of which were determined by a prescientific culture, and the institutions of which are still dominated by men trained in the legal or theological or philosophical assumptions of that culture. They are much more likely to believe that the methods of science, by their steady progress from the physical to the biological to the social sciences, are moving toward an ability to solve even our political problems, and that scientists as such have an obligation to take political action to that end.

The Established Dissenters

But surprisingly few of them seem to be persuaded that such political action requires any fundamental change in our political institutions. In spite of their general distrust of the processes of politics and politicians, the Outsiders are still willing to put their faith in an oversimplified version of Jefferson's ideas about political machinery, even though they may have lost their confidence in applied science and its relation to Divine Purpose that was the basis of Jefferson's belief in progress. Their ideal would be an egalitarian democracy, with all issues decided by the votes of private citizens who have not been corrupted by service in the bureaucracy, and all of whom are earnestly studying science. The ideal has been depicted—with an admission of its lack of realism but still as an ideal—as a system of electronic communication in which every citizen could watch and listen to a Congressional debate and then register his vote instantaneously in a national referendum.[2]

In their different ways, both the Insiders and Outsiders are too deeply absorbed in current issues to think about the basic theory of their political status. To develop such a theory, besides, would call for a command of nearly all branches of scientific and humane knowledge. No professional scholar has any incentive to undertake such a formidable task; the specialized structure of the academic world makes the undertaking a disreputable one. But the scientist or administrator who is involved in the new relationship of politics and science is forced to worry about this problem and to have at least some tacit theory to guide him in dealing with it. As a beginning toward formulating such a theory, he might well recall the way in which science was freed from the domination of the traditional learning.

The Conquests of Science

The political challenge of science was implicit in its seventeenth-century rivalry with theology and scholastic philosophy. Before that time, the scientists as well as the priests and poets were trying to understand the universe in terms of a set of analogies with man, and to understand man and the physical universe alike in terms of Divine Purpose. As the mystic, Jacob Boehme, wrote, "*man* is the great mystery of God, the *microcosm,* or the complete abridgement of the whole universe,"[3] and in his day this notion guided astronomers as well as poets and theologians. This was the point of view against which Boehme's contemporary, Francis Bacon, rebelled at the beginning of the seventeenth century. "It is incredible," he wrote, "what a number of idols have been introduced into science by the reduction of natural operations to a correspondence with human actions, that is, by imagining that nature acts as man does, which is not much better than the heresy of the anthropomorphists."[4]

Within the two centuries after Bacon, the tables were turned. When that period began, astronomers were just beginning to give up their belief, to which Copernicus had been fully committed, that they had to treat planetary orbits as perfect circles because only such perfection of form could embody Divine Purpose. When it ended, men were beginning to question the usefulness of Genesis as a textbook in biology and geology. When it began, philosophers and theologians were still insisting that nature could be understood by reducing its workings to correspond with the hopes and fears of men, and with what they liked to believe was the will of God. When it ended, nature was seen as a great piece of clockwork, with all of its movements obeying the same laws of mechanics, so that Laplace's ideal scientist, if he could know the position and motion of every atom in the universe at an instant, would be able to predict everything that would happen thereafter to eternity.

With this notion, it was not surprising that Bacon's "reduction of natural operations" would begin to work backward, and that men would begin to try to understand themselves and their society by *reducing themselves* to natural operations. Today Bacon might find it incredible to see what a number of models, if not idols, have been introduced into the social sciences, to reduce human actions to natural operations. The primary article of faith among the orthodox natural scientists (there are, of course, many skeptics and dissenters) is that rigorous scientific method is being gradually extended from the hard sciences to the soft sciences—from mathematics and physics, through chemistry and biology, to psychology and the social sciences. This is the spectrum of the sciences as described by August Comte, and his positivist followers ever since have expected the scientific method to make a progressive advance along this line: philosophy and theology were the enemies, and their defenses were to be steadily reduced as the rigorously impersonal method of the sciences conquered one field after another, occupying at last the practical field of government.

By the time of Thomas Jefferson, scientists were already assuming that this progressive advance of the sciences would revolutionize society and destroy the influence of the ecclesiastical establishments, the stronghold of authoritarian tradition. Jefferson was too much

The Established Dissenters

the practical politician to push his scientific theories to their abstract conclusions: he never agreed with the scientific doctrinaires of the French Revolution who would exclude Divine Purpose from their system of thinking about the future of man and society.[5] He was not interested in overthrowing one type of scholastic establishment and replacing it by another; he expressed great contempt for those charitable organizations that "spent themselves in founding schools to transfer to science the hardy sons of the plough."[6] This attitude, which held that science needed to justify itself to society by its practical applications, was superficially very similar to the attitudes expressed in England in the seventeenth century by the followers of Bacon.

The similarities show up most clearly if we compare the purposes of the Royal Society, founded by Bacon's followers in 1660, with those of the American Philosophical Society, founded in 1743 by Benjamin Franklin. The American society's purposes were expressed in Franklin's "A Proposal for Promoting Useful Knowledge," with an emphasis on "Experiments that let Light into the Nature of Things, tend to increase the Power of Man over Matter, and multiply the Conveniencies or Pleasures of Life." That Proposal was in the same spirit as the earlier purposes of the Royal Society, as Robert Hooke defined them in 1663: it proposed to avoid dogmatic philosophy, or "the explication of any phenomena whose recourse must be had to originall causes (as not being explicable by heat, cold, weight, figure, and the like, as effects produced thereby)"; and to work on "Manufacturers, Mechanick practices, Engynes, and Inventions by Experiments."[7]

And yet the political temper of the two groups of scientists, in their formative years, was quite different. One received a Royal charter; the other was finally chartered in 1780 by a statute signed by the clerk of the General Assembly of Pennsylvania, Thomas Paine. The leaders of the Royal Society proclaimed that they were "not meddling with Divinity, Metaphysics, Moralls, Politicks, Grammar, Rhetorick, or Logick."[8] The leaders who won control of the American Philosophical Society in 1769 were, in practice as well as in theory, revolutionaries.

The founders of the Royal Society had been associated with the Calvinist wing of religious thought that had been the active force in the Puritan rebellion and the execution of Charles I, so that their renunciation of politics may have been only the price to be paid for sponsorship by Charles II. But it was also in accord with the temper of the time: England was "satiated with Religious Disputes" and civil war, and scientists, like others, were looking for a chance to cultivate their gardens and avoid useless quarrels.[9] By contrast, Franklin and Jefferson, who served as presidents of the American Philosophical Society for nine tenths of the period from 1769 to 1814, thought of science as the basis for world-wide political revolution and for continuous political progress thereafter. In the last letter Jefferson wrote, he attributed the beginnings of the rebellion against "monkish ignorance and superstition" and in favor of "the rights of man" to the "general spread of the light of science."[10] By his own role in politics, Jefferson set an example of political initiative on the part of a scientist; by the nature of the administrative institutions and legislative procedures that he helped to establish, he cleared the way for scientists to concern themselves with the ends of policy, as well as the technical means toward such ends. But all the while he assumed that science would not become a new establishment, and that it would justify its existence by the type of practical and applied work which it would undertake.

But it is striking to see how soon in the history of the American republic the scientist as such disappeared from political leadership. After Jefferson, the presidents of the American Philosophical Society were political nonentities, and American scientists seemed almost as eager to forget about republican egalitarianism, and to be accorded honors befitting their intellectual eminence, as the members of the academies of Paris or Berlin or St. Petersburg—which were the models for the scientists who, just before the Civil War, were advocating the creation of a National Academy of Sciences. The United States, like Great Britain, never managed during the nineteenth century to set up a strong set of institutions for the pursuit of advanced theoretical science, such as Napoleonic France developed in the *Ecole Polytechnique,* the *Ecole Normale,* and the revitalized *Academie des Sciences,* or such as the German renaissance after Napoleon produced in an impressive number of universities.

But even after the revolutionary ardor of American scientists cooled off and they seemed to become similar to the British in their concentration on practical rather than theoretical interests, there still remained a significant difference: the institutional and academic politics that hampered theoretical science in the two countries came from opposite motives.

In Great Britain, science (in spite of the political prudence of most British scientists) was quite correctly identified at the

The Established Dissenters

beginning of the nineteenth century as an intellectual force that had helped produce the American and French revolutions. During the reaction against republicanism in governmental politics, science suffered in academic politics. The ecclesiastical establishment that dominated the older universities had no sympathy for science; they were willing to tolerate mathematics and "pure" science, but nothing of an applied nature. This academic preference for pure over applied science did even theoretical science little practical good; it remained strictly a poor relation within the household of the unreformed academic establishments, dominated by the Church of England and the Tory party. It was no accident, then, that the principal leaders of science in Great Britain came from the Scottish universities, like Kelvin, or from obscure dissenting sects, like Faraday, or from among the Unitarians, like Priestley, or the Quakers, like Dalton. (It seems a little unfair to blame the slow development of basic science during this period on religion as such, for the dissenting sects were typically more earnest and puritanical and often more literal in their religious beliefs than the Church of England; the problem was not religion, but the politics of the ecclesiastical establishment.)[11] When more active support came for experimental science, it was in the dissenting academies, or in London and the newer universities founded on German models. The advancement of the sciences was thus left, in terms of the academic caste system, to the lower middle class.[12]

In the United States, on the other hand, theoretical science was handicapped not because Jefferson and Franklin, with their union of applied science and radical politics, were held back by an ecclesiastical establishment, but because they triumphed over it so completely.

In the eighteenth century, while science was still (under the name of natural philosophy) justified in American colleges as an offshoot and ally of theology, its international standing was higher than at any time during the next century. More Americans were elected Fellows of the Royal Society in the eighteenth than in the nineteenth century. Curiously enough, in view of the conventional opinion that ecclesiasticism has been the great handicap to science, basic science seemed to flourish in the United States during the eighteenth century, when "natural philosophy was generally held to be the friend and not the enemy of revealed truth," and when the contemporary science was a part of the program of training for the ministry. By contrast, the nineteenth-century flowering of mechanical invention was comparatively barren of theoretical science.[13]

During this period, the great handicap was not the opposition of an upper-class establishment, but the popular acceptance of a vulgarization of Jefferson's philosophy: the notion that the practical ingenuity of the Yankee mechanic was better than theory for the advancement of science. Washington and most of our other early presidents might advocate the establishment of a national university, but Congress was quite content to do without such an extravagance. There is something symbolic in the fact that, when an Englishman offered the United States an endowment for a national scientific institution (being persuaded that only in the United States could science continue its liberating alliance with radical politics) Congress refused to accept the gift for many years, and when it finally did so, it invested the Smithsonian bequest in bonds of the State of Arkansas, which defaulted on them.[14] And when Congress did get around to providing national support for higher education, it was not for the 'diffusion of knowledge among men,' but for the advancement of the agricultural and mechanic arts.

There was, indeed, a theological reaction in the United States against the scientific radicalism that Jefferson typified. For example, Transylvania College, the first college west of the mountains, had made a brave beginning in science under the leadership of Jeffersonian free-thinkers and Unitarians, but all that was stifled when it fell under the control of the Presbyterians during the great religious revivals of the early nineteenth century.[15] But in the metropolitan centers of the United States, from that day to this, theological obscurantism has been stronger in the lower than the upper classes. The elite universities were more independent of conservative theological pressures than were the backwoods denominational colleges or even the state land-grant colleges, which were formally quite apart from ecclesiastical influence. It was not theological prejudices that kept Harvard from throwing all its weight behind the theoretical sciences; when it founded the Lawrence Scientific School in 1847 it followed good Jeffersonian doctrine in putting its emphasis on the training of men who would serve "as engineers or chemists . . . applying their attainments to practical purposes."[16] The upper-class institutions of higher learning were simply becoming the technological servants of private industry, rather than of Jeffersonian democracy.

Jefferson had bet on the wrong horse. He had wanted to make

The Established Dissenters

sure that science would be applied to the purposes of an agrarian democracy. And so he proposed that in the universities of America agricultural science be recognized as "the crown of all other sciences." He was the first of our scientists to propose that his particular field, on account of its social utility, be given academic preferment with government aid. "The same artificial means which have been used to produce a competition in learning, may be equally successful in restoring agriculture to its primary dignity in the eyes of men . . . In every College and University, a professorship of agriculture, and the class of its students, might be honored as the first . . ."[17]

Hamilton, of course, had taken a quite different line. His *Report on Manufactures* had proposed government subsidies for the advancement of technology, but for the benefit of industry more than agriculture. All the forces of technology in the industrial revolution, and of science in the later scientific revolution, were to conspire to make twentieth-century America far more like his dream than like Jefferson's. And his victory was less the result of the conspiracy of corporate interests than of the failure of Jefferson's theory of the way in which man's moral and political purpose was to be advanced in practical politics. For that theory took for granted the essential goodness and harmony of men's purposes, provided that men were not constrained and oppressed by ecclesiastical and feudal establishments; it held that the accumulation of practical knowledge in a free and egalitarian society would automatically guarantee the advancement of both knowledge and human welfare, under the guidance of a "natural aristocracy" of talent.[18]

Within a few decades it was plain that popular politics in the United States would not be willing to support either a natural aristocracy in politics or the advancement of science. One half of Jefferson's theory defeated the other half. Jacksonian democrats were quite willing to follow Jefferson in opposing establishments and class privilege, and relying on applied rather than theoretical science. But they were not interested either in calling to office Jefferson's "natural aristoi," or in building up (as John Quincy Adams proposed) scientific institutions that would bring America up among the leaders of science. Hence, in spite of the unusual freedom of scientists to advance themselves and their interests in public affairs, and in spite of the widespread support of applied science for both agricultural and industrial purposes, basic science in America remained second-rate throughout the nineteenth and early twentieth century. It did so, not because it was held back by an upper-class establishment, allied with ecclesiastical politics, but because the scientists who had helped shape the politics of the Revolutionary period had come so close to getting just what they wanted. And this was a social and political system with no establishments, in which scientists would be given support on the basis of the practical utility of their research, and in which public affairs would be administered entirely by men who would hold office, or lose office, every time the electorate changed its mind.

But, as things turned out, the Jeffersonian hopes were disappointed. It was not enough to free science from the shackles of theological influence, and politics from the domination of the church and the bureaucracy or nobility. Once the academic and political worlds were freed of their subordination to such ideas and institutions, they were not content with the high thinking of pure science or the plain living of the small farmer. For the more that technology and science contributed to the material welfare and comfort of mankind, the more science seemed to be dependent on the patronage not of an egalitarian democracy, but of a new type of highly organized power, the industrial corporation and its philanthropic offshoots.

When support began to come for science as basic research, rather than in connection with specific applications, it came not from the influence of popular political leadership, but from a source that Jefferson would not have expected and might not have welcomed: a union of great wealth and religious motivation, now characteristically incorporated in an institution that is a legal descendant of the Established Church of England, namely, the private foundation.[19]

The first major step, in frank imitation of the continental European institutions, came with the founding of Johns Hopkins, the first American university to put major emphasis on graduate research in the natural sciences. But the continuing push in that direction came from the general educational foundations that were established soon after the turn of the century. The several Carnegie and Rockefeller foundations had been established by industrialists who were motivated by strong religious beliefs, but the academic strategy that they followed was the opposite of support for an ecclesiastical establishment, or for classical theories of education. Andrew Carnegie, by making his pensions for professors available only to colleges that were not controlled by churches, led a great many academic institutions to separate themselves from the control of Protestant denominations; Congress would not dream of attaching such a condition today to the federal funds pouring into American universities, in spite of the tradition of separation of church and state. And it was under the guidance of Frederick G. Gates and Wallace Buttrick, two Baptist ministers, and Wickliffe Rose, a philosopher, that John D. Rockefeller's fortune became dedicated first to the advancement of medicine and general education, and then to this proposition: "All important fields of activity, from the breeding of bees to the administration of an empire, call for an understanding of the spirit and technique of modern science . . . Appreciation of its spirit and technique, moreover, determines the mental attitude of a people, affects the entire system of education, and carries with it the shaping of a civilization."[20]

This was the point of view that had come to dominate the academic and intellectual institutions of the United States, and the thinking of the business and political leaders who financed them. There was no important challenge to its influence; science was indeed ready to move on "from the breeding of bees to the administration of an empire." The ideas of objective techniques of inquiry, with notions of purpose and values rigorously eliminated, invaded the social sciences and then began to influence even the study of administration; universities undertook to teach that subject, foundations supported them in research as well as teaching, and government agencies began to recruit their graduates. As all this went on, the model most frequently held up for emulation was the Administrative Class of the British civil service. Yet after a half-century or so of effort, it is quite apparent that the United States has nothing in its governmental system like the established corps of general administrators, educated primarily in historical and classical subjects, whose influence is so great over the policies as well as the management of British government.

The reasons for this divergence are partly political, and some of them were dealt with in the previous chapter. But they are also partly academic and intellectual. Professors of political science assumed that the basic values and purposes of man were determined by his religious beliefs, his philosophical ideas, or other irrational notions, and that science did not deal with such matters at all. They tended, next, to assume that in government the major issues of policy properly depended on value judgments, and that these matters should therefore be reserved to politicians; administrators would be subordinate, and *their* work should be made as objective and scientific as possible.

This theory was supported by Woodrow Wilson's essay, "The Study of Administration,"[21] which held that administrative science was the same no matter what the policy or the purpose to be served: "If I see a murderous fellow sharpening a knife cleverly, I can borrow his way of sharpening the knife without borrowing his probable intention to commit murder with it . . ." Accordingly, in imitation of the way that scientists renounced any interest in purpose and values, administrators were supposed to renounce any interest not only in the election of their political superiors, but also in the decisions which politicians would make on policies. The theory that science has nothing to do with values and purpose has its practical political corollaries: the Hatch Act forbids civil servants to take part in political campaigns, and the Internal Revenue Code denies tax exemption to scientific institutions that use their funds to influence legislation.

This approach, it was generally assumed, was an imitation of the British civil service with its impartial administration, but it was quite different in theory as well as in practice. For it asked the administrator not merely to abstain from public participation in contests for power, but to avoid an interest in the substance of governmental programs. This approach, when followed in university programs of training for government service, turned out experts in managerial techniques—such as specialists in budgeting or personnel administration—far more successfully than it produced general administrators. A little later, in imitation of industrial management, the application of science to training for public administration came to include the use of psychology and sociology and cybernetics to deal with the morale of the workers, the effectiveness of their interpersonal relations and communications, and the technical aspects of the decision-making process. But this approach, though it took a broader view of the concept of efficiency, still refused to deal with the policy objectives of the organization. Consequently, the label "administrative," which in the British civil service means the top career men concerned with policy issues, came in the U.S. service to apply to jobs and to men charged with the means rather than the ends of a program, and therefore properly to be subordinated to the "executives" responsible for the substance of policy.

The substance of policy, on the other hand, was generally

assumed to include the scientific and technological aspects of the program. Scientists, however rigorously they may think they keep ideas of purpose out of their research, are not so inhibited on questions of policy. They are likely to assume, in the best Jeffersonian tradition, that the pursuit of science is not only a good end in itself, but a means toward political ends that are so obviously desirable that others ought to accept them automatically, or at least permit the scientists to propagandize for them while holding public office on a nonpartisan career basis. This is not merely the way scientists think; it is sanctified by public acceptance. If a career official in the Internal Revenue Service or the Post Office or the Commerce Department were to campaign publicly and conspicuously for higher income taxes or the public ownership of the telegraph system or more government regulation of business, it would be considered at least mildly improper, and perhaps even grounds for dismissal. If a rocket expert or a nuclear engineer or a psychiatrist in government service advocates vast appropriations for his field of interest, or major shifts in the relationship of the federal government to private institutions, he may be thought of as zealous to a tiresome degree, but he is only doing his duty.

"Establishment" has come to be a fashionable term for purposes of political ridicule, as young English authors deride the upper classes. But it is a pity to let the dramatists spoil a useful political term by making it mean any type of clique or class with a powerful influence. It is useful for a more precise purpose, to define a social institution that is given permanent public support and status apart from current shifts in political power. Thus the Church of England is established, and so are the dons at Oxford and the permanent parts of the British civil service. The intellectual disciplines that dominate this interlocking establishment are those on which the traditional values were founded; those whom this system has promoted to high rank are licensed to counsel the government on its most important policies, as long as they do so privately and discreetly, and do not get involved publicly in partisan disputes.

In the United States, the intellectual and academic tradition was different, and it produced a quite different institutional system, even though it had some of the features of an establishment. In the Jeffersonian tradition, the system was founded partly on the land-grant colleges, whose scientists created the unique American agricultural system; then Jeffersonian theory mixed with Hamiltonian practice established the great foundations, and made the principal private universities, once thought of as centers of pure scholarship, into decentralized systems for furthering not merely the advancement of science, but its application to public policy.[22] And if the mark of an establishment within the government is the ability to maintain a continuous access to the ear of the chief executive, the scientists have gained this status. The change in party control of the White House in 1961 brought in a new Council of Economic Advisers, and a new Budget Director, but the President's Science Advisory Committee was hardly affected. Both of the men who had served as chairman under Eisenhower remained on the committee under President Kennedy, and he chose as his new chairman a scientist who had been on the Eisenhower committee.

G. K. Chesterton once remarked that Great Britain could take pride in the fact that the sailors in the Royal Navy had never—well, hardly ever—mutinied, except for more pay. A social system is stable as long as its disputes are not over fundamentals. On this principle, the present scientific establishment in the United States is healthy enough; its internal arguments are mainly over the ways in which its grants and contracts are distributed, and from the outside it is challenged mainly with respect to the amount of money it gets, or the specific uses to which the money is put. With one exception, there has never been in American politics a serious effort to present the arguments, from the point of view of a conservative philosophy, against the intellectual approach of the scientific establishment whose theories have so profoundly influenced our national policies.

That exception was not altogether serious; it had some tragic elements, but they were mixed with low comedy. It was the effort made by a special committee of the House of Representatives, under the chairmanship of Congressman B. Carroll Reece (Republican of Tennessee) to investigate the work of the tax-exempt foundations. And the intellectual core of the investigation was an attack on the "growing movement to apply the methods used in the natural sciences to research in the social sciences."

This movement, the committee report argued in 1954, had led the social scientist to believe that the main purpose of his discipline was to catch up with the rigorous and value-free methods of the natural sciences. The effects of this belief were "an excess of empirical research," based on "inductive reasoning from observed data," and this in turn led to "'moral relativity,' to the detriment of our basic moral, religious, and governmental principles."

It was, of course, the final political result of this methodological influence of the natural sciences that the writers of the report were interested in. They said of the scientific method: "Its natural outcome is an approach to Marxism—it is not surprising that so many of the social scientists tend to collectivism." This is dangerous both because "public opinion is greatly determined, in the long run, by the influence of intellectuals," and more specifically because "the government has come to rely upon foundations and foundation-supported organizations to provide 'social scientists' for research and in advisory capacities," with the effect of "infiltrating government with subversives."[23]

Except for the point about subversives, the argument was one that might have gained considerable support from any of the several conservative schools of thought that were becoming fashionable in American academic life, and that were undertaking to defend the traditional against the scientific culture. For there were many respectable scholars who had been arguing that the structure of American society had been so shapeless, and its tradition so deficient in firm theological or philosophical principles, that it had no inner defenses against the domination of public affairs by a technology devoid of purpose or spiritual values. Science, this line of argument ran, had had its modern origins in Western Europe in the intellectual movement that was associated with the rise of Protestantism, and perhaps even earlier with the heretical ideas of the nominalists. Its radical implications were kept in some check in Western Europe by the traditional structure of society, but in the United States—with no aristocratic tradition, and no established church or bureaucracy—the scientists and their intellectual allies had no real opposition in imposing their ideas on public policy. Worst of all, they seemed to have an edge in the competition for foundation grants.

This was a legitimate though highly debatable point of view, and something like it had become current in various centers of academic and governmental thought. As examples, one might cite among the professional scholars the ideas of the neo-Thomists gathered at the University of Chicago under the leadership of President Robert M. Hutchins and Mortimer Adler,[24] and among public officials, the quite different ideas of George F. Kennan, who had never been persuaded by liberal scientists that the atomic bomb had made us into One World, or that technical assistance was rapidly turning all the underdeveloped countries into democracies.

But intellectuals of the genuinely conservative tradition were not the allies that Mr. Reece was seeking: he listed Messrs. Hutchins, Adler, and Kennan in his report among those whose names were in the files of the House Committee on Un-American Activities, and used their association to help document the subversive guilt of the foundations. And Mr. Reece's purpose was certainly not to establish a conservative political authority in the United States; it was only to prove the charge that he announced as he started his inquiry: "Here lies the story of how communism and socialism are financed in the United States."[25] The success of his effort depended on his ability to persuade the country that the main ideas in American intellectual life had been invented by a big-money conspiracy, a feat so obviously beyond the competence of "big money" that it was hard for politicians to take the charges seriously, even in the era of McCarthyism. The investigation collapsed shortly after a minority member of the committee read aloud (without identifying) excerpts from Papal encyclicals, and a member of the committee staff said that they were "closely comparable to Communist literature," and that their objectives "parallel very closely communistic ideals."[26]

The Reece report was a good example of the empirical research that it denounced: it amassed a great deal of detail to prove what every academic administrator in the United States knew—that the major foundations, the major universities, the major scholarly associations and their federations, and the major government agencies all kept in touch with each other and exchanged ideas and personnel, and that science was the main source of the ideas they respected most. But it was tragically deficient in the theoretical interpretation of its data. It did not recognize that the main source of the intellectual tradition that it was attacking was not Marxist, but Jeffersonian—just as its own attack was based on a Jeffersonian dislike of concentrated economic influence, rather than on a conservative philosophy drawn from the prescientific theological tradition.

For better or for worse, science escaped from the institutional domination of the older culture very early in the history of the United States, and in its relation to the administrators of academic and public affairs it has been in a position of predominant influence ever since. The traditional culture, derived from theology and the old philosophy, has had comparatively little organized influence on politics; there is simply no conservative political faction of any consequence that has its intellectual roots in the old tradition,

The Established Dissenters

to counterbalance the newer and more radical influence of science. This is perhaps a weakness in American politics; the most ardent conservatives are, like the late Congressman Reece, not conservatives at all in the historical and philosophical sense of that term; they are radicals committed to a particular set of economic and technological interests.[27]

Science in the United States might as well quit rebelling against the older culture from which it sprang. It has become independent of its father long since; its more dangerous rival is its technological offspring. If science wishes to continue to guard its freedom and emphasize its purpose of knowledge and understanding for their own sakes, it might well begin to worry about the prospect of a society dominated entirely by technological purpose. Science might well wonder whether it might not have fared better in a society in which the theological and political traditions of free institutions remained powerful. But if that is so, science cannot count on being protected by the older tradition, which unaided is much too feeble in the United States to set limits on the purposes of technology.

The Self-Restraint of Science

Out of its own methods and its own approach, science will have to make some contribution to a new theory about its proper relation to politics. We can best judge what that contribution may be, not by listening to what scientists say specifically on political subjects, but to what they say about their own work as scientists.

The average citizen who reads Sunday supplements or the political scientist who reads Congressional hearings may get the impression that scientists now think that science may some day, even if it cannot now, provide the answer to any question of policy. Many scientists feel obliged to assert their potential jurisdiction in this way; they believe that science, for more than three centuries, has been winning its intellectual battle against theology and traditionalism, and do not see why it should accept any limits on its victory except as a temporary tactic. At times, this point of view—which is characteristically expressed more often by the Outsiders, who are most conspicuous as critics of public policy, than by the Insiders, who have to help administer it—seems to represent nearly a consensus in the scientific community. Many scientists, even when they support the Insiders as a practical necessity, seem to think that they are making unworthy compromises with politicians and administrators, much as pious vestrymen feel guilty if they support local politicians who tolerate a certain amount of commercial vice in order not to hurt business.

On the other hand, if the layman takes even a brief excursion into the writings of leading scientists, and takes note of what they say about their own business, he is not persuaded that science is a form of knowledge whose practitioners are growing in confidence about their ability to understand and interpret reality, especially with respect to problems that are related to human purposes. Still less is he persuaded that scientists themselves are inclined to unite in an organization that could help to persuade the general citizenry to accept science as an authoritative guide to policy decisions.

For example, the revolution in physics over the past half-century left many of the more philosophical physicists, especially the leaders of the older generation, with much less confidence that physics can ever reach a complete understanding of concrete reality. The majority of the younger generation may not accept this philosophical pessimism, and may hold to a faith that science can in principle answer any question that is scientifically meaningful, but they set such limits on the kinds of questions that they consider to have real meaning that they exclude many of the philosophical or political questions that most interest the layman. During the same period, scientists in other disciplines have come to be much less inclined to think that it will ever be possible to develop a single mechanical and deterministic science, to which all other sciences can be reduced in a grand and unified system.[28]

I am not concerned here with the issue whether in theory physics (or any other science) may some day actually provide a complete understanding of nature, or solve any concrete political problem. That is a metaphysical issue that has no operational meaning to a student of politics. I am concerned rather with what scientists themselves think about that issue, for it is hard to imagine that science could provide the intellectual basis for a new theory of politics unless scientists generally believed that their methods contained some promise of dealing comprehensively with major political issues—as the materialist dialectic proposes to deal with problems of history and politics as well as problems of physics. And the most pertinent fact is that most American scientists seem to think that such an idea is either irrelevant to their interests, or merely silly.

Their attitude comes in the main not from any loss of self-confidence on the part of the scientist in his particular discipline. Few doubt, moreover, that there is in some sense a fundamental unity of science, and that over the past half-century the several sciences have greatly enlarged their common stock of general principles, and of their conceptual tools of inquiry. Many hold more firmly than ever to their belief that scientific concepts will be progressively unified in principles of increasing generality. Nevertheless, all this is quite different from the much simpler scientific faith of the nineteenth century, which showed more confidence in the complete adequacy of science as a means of understanding reality, and in the possibility of extending the principles of mechanics so as completely to understand and then to predict and control human and social affairs. That was the kind of intellectual faith on which a genuinely authoritative political philosophy could be based.

Physicists began to lose that kind of confidence in the nineteenth century as they went beyond the solid and predictable matter that seemed to correspond to the ordinary man's notion of what was real. The electromagnetic theory of Faraday and Maxwell, for example, made Kelvin uncomfortable because he could not devise a mechanical model of it.[29] And as the physicist got inside the atom, he entered a universe to which some of the older generation never became reconciled; to them it seemed to contain phenomena that were for the first time, even in principle, unknowable and unmeasurable; and individual bits of inanimate matter seemed to behave without obeying the classical laws of cause and effect.

The younger generation of physicists apparently got used to all this quite promptly. They did not even expect to think in terms of the mechanical models, or the aesthetic analogies, that had been the foundations of the scientific faith of their elders. Einstein tried to convey to the layman some notion of the mathematical and abstract nature of modern physics by saying that the scientist "certainly believes that, as his knowledge increases, his picture of reality will become simpler and simpler and will explain a wider and wider range of his sensuous impressions." At the same time, he warned, the scientist has to understand reality in the way a man might if he had to study a watch without opening it. "He will never be able to compare his picture with the real mechanism and he cannot even imagine the possibility or the meaning of such a comparison."[30] The younger physicists characteristically did not even care whether there was a watch there in the first place; if they could identify the things they could observe, and measure and predict their relationships, they were not interested in the kind of "reality" that was beyond their observation, and were not sure that it made sense to assume that it existed.

The great advances in the physicists' understanding of the material world have apparently come from this kind of selective interest. Science has achieved its great power by insisting on defining for itself the problems it proposes to solve, and by refusing to take on problems merely because some outside authority considers them important. But that power, and the precision of thought on which it depends, is purchased by a refusal to deal with many aspects of such problems. Some of those aspects are those that always appeal to the child and the poet, and that used to concern the philosopher—notions of ultimate cause and of human purpose. Thus Newton refused in the *Principia* to try to answer the question how one celestial body could move another without touching it; by setting aside the question that Aristotle and Descartes had considered important, he made it possible not only to predict the movements of the planets, but to relate them to the general laws of mechanics on earth. The demand of each scientific discipline for the right to choose its own problems, and fit them to its concepts and techniques and instruments, suggests that science is not eager to undertake to solve the problems of society as society would define them—especially since politicians so often insist on defining such problems in terms of purpose.

A generation ago, a number of physicists were so impressed by the new quantum mechanics, and especially the new uncertainty principle—resulting from the discovery that it was impossible at the same time to determine with precision the position and the velocity of an electron—that their confidence was shaken in the regularity of natural phenomena, and the operation of cause and effect. As a result, a few of them took to mystical speculation, and most of them concentrated on their specific research interests and ignored the philosophical implications, but those with the broadest interests undertook to grapple with the problem in a scientific spirit. In recent years, for example, the less mystical and more positivistic among the physicists—for example, the late Percy W. Bridgman—have been likely to worry about the limits on the ability of science to know and to predict. Even if the physicist retains full confidence, in principle, in the regular sequence of cause and effect, in practice he acknowledges that it is impossible to predict

The Established Dissenters

the future from the present position and motion of the atoms without having a limited number to observe under controlled conditions, which means without letting anything come in from outside to upset the experiment. The idea of determinism, in short, has meaning only within a controlled experiment of reasonable size; to talk of determinism throughout the universe, Bridgman argued, becomes meaningless for any but metaphysical or religious purposes.[31] Moreover, there is the limit that is set on the exactness of science by the need to take into account, in any observation, the instruments which give you the knowledge of the things you are studying, as well as the things themselves. As Bridgman noted, this problem comes up not only in dealing with the very small-scale phenomena—as when it becomes impossible to determine simultaneously the position and velocity of an electron precisely—but in dealing with very large systems. For you cannot understand and control your data unless you understand and control your instruments as well, and once your data reach a certain quantity the control of those instruments will require other instruments, and so on "in infinite regress."

Bridgman summed up these limitations—in a bit of fanciful speculation—by considering the problem of studying the functioning of the human brain by looking at its individual atoms. In addition to the time required to observe all their vast number, and to consider their interrelationships, there would be the time needed to put the observations into words, and then argue about those words. This would lead, he gloomily observed, to another infinite regression.

The biological or social scientist is not nearly so frightened by the quantity and complexity and (in practice if not in theory) the unpredictability of the data he has to work with. He is used to dealing with statistical models and probabilities, and inclined to scoff at the timidity of the professor of the supposedly more rigorous discipline who considers it impossible to think at all scientifically about a subject unless it is subject to completely deterministic rules. But the "harder" sciences seem less eager than they once were to extend their jurisdiction, or to assert their readiness to solve all problems. They are inclined to avoid many questions that the layman would wish to ask, because they consider them either too difficult or meaningless, and they seem to take pride in the discovery that they have reached limits on what can be known about certain physical phenomena.

The main purpose of science as such can no longer be defined in terms of "useful knowledge"; it is less a matter of providing answers than of opening up new questions. James B. Conant defined science as a series of concepts arising from experiment and observation, and fruitful of further experiments.[32] This emphasis, as Gerald Holton has pointed out, has led in its extreme form to an interest in highly specialized and sharply defined problems, and simultaneously a complete suspension of curiosity in all other directions; and in its less extreme form, to an "existential acceptance of the known and unknown."[33]

Thus the logical affinity of modern science, in its most rigorous and positivistic forms, does not seem to be with nineteenth-century idealism, the philosophy which was allied with a belief in the unity of all knowledge and which was taken to serve as the basis for powerful authoritarian systems of politics. Instead it seems to be with existentialism. Science does not seem to expect to establish a body of set truths that can serve as a dogmatic basis for political action. The main philosophical threat to our freedom is not that science will tempt us to invent a new materialist dialectic, or establish a "1984" style dictatorship. It is rather that if we rely on science alone we will be left with no sense of the purpose of existence, and thus no basis for determining our political goals to guide the blind forces of applied technology.

Let us leave the physicists for the moment, move along the line from the hard toward the soft sciences, and look at biology. Here we find a number of leading biologists worrying about the relevance to science of the idea of purpose, and openly in rebellion against the "reductionist" philosophy, which proposed not only to make biology more scientific by eliminating notions of purpose, but also by reducing it to the analytical approaches of physics and chemistry. Niels Bohr once noted the limitation on the methods of physics in studying a living organism: to make a complete analysis would destroy it and ruin the observation. But the point made by biologists is even more fundamental: as René Dubos argued, even if you could carry on such an analysis, the analytical process inherently ignores the fact that "the traits, properties, and activities associated with the living process are the expressions of the interplay between the constituent parts, rather than of their individual characteristics." The analytical techniques associated with physics and chemistry cannot account for the phenomena most characteristic of life, especially "a continuous interplay with the environment involving 'purposiveness' or at least 'directiveness.' "[34]

The Established Dissenters

If Dubos shows a little unwillingness to commit himself altogether to the word "purposiveness," he may well be trying to distinguish his position carefully from those who, like Teilhard de Chardin or E. W. Sinnott, are considered by some of their colleagues to be guilty of sympathy with the scientific heresy of vitalism, which skirts close to the edge of mysticism.[35] Even those biologists who dislike to use the term "purpose" in connection with the evolution or development of biological systems are likely to be just as insistent as Dubos on the limitations which science must acknowledge when it undertakes to deal with living organisms. Ernst Mayr, for example, will have nothing to do with any teleology (in the sense of anything that smacks of the notion of evolution guided by a final goal or purpose) but insists that biology, unlike most physics, has to admit a high degree of unpredictability or indeterminacy in its subject matter. Individual events take place essentially at random, particularly in heredity; each animal is truly unique; each is so complex that a complete description of it is quite impossible; and in the interaction of living beings new qualities emerge that are not logically predictable from their previous properties. For all these reasons, though statements in biology can have scientific validity, it is a statistical validity, and the future of an individual organism is not predictable.[36]

As we move along Auguste Comte's spectrum from physics to biology, and on to the social sciences, we find all these same difficulties intensified. Social scientists generally have hoped that, by making their disciplines more exact, and by imitating the quantitative and rigorous methods of the natural sciences, they could (a) provide more reliable guides to those who have to make policy decisions, and might even (b) provide the answers to the main policy problems. These two hopes, at first thought, seem very much the same. But they are fundamentally different, and the difference turns on some of the points I have been discussing.

The critics of the social sciences have been inclined to say that they will neither provide reliable guides to the policy maker nor provide the answers to policy problems, for two reasons: first, their subject matter is too complex, and second, they mix up their scientific approach with value judgments. There is no doubt that these two limitations, as a matter of degree, have been severe. In the same way that biology is more complex than physics, and therefore involves less certainty and predictability, so the various social sciences are more complex and difficult than biology. Moreover, as in physics, problems arise not only from the magnitude and complexity of the data, but from the unreliability of the instruments of observation. Man in society is hard to study scientifically less because he is a complicated object of observation than because he is the instrument of observation, and a refractory one indeed. If modern psychology has taught man anything, it is just how irrational and perverse and unreliable an instrument he is for scientific purposes. It is certainly much harder for him to purge his mind of prejudices and value judgments when he is dealing with human and social problems than with the data of the physical sciences.

Yet these two limitations can be overcome to a very considerable degree, and are being overcome, by those aspects of the social sciences that rely on quantitative techniques, such as econometrics, or that are developing more reliable methods that are linked with biology and psychology, such as the behavioral sciences.[37] Every advance in the precision of our understanding of facts can also contribute to the sharpening of our value judgments. As a result, these disciplines are beginning to furnish the politician or administrator who must decide policy questions with an increasing quantity of data and of methods that can be useful to him. There is every reason to believe that, as they become more exact and reliable, they will continue to do so.

But that is fundamentally different from the question with which we are concerned: namely, whether scientists believe that science can solve major policy problems, and thus provide the basis for a new system of political decision. And on that question, as the social scientists succeed in pushing rigorous and exact methods of research toward the "soft" end of Comte's scientific spectrum, they are less inclined to try to relieve political and legal authority of its burden of making decisions in which unscientific value judgments will play a major part.

The most widely discussed use of the social sciences in a major governmental decision in the United States was probably the use by the Supreme Court of sociological evidence in its decision forbidding racial segregation in public schools. A good many social scientists were at first eager to take as much credit as possible for this decision, and to argue that it proved what objective scientific method could accomplish if freed from irrational beliefs and prejudices. Then came a tangled public argument between those anthropologists and psychologists who held that science proved that the races were intellectually equal, and hence should not be segregated, and those who argued that they were not, and hence

The Established Dissenters

should be. And so the Committee on Science in the Promotion of Human Welfare of the American Association for the Advancement of Science concluded in a public report that the question of intellectual equality was too complicated to be proved one way or the other, and in any case was not really germane; the main question turned on a political and legal principle that was at bottom a matter of ethical belief.[38]

This suggests that the social sciences may now be following the earlier examples of the physical and the biological sciences not merely in trying to achieve greater precision and reliability in their methods, but also in understanding that such precision is purchased by an abstraction, and an exclusion of concern for purposes and values, that make it impossible to deal simultaneously with all the aspects of any concrete problem. The maturity of a science may be measured not only by its power, but by its discrimination in knowing the limits of its power. And if this is so, the layman does not need to worry lest the social sciences, as they become more scientific, will be more likely to usurp political authority. On the contrary, they will stop short of trying to solve completely our major political problems not because they are unlike the natural sciences, but to the extent that they are like them. And the more they get to be like them, the more they will be of specific service to the policy maker, and the less they will pretend that their methods can measure all relevant aspects of any concrete problem and supply its final answer.

The scientist at work in his laboratory has not, during the twentieth century, been pursuing the ideal of a single scientific method that is gradually giving a single comprehensive view of reality. He has been developing the particular method of a particular discipline, the one that works well and produces results with respect to a special aspect of reality. And when he undertakes to join with his fellow scientists to advance his discipline, he finds it most useful to associate not with a continuously broadening group, but a narrower and more specialized one.

The first scientific organizations in the United States were comprehensive, like the American Philosophical Society, which in the eighteenth century included all the sciences together with all other branches of learning, or, in the next century, like the American Association for the Advancement of Science, which united at least all the natural sciences. But the more advanced the science, the less it seemed to be interested in building up a comprehensive organization; the physicists and chemists concentrated their attention so much on their respective specialized societies that they were much weaker in the American Association for the Advancement of Science than the biologists and geologists.

Even when new scientific concepts and techniques began to integrate the methods of certain sciences, the result was not to unite their organizations but to split them further. As the techniques of chemistry began to be more useful in biology, the result was not to unify the associations of chemists and biologists, but to add a new American Society of Biological Chemists. The scholarly and professional motives of the scientist led toward ever-increasing specialization; the 1960 catalogue of scientific and technical societies in the United States and Canada listed 1,836 organizations.[39] Scientists have indeed managed to maintain comprehensive organizations. But they have done so only when they have been interested in some purpose beyond science itself. For example, they established the Federation of American Scientists, and in recent years built up the American Association for the Advancement of Science, out of an interest not only in science but also in its social and political implications. Similarly, they have set up organizations to represent them in doing business with the government—the purpose that led to the creation of the National Academy of Sciences in the nineteenth century, and the American Institute of Biological Sciences in the twentieth.

The Retreat toward Abstractism

So it seems obvious that science is not moving toward the development of a unified system of knowledge that can solve political problems. And it seems equally obvious that scientists are not developing a unified and disciplined organization through which the scientific community will become a powerful political force.

One might then ask whether the intellectual world is moving in the opposite direction. From the point of view of the scientist, are we on the road to reaction? If the methods of the natural sciences have not proved adequate to deal with the complexities of social problems, are we about to give up the effort of the Enlightenment to introduce rationality into politics, and surrender to a revival of theological authority over moral and political purpose?

This possibility might seem a plausible one but for one curious fact: it was not the conservative but the liberal wing of theology

The Established Dissenters

that tried to take advantage of the uncertainty that developed in the self-confidence of science. When a few of the twentieth-century physicists began to note that certain things were in principle unknowable and others did not seem to follow the classical laws of cause and effect, it was mainly the theological liberals who thought that we might smuggle back into our philosophical system some notion of Divine Providence intervening occasionally in the affairs of the world. If the biologists, they went on to suggest, find that the study of living matter requires us to think in terms of its purpose, may not Evolution be seen as the working of a Divine Plan? Some of the more liberal theologians thus undertook to reconcile science and religion, to the great relief of many of their followers who had been made uncomfortable by finding the old unity of faith and learning disrupted. So they were reassured to think that, in Henry Drummond's words, "science has supplied theology with a theory which the intellect can accept and which for the devout mind leaves everything more worthy of worship than before."[40] Some of the scientists, too, were willing to take on the mantle of prophets, and to draw religious or mystical consequences from the new uncertainties of their science. Thus Sir James Jeans argued that the mysteries of Nature could be understood only as phenomena of Mind or Spirit—or, as he said in his presidential address to the British Association for the Advancement of Science in 1934, the compulsion of determinism may originate in our own minds.[41]

Now it is quite clear that the leaders of scientific and those of religious thought do not waste as much time quarreling with each other as they did a half-century ago. But this cessation of hostilities did not come about through a real reunion, with more scientists discovering grounds for faith through their science and more theologians relying on science for evidence of their beliefs. On the contrary, during the past quarter-century the most important leaders in both fields have been inclined simply to pull their troops back from the battle and to respect the territory of the other camp.

Thus the Catholic philosopher Jacques Maritain, while welcoming the spiritual effects on certain scientists of the "troubled and divided state of mind" resulting from the crisis of modern physics, goes on to argue that "most of the great contemporary physicists who turn to philosophical problems"—he had mentioned Jeans, Sir Arthur Eddington, Arthur Compton, and Erwin Schrödinger—get into all sorts of logical weaknesses and confusion by trying to extend their scientific methods into another field. By contrast, he praises the scrupulous logic, within fields which have meaning for the scientist as such, of the logical positivists, who are interested only in things which can be observed, measured, and dealt with by mathematical symbols. The concepts of modern science like physical indeterminism may in the end help establish true faith, but only if science and theology are seen as distinct fields of knowledge.[42]

In this point of view, Maritain is at one with the most influential leaders of the new Protestant theology. In different ways, Karl Barth, Paul Tillich, and Reinhold Niebuhr neither try to fight against science nor make use of it; they are concerned with things that operate on another plane altogether. There is clearly, among such theologians, much less of a disposition today than a quarter-century ago to buttress theology by finding uncertainties or mysticism within the ranks of the scientists, or analogies between theological and scientific concepts.[43]

It may be significant that this reaction against the earlier type of theological liberalism has not led theologians to try to develop more precise moral codes on the basis of their theoretical doctrines, or in practice to argue that organized religion should have greater political authority. The new leaders of Protestant theology not only seem to have no ambition to re-establish the controls over public morals in which their Calvinist ancestors took such pride, but they have given up the interest of their immediate liberal predecessors, the advocates of the Social Gospel, in striking up an alliance with applied science to solve specific social problems. This is true, obviously, of the theologians like Tillich[44] who represent the existential wing of contemporary religious thought, but it is even more true, perhaps, of the neo-orthodox, like Barth, whose God is abstracted nearly as effectively as the space-time continuum from the practical moral and political issues of the world today.[45] And those neo-orthodox theologians who are most interested in practical politics, like Reinhold Niebuhr, are as eager to avoid the belief that man can translate Divine Purpose into political decisions as they are to base their faith on something other than the evidences of science.[46]

If science and theology are less in conflict today, it is only partly because science is now less inclined to insist that its method is the only way to think about man and the universe. It is more because theology—or at any rate, leading theologians—make much less confident claims today than a century ago that their form of knowledge can be related with certainty to material and political affairs. Academic theologians may indeed have gone too far in this

The Established Dissenters

direction for the taste of the average scientist and engineer, as well as the average man. If one straw can show which way the wind is blowing, it may be significant that the main strength of the more fundamentalist Christian association in American colleges and universities, the organization created by those who considered the World Council of Churches and its student affiliate too modernist and not literal enough in their beliefs, has been drawn from faculty members and students in the natural sciences and engineering.[47]

Some philosophers of science may look forward to the day when science will displace the traditional values of morals or politics. But the working natural scientist usually seems to be bored by the idea. Typically, the notion appeals more to certain types of social scientist or political theorist; it was Thomas Hobbes, after all, who anticipated the physical scientist's taste for reducing human actions to physical phenomena, by building his political theory on the assumption that all change is nothing but motion.[48] The recent skepticism of the natural scientists about their ability to attain ultimate and certain knowledge, and their growing unwillingness to reduce the sciences themselves to a single operational or philosophical system, do not offer much intellectual basis for the development of a new ideology or a new ruling priesthood. Scientists, in the way they think, are still dissenters, even after they have gotten themselves established.

As individuals, scientists have no great trouble in reconciling either their skepticism, or their confidence in determinism, with moral purposes and values. Some of the physicists and mathematicians, when reality seemed to dissolve into meaningless symbols, took refuge in the sane realities of ordinary personal relationships. Hermann Weyl, for example, described the "ridiculous circle" of meaninglessness into which one may be led by the formalism of modern mathematics and physics, and said, "We escape it only when we understand the manner in which we deal in daily life with things and people to be an irreducible foundation.[49] And thus Bridgman was able to say, on the level of personal knowledge, "In the end, when . . . human weariness and the shortness of life forces us to stop analyzing our operations, we are pretty much driven to accept . . . a feeling in our bones that we know what we are doing." "We disregard determinism when dealing with ourselves; we have to disregard it also, within reason, in our everyday contacts with our fellows."[50]

If the scientist makes something like a leap of agnostic faith in his personal life, the sciences do something of the same sort when they deal with public issues. By eliminating the bias of human purpose from their methods, and by concentrating on material causes, they do not seem to destroy the political independence or sense of commitment of scientists, who as citizens seem no more inclined than laymen to be either determinists or skeptics. Perhaps they know better than anyone else that science does less to provide final answers to political issues than to open up new ones, and that men in authority will always have to make responsible choices without the assurance of absolute certainty. Far from despising moral and political values, or doubting their existence, they seem to think them so important that science ought to be concerned with helping to test and refine and clarify them—and to refuse to be used as a mere instrument of any political authority that is based on values that are not able to stand up to such testing.

But in undertaking to relate knowledge to the responsible use of political authority, the scientist runs into complications that do not confront him as he adjusts his personal philosophy to his individual behavior. Here is where the great power of the natural sciences does not do away with the need for a political or constitutional theory, but makes it all the more necessary.

This problem cannot be solved by encouraging science to extend its progress in a single dimension, along Comte's spectrum from the hard to the soft sciences, with the expectation that at the end it will conquer and occupy the old stronghold of theology and philosophy in the determination of the values that form the basis of our political decisions. For the fortress of politics has long since been deserted by the theologians and philosophers, at least by the more scholarly among them. And the value system of politics, like that of most individuals, is not a code of rules discovered in advance by abstract study, but is a less precise set of attitudes developed in a series of concrete actions. In politics those actions take place in a continuous process of cooperation and compromise between those who work to discover or develop abstract and precise systems of knowledge and those who make use of such knowledge to further human purposes.

This system of relationships runs along a spectrum in a quite different dimension from Comte's; it runs from the abstract and theoretical knowledge of science, which is by its nature free of human purposes and passions, first to the types of skills and knowledge organized and applied by the professions (like engineering and medicine) that are based on science, and then to those of administrators, and finally of politicians. These several types of skills and knowledge are in turn progressively less concerned with precise abstractions, and more with the responsible use of power in the application of value judgments to questions which science is never quite able to answer completely.

Along this spectrum, science is not in conflict with the disciplines of the older tradition of humane learning. On the contrary, it shares with them a common set of problems. It is impossible for either kind of scholarly knowledge, in a free constitutional system, to be translated directly into political decisions. In Western nations, the theologians have long since been forced to learn how to let lawyers and administrators serve as the intermediaries between their abstract truth and the politicians who exercise supreme authority. The scientists are newcomers to the status of being established with public support, and are not yet altogether persuaded that they need to develop a clear constitutional theory of their relation to political authority.

The scientists have one advantage: in theory it has been rather more clear to them than to most of the theologians that they can develop their kind of knowledge only by freeing themselves from assumptions about human purposes and values. Thus they have protected themselves, to some extent, from the temptations of power and the dangers of political control. By the very nature of their discipline, they remain dissenters, with no interest in founding a new political dogma. But they need a great deal of money from the government, and what they do with it has an obvious impact on public policy. Even as dissenters, they must be established, and the future status of their estate must be developed with care if we are to adjust our constitutional system to modern technology without losing our freedom.

REFERENCES

1. Jerome B. Wiesner, "Science in the Affluent Society," address at centennial celebration of the National Academy of Sciences, Oct. 23, 1963 (mimeo).

2. Simon Ramo, address at the University of California at Los Angeles, May 1, 1961 (mimeo). The idea was subsequently noted in the *Report of the American Assembly: 1962–1963* (New York: Columbia University Press).

3. Jacob Boehme, *The Signature of all Things* (New York: E. P. Dutton, Everyman's Library, 1934), p. 3.

4. This passage appears, with only slight variations, in *The Proficience and Advancement of Learning, Divine and Human,* Book II, and in *De Dignitate et Augmentis Scientiarum,* Book V, chap. iv. I am indebted to Dr. Marjorie Hope Nicolson for calling it to my attention (see her *The Breaking of the Circle*), and I have used her translation, except for the substitution of the word "science" where she read "philosophy." In this context, Bacon's "philosophy" clearly meant what we mean by science; it was translated as "Natural Philosophy," for example, in *The Philosophical Works of Francis Bacon,* ed. John M. Robertson (London, 1905), pp. 119, 517.

5. Jefferson, in a letter to John Adams, April 8, 1816, affirmed his confidence in human goodness and social progress, and based that confidence on a refutation of the determinism of Diderot, D'Alembert, and D'Holbach and on a belief in both a theistic "first cause" and the effective workings of "final causes." Jefferson was strongly anticlerical, and opposed all forms of ecclesiastical establishment, but was a little contemptuous of the tendency of scientific radicals in the Catholic countries to turn atheist; he noted that the Protestants, when they defected from Platonic Christianity, turned Deist. See also his Letter to Thomas Law, June 13, 1814, *The Life and Selected Writings of Thomas Jefferson* (New York: Modern Library, 1944), pp. 667–668, 636–640.

6. Jefferson to David Williams, Nov. 14, 1803, *The Writings of Thomas Jefferson,* ed. Albert E. Bergh, 1903, vol. X, p. 429.

7. A facsimile of Franklin's "Proposal" is given in each of the recent Year Books of the American Philosophical Society, Independence Square, Philadelphia. The Robert Hooke quotation is from C. R. Weld, *A History of the Royal Society with Memoirs of the Presidents* (London: John W. Parker, 1848), I, pp. 146–147.

8. Weld, I, 146–147.

9. Thomas Sprat, *History of the Royal Society,* 1667, reprinted in Washington University Studies (St. Louis, 1958), p. 152. Edwin G. Conklin, "A Brief History of the American Philosophical Society," *Year Book* of the Society (Philadelphia, 1962), pp. 39–40.

10. Jefferson to Roger C. Weightman, June 24, 1826, *Life and Selected Writings,* Modern Library, p. 729.

11. Lewis Feuer argues to the contrary: that science is held back by religion, and fostered by a kind of Epicurean materialism. See his *The Scientific Intellectual* (New York: Basic Books, 1963).

12. Everett Mendelsohn, "The Emergence of Science as a Profession," in *The Management of Scientists,* ed. Karl Hill (Boston: Beacon Press, 1964). See also Sir Eric Ashby, *Technology and the Academics* (London: Macmillan, 1959). For a delightful account of the persistence into the twentieth century of the unreformed establishment at Oxford, see E. L. Woodward, *Short Journey* (New York: Oxford University Press, 1946).

13. I. Bernard Cohen, *Science and American Society in the First Century of the Republic* (Columbus: Ohio State University, 1961).
14. Brooks Adams in his introduction to Henry Adams, *The Degradation of the Democratic Dogma* (New York: Macmillan, 1920), p. 58.
15. Niels H. Sonne, *Liberal Kentucky 1780–1828* (New York: Columbia University Press, 1939).
16. Cohen, *op. cit.*, p. 6.
17. Jefferson to David Williams, cited above, pp. 429–430.
18. For a summary of Jefferson's views on the expectation that a natural aristocracy would be produced by the progression forces of science, see his letter to John Adams, Oct. 28, 1813, *Life and Selected Writings*, Modern Library, pp. 632–634. For a very suggestive discussion of the political consequences of the lack of philosophic depth in the thinking of Jefferson and his associates, see Daniel J. Boorstin, *The Lost World of Thomas Jefferson* (Boston: Beacon Press, 1960).
19. For the legal ancestry of the private foundation and its roots in the status of the medieval church—but also in the political radicalism of the fourteenth century—see Henry Allen Moe, " 'The Vision of Piers the Plowman' and the Law of Foundations," American Philosophical Society, *Proceedings*, 102 (1958), pp. 371–375. For the subsequent story of the development of foundations in England, see W. K. Jordan, *Philanthropy in England, 1480–1660* (London: Allen and Unwin, 1959), and David Owen, *English Philanthropy 1660–1960* (Cambridge, Mass.: Harvard University Press, 1964). Owen (p. 326) quotes Thomas Hare, who is better known for his advocacy of proportional representation than as a leader in the Social Science Association and in the organization of philanthropy, as remarking in 1869, "I regard endowments as an important element in the experimental branches of political and social science."
20. Memorandum of 1923 by Wickliffe Rose, General Education Board, quoted in Raymond B. Fosdick, *The Story of the Rockefeller Foundation* (New York: Harper, 1952), p. 141.
21. *Political Science Quarterly*, June 1887, reprinted in *Political Science Quarterly*, December 1941, p. 481. Wilson's essay actually recognized and gave priority to the role of administration in policy: "It is the object of administrative study to discover, first, what government can properly and successfully do, and, secondly, how it can do these proper things with the utmost possible efficiency." But he put such strong emphasis on the second point that the influence of his essay was heavily in the direction of making administration a value-free science.
22. Clark Kerr, *The Uses of the University* (Cambridge, Mass.: Harvard University Press, 1963).
23. *Tax-Exempt Foundations*, Report of the Special Committee to Investigate Tax-Exempt Foundations and Comparable Organizations, House of Repre-

sentatives, 83rd Cong., 2d Sess., House Report No. 2681 (1954), pp. 17-19, 56, 60, 67, 73, 200.

24. Among the scholars who propounded systematic conservative theories was Richard M. Weaver, of the University of Chicago, who argued in his *Ideas Have Consequences* (Chicago: University of Chicago Press, 1948) that the defeat of logical realism by nominalism in the theological debates of the Middle Ages was the great turning point in Western history, from which resulted our modern liberal and scientific decadence. William of Occam, he argued, led a philosophic attack that, with later support from Bacon and Hobbes, is responsible for the current onslaught on our "last metaphysical right" of private property.

25. *Tax Exempt Foundations*, p. 422.

26. *Ibid.*, p. 425.

27. The lack of a genuinely conservative political tradition in the United States is discussed by Louis Hartz, *The Liberal Tradition in America* (New York: Harcourt, Brace, 1955).

28. Ernest Nagel remarks, for example, on the decline in the early belief in mechanics as the perfect and potentially comprehensive science, and the growing belief that the reduction of one science to another that is more abstract and simple—for example, biology to physics—does not necessarily produce a more useful method. *The Structure of Science* (New York: Harcourt, Brace & World, 1961), pp. 154, 363. For a classic example of the reductionist and deterministic type of biology, see Jacques Loeb, *The Mechanistic Conception of Life*, ed. Donald Fleming (Cambridge, Mass.: Harvard University Press, 1964); the first edition was published in 1912.

29. Einstein noted that James Clerk Maxwell's equations, which could not be interpreted mechanically, made it necessary to give up mechanics as the foundation of all physics. See his "Autobiographical Notes" in Paul A. Schilpp, *Albert Einstein: Philosopher-Scientist* (Evanston: Library of Living Philosophers, 1949), p. 25. As for Kelvin's view, see Nagel, p. 114.

30. Albert Einstein and Leopold Infeld, *The Evolution of Physics* (New York: Simon & Schuster, 1938), p. 33.

31. P. W. Bridgman, in *The Way Things Are* (Cambridge, Mass.: Harvard University Press, 1959), pp. 170–172, makes this point, even while citing the effect on human conduct of belief in determinism, with the history of Calvinism as an example. "A deterministic universe was demanded by the religious and philosophic notion of an omnipotent and all-knowing God."

32. James B. Conant, *Modern Science and Modern Man* (New York: Columbia University Press, 1952), p. 54.

33. Gerald Holton, "Über die Hypothesen, welche der Naturwissenschaft zu Grunde liegen," in *Eranos-Jahrbuch* XXXI (Zürich: Rhein-Verlag, 1963), p. 408.

34. René Dubos, "Logic and Choices in Science," American Philosophical Society, *Proceedings*, 107 (1963), p. 370. See also Theodosius Dobzhansky, "Evolutionary and Population Genetics," *Science*, Nov. 29, 1963, p. 1131.

35. See, for example, the various quotations from Teilhard de Chardin's writings available in Nicolas Corte, *Pierre Teilhard de Chardin: His Life and Spirit* (New York: Macmillan, 1960). Edmund W. Sinnott, in *The Biology of the Spirit* (New York: Viking Press, 1953), argued for a new and biologically respectable concept of purpose. George Gaylord Simpson criticized their positions in his *This View of Life* (New York: Harcourt, Brace & World, 1964). At the same time he took an anti-reductionist position and dealt at length with the special problem of considering purpose in biological science.

36. Ernst Mayr, "Cause and Effect in Biology," *Science*, Nov. 10, 1961, pp. 1501–1506.

37. Bernard Berelson and Gary A. Steiner give a summary of the current accomplishments of the behavorial sciences in their *Human Behavior: An Inventory of Scientific Findings* (New York: Harcourt, Brace & World, 1964).

38. "Science and the Race Problem," *Science*, Nov. 1, 1963. See also letter of rebuttal in *Science*, Feb. 28, 1964, pp. 913–915.

39. National Academy of Sciences—National Research Council, *Scientific and Technical Societies of the United States and Canada, 1960–61*, ed. John H. Gribbin (Washington, D.C., 1961).

40. "The Contribution of Science to Christianity," in *Henry Drummond, an Anthology*, ed. J. W. Kennedy (New York: Harper, 1953), p. 75.

41. British Association for the Advancement of Science, *Report of the Annual Meeting* (1934), p. 13.

42. Jacques Maritain, *The Range of Reason* (New York: Scribner, no date), pp. 406, 87, 210.

43. John Dillenberger, in *Protestant Thought and Natural Science* (New York: Doubleday, 1960), gives an excellent summary of these developments. "There is a great danger of filling the gaps in science with theological answers, or of seeing too readily the footprints of God in the world, or of assuming that one is thinking God's thoughts after Him. Few indeed are those who see an argument for free will in the concept of indeterminacy or who follow du Nouy in finding a theistic frame of reference in biology . . . The respect for mystery which has emerged in contemporary science does not necessarily imply a spiritual or religious interpretation of the world" (pp. 283–284).

44. Paul Tillich, *Dynamics of Faith* (New York: Harper, 1958), p. 33.

45. Karl Barth, in his major theological work, looked on politics and political questions as "fundamentally uninteresting." *Community, State and Church*

(New York: Doubleday Anchor Books, 1960), p. 23. Dillenberger's comments are pertinent: "While theologians and scientists previously crossed into each other's territory, Barth and Tillich have so separated these spheres that they have disregarded the knowledge of the world contributed by natural sciences . . . To be sure, the thrust of existentialism was not merely against science: it protested wherever man became an object . . . The emergence of existentialism in the theological renaissance of the twentieth century stands for a recovery of man more congenial to classical theology, than the notion of man as the embodiment of value or as moral personality." Dillenberger, pp. 262-264.

46. Reinhold Niebuhr, *The Nature and Destiny of Man* (New York: Charles Scribner's Sons, 1947), Part I, pp. 198-203, 298-299.

47. Not only does the Inter-Varsity Christian Fellowship attract student support from among those concentrating in the sciences, but the faculty advisers at two thirds of the colleges reporting came from the natural sciences, and the academic members of the National Board are predominantly from the sciences. Lawrence Neale Jones, "The Inter-Varsity Christian Fellowship in the United States," unpub. Ph.D. dissertation, Yale University, 1961.

48. *The Leviathan*, Part I, chap. i.

49. Hermann Weyl, "Wissenchaft als Symbolische Konstruktion des Menschen," in *Eranos-Jahrbuch* XVI (Zürich: Rhein-Verlag, 1948), pp. 427-428. I am indebted to Gerald Holton for calling this article to my attention, and for the translation of this passage.

50. Bridgman, pp. 43-44, 259.

GYORGY KEPES

The Visual Arts and the Sciences:
A Proposal for Collaboration

THESE LINES are hesitantly written by a painter, whose tools are images, not words, who feels at home in the visible world rather than in the complexities of concepts, and whose commitment is to qualities of the seen world, not to disciplined interpretations of measured phenomena. The thoughts presented here have grown out of an internal dialogue between dreams of the full life and the recognition that our circumstances seldom permit them to come true.

I sometimes dream about being just a painter, painting and forgetting everything else—living in the richness of the moment—like the feeling I remember of swimming without any sense of time or goal, feeling the cooling touch of water, the warmth of the sun, the effortlessness of movement. But such experiences of timeless blending into the enveloping natural world are rare. A painter, too, may find a sense of abandon when the interplay between brush strokes and not-yet-visible but intensely felt hidden images develops freely into life. But such glimpses of felt unity with the "primal sanities of nature," disregarding measured time and parceled space and finding an exalted confidence in mere being, also come only rarely and do not last. Each moment of our contemporary existence reminds us that we are growing out from yesterday and moving toward tomorrow, and that our individual survival and self-realization can be guaranteed only by the cooperative acts of other men. We live in history and we live in society. Yet even though we may recognize that our lives are secured by the combined efforts of the social body, our explosive, unresolved mid-twentieth-century life compels us, as individuals, to return again and again to the basic questions: What am I? Where have I been? Where am I going?

One of the most evident signs of the contemporary self-consciousness is the obsessive questioning of what roles we are to play; and nowhere is this more true than in the urgent concern over questions of the justification, the scope, and the significance of artistic forms. In no other area of contemporary civilization are claims and counter-claims made with such vehemence, such offensive and defensive rigidity. Quacks and peddlers of fake solutions, with their artistic nostrums, are hard to distinguish from persons with honest beliefs and deep commitments. The part controls the whole. So many of our artists single out fragmentary aspects of a complete image of human experience. At one moment they are busily improvising an image of speed, casting away repose and introspection. At other times they are manufacturing new fertility symbols or paying homage to the increasing production rate of our industrial society, rejecting the broad panorama of nature. Lately, infatuated with the isolated kinesthetic act, they accept the autobiographical note of an accidental moment at the expense of the rest of life.

Some fifty years ago the Italian Futurist Filippo Marinetti orated about "the racing space, the acrobatic somersault, the slap in the face and the blow of the fist—'war,' the bloody and necessary test of the people's force." Naum Gabo and Antoine Pevsner answered him thus:

The pompous slogan of "Speed" was played from the hands of the Futurists as a great trump. But ask any Futurist how does he imagine "speed," and there will emerge a whole arsenal of frenzied automobiles, rattling railway depots, snarled wires, the clank and the noise and the clang of carouselling streets . . . does one really need to convince them that all that is not necessary for speed and for its rhythms?

Look at a ray of sun . . . the stillest of the still forces; it speeds more than 300,000 kilometres in a second . . . behold our starry firmament . . . who hears it . . . and yet what are our depots to those depots of the Universe: What are our earthly trains to those hurrying trains of the galaxies?[1]

Mere revelry in the novelty of immediate visual dynamics without an understanding of their roots and of their direction of growth only prevents us from finding the way out of our blind alleys. Some attempts to come to terms with our explosive world have bogged down in just such easy-to-come-by excitement; the central interest of many artists has been riveted to the mimetic surface aspect of our surroundings.

This is not to deny that other artists have searched with admirable discipline for visual idioms capable of rendering the fundamental dynamic character of twentieth-century experience. The first, in

The Visual Arts and the Sciences

significance as well as chronologically, were artists working in the early part of this century. Artists of the Cubist era realized that the visual qualities of our surroundings cannot be projected in an artistic image seen from a single fixed view. The Cubist's painted image of physical space was not the painted replica of his optical image. It was an evocation and ordering of the changing views collected by his moving, exploring eyes.

Although these painters limited themselves to a single and one-sided goal, to an exploration of the structure of images, their efforts led to the rediscovery of three fundamental aspects of artistic vision: *complementary unity*—the unity of interaction of observer and observed, of order and vitality, of constancy and change; *rhythm*—basic to all living process, and so, too, to the creation or reliving of an artistic configuration; *sequence* in the life span of created experience. Images are created and perceived as structured sequences of patterns; melodic line and contrapuntal organization are inherent not only in musical patterning but in all created forms. It is to these three conceptions that I shall relate the thoughts that follow.

Artists after the Cubists, however, went other ways. The Italian Futurists were typical. They closed their eyes to their inner world and focused on the dynamic outside environment. Living in a country that was lagging behind industrially and was dreaming of past glories—a country of museums with little relevance for twentieth-century man seeking his identity—they held that the two worlds of the old and the new could not coexist and, rejecting their heritage, they blasted away at all the inhibiting memories of the past. Thus they used techniques of recording the motion of objects that closely resembled the photographic motion studies of the great nineteenth-century physiologist E. J. Marey, and then held them to be art-saving, revolutionary innovations. They claimed complete authority for this one-sided vision and denied the existence of other forms of visual expression.

In the same way that the Futurists were blind to the past, more recent artists have been blind to the future. They have renounced the public forum and recoiled to the innermost privacy of unsharable singular moments of existence. They shrink the world to a rebellious gesture, to violent graphs of the cornered man. "The big moment came," as an articulate spokesman of this group has put it, "when it was decided to paint . . . just to paint. The gesture on the canvas was a gesture of liberation from value—political, aesthetic, moral."[2] But in fact, these artists recoil from the necessary vital interaction with the outside environment and thus have broken again the essential unity of the seer and the seen.

Later, the interest of a new group of motion-addicted artists swung back again to the outside world. Instead of looking for new qualities of twentieth-century life, they produce substitute moving objects, either cerebral, impeccable, watchwork-like toy machines or self-destructive Frankenstein monsters made from corroded fragments of industrial waste. Some painters also experiment with motion, and their sophisticated knowledge of visual illusions produces amusing, well-groomed eye teasers by mobilizing every optical trick to animate surfaces into virtual motion.

A most recent group of artists has returned from abstract images to concrete objects in their environment. They have become fascinated by vulgar features of everyday life, and they have chosen them as emblems. Seductive selling devices of the competitive society—advertising pictures, containers, packages, and the mass-produced heroes of the comic strips—are their preferred images. These artists have a just resentment against the gigantic, semantic conspiracy of newspapers, billboards, and television to catch public attention through deliberate doubletalk. They recognize how language—verbal and visual—is exploited to force the responses of a passive public. But, parallel with this awareness, they have developed an attachment to objects that never left their visual field. Their unresolved mixture of private attachment and public critical social commentary takes no account of the revolutionary artistic achievements of the earlier part of the century.

Most of the mushrooming art movements seem to have forgotten the essential role of artistic creation. By and large, the art world has become the scene of a popularity contest manipulated by appraisers and impresarios who are blind to the fundamental role of the artistic image. To find our way in this bewildering scene, we must return to fundamentals and ask basic questions. We all wish that we could live without these clumsy confrontations, but we cannot evade the specific problems that we encounter in art nor the fundamental questions of our condition. The eager prophets of the *dernier cri* are blind to the basic principle that what makes today is not only today. "From the oldest comes the newest," commented Béla Bartók, an authentic spirit of our time.

Vision is a fundamental factor in human insight. It is our most important resource for shaping our physical, spatial environment and grasping the new aspect of nature revealed by modern science.

The Visual Arts and the Sciences

It is at its height in the experience of artists, who elevate our perception. Artists are living seismographs, as it were, with a special sensitivity to the human condition. Their immediate and direct response to the sensuous qualities of the world helps us to establish an entente with the living present.

Yet artists today lack orientation in the contemporary world. They come together in small groups in great cities, where, in the safety of little circles that shut out the rest of the world, the initiates share one another's images. They generate illusory spontaneity, but miss the possible vital connections with contemporary intellectual and technological reality. It is unfashionable today, if not taboo, for artists to think and act on the broad terms of cultural and social ideals. No doubt moralizing in art can lead to creative suicide, just as market-policed and state-policed art can lead to the murder of artistic honesty. But the other extreme—lack of intellectual curiosity and rejection of commitment—leads to emaciation of artistic values.

It seems to me that the overwhelming task of creating modern science on its present, large scale has used up some of our most important intellectual and emotional equipment. When a vital part in a complex machine is worn out or out of adjustment, it is wiser to stop the mechanism than to grind on to destruction. Engineers, therefore, devise arrangements that ensure orderly shutdown when a part gives way. It may be that our cultural life has had such a "safety failure," as the engineers call it. Our artists may have served us by preventing a disaster.

Nevertheless, an emotional return to the archaic, ancestral cave would obviously be a failure to function in contemporary terms. Let us not mistake this temporary standstill for a genuine answer to our long-range needs. We cannot renounce the dimensions of the twentieth century—of which the new perspectives opened by scientific triumphs are a part—just because in certain respects adjustment to them is not achieved without distress; we may suffer from exposure to the new scale, but it is necessary for us to meet it. Only complete acceptance of the world that is developing can make our lives genuinely acceptable. Such acceptance involves two tasks: to advance in every field to the furthest frontiers of knowledge possible today; and to combine and communicate all such knowledge so that we gain the sense of structure, the power to see our world as an interconnected whole.

Today there is a growing general awareness of art as an important human faculty to provide this sense of structure. Museums, art centers, art magazines, and proliferating galleries are doing an important job in helping the artist to communicate with the public. But with all this, there are significant areas still in the shadows, areas that will remain in the shadows unless we can find means of stimulating discourse of two kinds. One is discourse between artists who work in various media and have common interest in exploring the many potentials for them that lie in technical developments. The other is the interaction between artists and the major scientific and technical contributors of our time. Particularly in the second of these areas of interaction, the need is evident enough, if one may judge by the frequent expressions of hope for some kind of fruitful plan. Fully aware of the considerable difficulties, I wish to put forward a modest proposal.

I propose the formation of a closely knit work community of eight to ten promising young artists and designers, each committed to some specific goals. The group, located in an academic institution with a strong scientific tradition,* would include painters, sculptors, film-makers, photographers, stage designers, illumination engineers, and graphic designers. They would be chosen for their demonstrated interest and alertness to certain common tasks. It is assumed that close and continuous work contact with one another and with the academic community of architects, city planners, scientists, and engineers would lead to a climate more conducive to the development of new ideas than could be achieved by individuals working alone, exposed only to random stimulations and subjected to the pressures of professional competition and the caprices of the art market.

Beyond any doubt, unique, authentic, and essential contributions come from the hidden layers of the personality. These deeper sources of creative imagination cannot be manipulated externally, nor can they be released simply by financial aid or even optimum physical working conditions. On the other hand, the past has given us ample evidence that major creative achievement comes from the confluence of many types of creative personalities.

George Gaylord Simpson, the paleontologist, has commented that as organic evolution was brought about by interbreeding, so must our further cultural evolution today come about through

* A proposal based upon these ideas has been submitted to the administration of the Massachusetts Institute of Technology.

The Visual Arts and the Sciences

broad-scale "interthinking." An experimental effort to encourage such interthinking between different disciplines in the visual arts and scientific and technical fields is more than overdue. As the twentieth century has grown older, such intercommunication has become seemingly more improbable. Lacking orientation in the total contemporary world, which holds as much promise as it does menace, many artists have inevitably withdrawn into themselves. Their only honest response to this world has been the expression of complete isolation. In their frantic retreat, many of them have adopted a scorched-earth policy and have burned their most valuable cultural belongings. Cornered and confused, some of them disguise brutality as vitality and intellectual cowardice as existential self-justification.

In a less fragmented life, before the common life of society was frozen into separate compartments each with its specialized interests and jargon, priests and laymen, scholars and artisans, poets and artists could communicate to a larger degree in the same language and could pool their feelings and knowledge in a common cultural stream. A hope for such unity can hardly be entertained when we are faced with the complexity and scale of the present cultural situation. We cannot improvise a new central theme for our lives, nor can we create a unity with a well-defined scale of values for all aspects of our civilization. But we can mobilize latent aspects of our cultural life that offer a strong centripetal pull.

The proposed small work community, by recognizing common problems of adjoining or related fields, could accomplish the dovetailing of knowledge and feeling, or of knowledge and knowledge. Engineering knowledge could serve to reinforce the insights of artistic sensibilities. The approach and craftsmanship of one artist or designer could serve to complement that of another and lead into new directions.

Among the wide range of artistic goals today, there are many that could and should be of equal concern to painters, designers, film-makers, sculptors, and others. Themes that suggest themselves for the initiation of such a program include (1) the creative use of light; (2) the new aspects of environmental art—the gearing of sculptural and pictorial tasks to the dynamic scale of the urban environment and to the new wealth of technical tools and implements; and (3) the role of visual signs in artistic communication—an investigation that could branch out into a creative exploration of subjective icons as well as of the common visual symbols in the cityscape, and a scientific exploration of communication and the use of graphic signs for didactic purposes.

Of these and many other possible themes, I have selected the first two for concrete discussion. Each of these two cases will indicate that the task defines itself differently for different groups within the work community. The supporting personnel for each can be drawn from various segments of the academic host institution, such as electrical engineering, metallurgy, psychology, communications engineering, city planning, or architecture, as the given undertaking requires. In such a cooperative effort the value will come not only from an exchange of complementary ideas, but also from the friction of the conflicts that inevitably arise when such a group of individuals, each with his own angle of approach, works toward a common goal.

Following are more explicit statements of the scope and approach of the two selected themes suggested for cooperative treatment.

1. The Creative Use of Light

Both natural and artificial light serve as essential creative tools in a variety of areas. Most of the recent representation and communication devices that speak to the eye are based on the modulation of light—for example, photography, motion pictures, television, and, to some degree, stage design. But beyond this, light has, or might have, a dominant role in contemporary architecture and the new cityscape, as I will indicate later on. Up until now, the imaginative use of light has been a neglected area in design. With other means, architects, planners, engineers, and artists have gone far in establishing a basis for a physical environment that is, at its best, authentic in its solution of twentieth-century needs and promising in its enrichment of our life. While there have been considerable technical advances in lighting, and designers with light have made some notable contributions, there are many directions that they have not begun to explore, nor even begun to dream of.

In large part both the forms of contemporary architecture and the nature of present-day urban life have been modified by technical advances in illumination. The transmission of natural and artificial light through large sheets of glass has helped create a fresh sense of space as well as an augmented demand for light within structures. All hours of the day may now be exploited, for the sharp differentiation in nature between night and day has fused in our cities into a single time scheme of day-and-night. Without artificial lighting

The Visual Arts and the Sciences

in our houses and streets and vehicles, the circulation of people and goods would be reduced to a trickle. When evening comes and the lights are turned on, the city is transformed, however chaotic, blighted, or ugly its daytime face. Points, lines, plane figures, and volumes of lights, whether steady or intermittent, moving or still, white or colored, whether from windows, signs, spectaculars, headlights, traffic lights, or street lights—all compose a fluid, luminous wonder. It is—again at its best—one of the grand sights of our age. Although this impressive display is produced almost by accident, a byproduct of utility, its magnificence reminds us of the concentrated and ordered beauty of the great windows of thirteenth-century cathedrals. This accidental splendor contains the promise of a new art, the orchestration of light, on both limited and vast scales.

The use of light to clarify and inform architectural spaces and complex cityscapes is not yet a discipline. We do not yet command the principles, principles which must be based on a thorough understanding of the tools of lighting as well as on a full awareness of the requirements for raising the art of using light to a high level. Certain preliminary steps must be taken. We know how to make illumination both adequate and comfortable. This has been the goal of illumination engineers who have learned all that physiology and physics can teach them concerning both natural and artificial lighting. But architects and planners realize that there are immense opportunities in lighting, and they demand more than just comfort and amplitude. Stainless steel, reinforced concrete, extensive glass surfaces, and the new structural systems naturally collaborate with the tools of lighting. Together they suggest a whole new range of light qualities for architectural surfaces and spaces, analogous to the way the glass sheath of structures such as the U.N. building condense and abstract from their surroundings by reflecting the daytime sky- and cityscape. No one as yet quite realizes, however, how to take full advantage of these opportunities. Such knowledge will slowly grow. On the other hand, it is possible that a striking advance can be brought about by an effort directed at exploring light itself as a field for the creative imagination, not merely as an adjunct of architecture and planning.

By a coordinated exploration of the use of light in research areas that are at present unassociated, we shall move toward those fundamental principles that can fully mobilize both artistic sensibility and technical knowledge. We are able to perceive a higher unity achieved in certain traditional systems of working with light, as, for example, the techniques employed in the twelfth- and thirteenth-century stained glass, at York, Chartres, Le Mans, Sens, and the Sainte Chapelle, or in the vibrating play of light in the glass mosaics of Ravenna. We can see the same thing in the sculptural modulation of simple buildings, both ancient and modern, in the Mediterranean basin, where there is an unsurpassed use of sunlight to define form and enhance surface; or in the exploitation of mist and gray skies in the looming features of Central European castles, or in the Praxitelean use of multifaceted cutting of Parian marble to make the surface of a statue "breathe." We can see it in the use of light in modern stagecraft and photography, in advertising displays, in the electronic instrumentation of light, in projected light plays and electronically controlled lighting devices.

All the forms of light have in common certain principles, and these principles must be developed and exploited for ever wider purposes. Albert Michelson, the first American to receive the Nobel prize in physics, recognized the new scientific and technical dimensions of the twentieth century as legitimate tools and goals for artistic expression. He wrote:

Indeed, so strongly do these color phenomena appeal to me that I venture to predict that in the not very distant future there may be a color art analogous to the art of sound—a *color music,* in which the performer, seated before a literally chromatic scale, can play the colors of the spectrum in any succession or combination, flashing on a screen all possible gradations of color, simultaneously or in any desired succession, producing at will the most delicate and subtle modulations of light and color, or the most gorgeous and startling contrasts and color chords! It seems to me that we have here at least as great a possibility of rendering all the fancies, moods, and emotions of the human mind as in the older art.[3]

Artists a generation before us also recognized the need for a new frame of reference for their creative vision. They sought new ways to project their responses to the new possibilities. Painters, photographers, and film makers struggled to find valid new idioms with which to bring space and light into a vital focus. Magnificent artistic statements were made with pigments on canvas or recorded with light on photosensitive film. These artists were, nevertheless, frustrated and tantalized because the limits of their media narrowed and condensed the explosive range of the new experiences. Needed were a new scale of tools and a new scale of setting. Only by accepting light as autonomous, as plastic luminosity to be molded, shaped, and formed with the same limitless plasticity as the sculp-

The Visual Arts and the Sciences

tor's clay, could the artist hope to find a valid correspondence between his new scale of experience and his artistic expression of it. And only a spatial surrounding generous enough in scale to shelter the explosive luminous tools could provide an adequate background. The isolated, sheltered, small space of a room in the home or in a museum is suffocatingly narrow for the fluid power of light in action. The new, rich intensities of artificial light sources, if used creatively, must be woven into the bigger fabric of the night cityscape. The mirroring of the shop windows and the interpenetration of mobile vistas, with their continuous transformations of space and form, must be accepted as background to creative figures shaped by the moving contours of actual lights.

An example may be useful here. The opportunity to try out these new tools in their new setting was given to me some years ago by a commission for a mural in the offices of a leading airline in the heart of New York City. The theme was the richness of the appearance of the nocturnal city from the air. The tool chosen was light in action. The mural, over fifty feet long and eighteen feet high, is a gray aluminum screen with some sixty thousand random perforations and larger cutouts. The sources of light are a multitude of incandescent, fluorescent, and spotlight bulbs and tubes behind the mural surface, controlled by timing and switching devices that actuate the circuits. The purpose was to create, by means of these devices, a fluid, luminous pattern with random changes, alive through the continuous transformation of color intensity, direction, and pattern. To avoid the mechanical repeat inherent in a mechanized device, many thousand different color filters were placed behind the perforations in random distribution. The underlying design idea was based upon a principle used in Peruvian fabrics: maintenance of rhythmic interplay between a constant pattern and a changing pattern. On the one hand, on the permanent pattern of the perforation a shifting color scheme was superimposed, and on the other hand, on the recurring time pattern of brightness there were superimposed cutouts and perforations varying greatly in shape and linear direction. By such means, I tried to meet some of the older reservations about the justification of a mobile visual art form as expressed by Wilhelm Ostwald:

> According to this reasoning the legitimacy and the explanation of discords in the art of music depend upon the temporal sequence of concords. Is there anything comparable to this in the art of color? The answer is a very decided and fundamental "No," for the art of color—at any rate in

its present-day condition—is totally destitute of the temporal element. A discord which has been introduced into a picture, woven into a carpet, or printed on a wallpaper has to remain there, forever unresolved. It is not permissible to say that we can place the resolution beside it. There is nothing to compel the eye to look at the discord first and then at the resolution, for the exact opposition is just as likely to be the case.[4]

Although the mural has a defined architectonic role in the design of the office, which is on the street level, I intended, beyond this, to make it a part of the large space of the street outside, sometimes blending and sometimes competing with the rivers of light generated by moving automobiles, giving and taking light from the surroundings, both invading the outside space and being invaded by it.

Let me cite another example to show the imaginative teamwork of a group; it included the author, who is a designer and painter, a sculptor, a structural designer, a lighting consultant, and an architect and planner. They addressed themselves to the problem of providing a major, aesthetically and functionally valid landmark for a large city on the Eastern seaboard of the United States. The description that follows renders part of the joint report that outlines their plans, as recently submitted to the city authorities.[*]

A central gathering place for all the activities of the downtown part of the city is a park surrounded by the city's newest and tallest buildings. Night and day the area is a thoroughfare for businessmen, shoppers, visitors, and pleasure-seekers. Because of its location at such an important point in the life of the city, it was clear that plans for this site must envisage something more than a mere expanse of paving and shrubbery. Trees, benches, and paving stones can identify an area as a park; but to serve as a true landmark, to invite to relaxation or to rouse excitement, to intensify its character as a reference point for both citizen and visitor, a park must have a dimension, a distinctive significance, which truly sets it apart as a special place.

To achieve the desired effect, the planners in this case proposed a Tower of Light, to be located at one corner of the park, outside

[*] "Charles Center [Baltimore] Tower of Light, Special Study," Rogers, Taliaferro, Kostritsky, Lamb, July 1964 (mimeographed). The team consisted of Gyorgy Kepes as designer and coordinator; George Kostritsky, architectural and planning coordinator; William Wainwright, structural engineer; William Lamb, illumination engineer; and Michio Ihara, sculptor.

The Visual Arts and the Sciences

a paved ellipse, where it will enjoy maximum visibility and lighting effect from a nearby bridge and an elevated walkway, as well as from a large part of the central downtown area. On the Tower of Light is to be a 25-foot-wide reflective screen suspended 100 feet above the park. At night, the many facets of this screen, covered with bright, durable gold leaf, will arrest the rays of a powerful light from the pool below and reflect them back down upon the entire park area. By day, reflected sunlight from the plaza and buildings picked up by the screen will bring to life the warm surface of the man-made sun.

Set in a shallow pool of water, two 160-foot towers of steel cable spun over a slender frame support the elliptical disk. The towers are set 30 feet apart and are securely anchored to the concrete structure of the parking areas below. The deceptive slimness of the mast, spreaders, and stainless steel filaments hides a strength known to builders of sailing craft for years but never before so purely applied to an architectural problem. Pound for pound, the towers far exceed the strength of the steel frames in the tall buildings that surround the plaza.*

At night a cluster of powerful lamps, totaling 25 kilowatts, will direct a beam of light straight up into the air. The gold-leafed disk will scatter most of the reflected light back down upon the plaza, but portions of the beam will escape, creating slim shafts of light above in the night sky. The actual lighting elements will be contained in cone-shaped islets rising from the center of the pool. By day the reflective surfaces, pointing northeast away from the sun, will glow with light reflected from the windows of the surrounding office buildings. In contrast to the disk, the masts and cables will show a dark metallic luster. One will see them against the background of sky and glass as a tense, sharp network. Thus the impact

---

*One of the advances in metallurgy which enable the engineer to make radical refinements in the designs of yesteryear is the availability of high-strength steels. For masts and spreaders it is no longer necessary to design to working stresses of 20,000 per square inch (psi). Bethlehem Steel Company at its Sparrows Point plant now manufactures its V65 steel with a yield point of 65,000 psi and a tensile strength of some 80,000 psi. U. S. Steel's T-1, with a different set of properties, goes even beyond this. Bethlehem also manufactures locally a highly corrosion-resistant steel by the name of Mayari-R which does not require painting to retain its strength. With a choice of such finely engineered materials, the designer is in a position to do things with his structure that were unheard of only ten years ago. Similar considerations apply to the specification of powerful new low-voltage light sources.

of the Tower of Light lies not in bulk or monumentality but rather in its freshness and ingenuity, a spirited symbol of the energy of the new city.

The tower represents an opportunity to use typically twentieth-century forms and materials to produce, by imagination and technology, a solution to an urban problem. The problem of handling a small square at the nerve center of a city, set about with tall buildings, exists today on a scale more vast than ever supposed in any previous age. Of course there have been many light towers designed before, but they were mainly for a solely functional, decorative, or publicity purpose. This design is different in several essential ways.

First, it is not an entity in itself, but an integral part of an integrating factor in a city area, the plaza. Each architectural spatial form has a day and a night life, the two frequently without any consistency. During the day, the legibility of the buildings and their interspaces is based upon patterns of light and shadow formed by a single light source, the sun. At night, however, the original unity of the buildings and their spatial community is shattered by conflicting interior and street illumination. To counteract this destruction of spatial unity, the light tower was designed to be another central light source, which could restore the legibility of a single pattern of light and shadow instead of a wild jungle of intercepting shadows produced by a multitude of lamps. Indeed, the single light source could serve somewhat as a fireplace in a living room. The gold-leafed, light-reflecting screen will give a warm glow of changing patterns and thus recall the never-resting richness of the fire on the hearth, a constant central symbol in the increased scale of man-created environment.

The second consideration in designing the tower was the awareness that each historical stage has had its preferred technical tools, that the most potent artistic imaginations have always utilized the most advanced technical potentials. The stained glass of the thirteenth-century cathedrals, the Crystal Palace of the nineteenth century are cases in point. Artificial illumination and new structural principles are among the most fertile potential creative devices of this century. The tower and the reflecting screen are based upon advanced structural principles. The light sources exploit powerful illumination tools. Together they can stand as a new art form—a luminous sculpture radiating its image far beyond its actual location and function—a part of the total cityscape, a landmark.

The Visual Arts and the Sciences

On a smaller scale, there are possible pictorial and sculptural uses of light, the use of luminescence, or the channeling of light along an elaborate linear path by means of bundled optical glass fibers. Photosensitive glass, color filter overlays, polarized screens, diffraction grating are still other possibilities. Projected light could be explored in terms of its kinetic-graphic potential, as used in animated films. It could also be utilized in transient murals in which opaque or transparent flat surfaces or sculptural reliefs are brought into common play.

The devices of stage designers suggest other new possibilities. Light could be articulated in its time sequence, and the combination of stroboscopic illumination with stable light sources used to produce luminous animated sculptures.

At a more technical level, optical light and color phenomena could be applied to investigate natural processes. Technical investigation of chromatography, photoelasticity, and so forth could be developed on an exploratory basis without immediate scientific goals as possible new tools for reading nature. We should remember that at one time use of oil paint or photography was just as "foreign" to, and had to be just as much "learned" by artists as are these new tools for expressing ideas visually.

2. Environmental Art and the New Technology

There are now tremendous new opportunities to reshape our spatial environment. Our technical knowledge and competence offer us many solutions for a more comfortable world; they also offer us the means of revitalizing the urban environment by means of new artistic organization and new ways of projecting, in visible symbols, the current meaning of corporate existence.

For various reasons, these new opportunities have not yet been explored. Our best artists have concentrated on personal comments, communicating their feelings and thought through the channels of galleries, museums, or private collections. Their elegiac and lyric—or acrid!—personal comments are significant, to be sure; but there is a need for a parallel visual summation in the large-scale physical environment. In the last few decades, projects on an immense scale have transformed our cities, but very few of them have had a convincing artistic focus. In fact, there is not one new environment which is comparable to the work of some of our easel painters in expressive intensity. The gap between our new opportunities and the artists' willingness to grasp them—to say nothing of the adequacy of their knowledge for the task—is a serious one. The transference of thinking to such a broad artistic scale cannot be suddenly brought about. There are many human, aesthetic, and technical issues that the artist must understand before he can function within this new and vast scope. Some first attempts have proved abortive because the artists involved had not enlarged their vision or learned the technique of collaboration. They were untutored in those technical potentials of our industrial civilization that can offer them a new palette for their work.

There are, then, three basic conditions that must be fulfilled if our artists are to live up to the new tasks. First, they must cultivate those neglected areas of their creative imaginations which can render them responsive to the new scale. Second, they will have to learn to adjust to and communicate with architects, engineers, city planners, and many others who are working at reshaping the environment. Third, they will have to learn to explore the new technical potentials needed to implement their findings.

The visualization of new opportunities cannot be taught, but it can be stimulated. Intense work in a cooperative spirit by a group of artists invited to join in such an undertaking as has been proposed can bring about a type of imaginative thinking which the individual artist could hardly achieve alone. A prototype task would be, for example, the chromatic organization of factories and offices where all spaces, colors, textures, and light are structured in an ordered pattern with a contrapuntal sequence. This could then be worked out further at different scales, each with its own demands and opportunities. As another project, city areas and their component form elements could be evaluated in terms of their visual intensity in a sequence of experiences. The same thing could be done with large-scale sculptures and murals in such a way as to give value to their sequential meaning as well as their individual quality. Form in its broadest sense could be considered on pedestrian, vehicular, or aerial scales. Again, these rough outlines will achieve concrete direction and meaning only as they are worked out in the collaborative projects of the painters, sculptors, architects, city planners, illumination engineers, and others.

A continuous give-and-take among the group, together with help from the outside, will develop techniques of teamwork without curtailing the initial intensity of the creative ideas. Techniques of model-making, films, or slides could be used to simulate the full-scale reality. Furthermore, learning to use the new tools, implements, and media of industrial production will reinforce the ideas and techniques of collaboration. The sculptural possibilities of reinforced concrete, prestressed concrete forms, plastic, stainless steel, aluminum, new techniques of welding; and the potentials of prefabricated units, pictorial use of baked enamel on steel, luminescent walls, photosensitive glass, spraying techniques ranging from metal spraying to color spraying, and new adhesives are only a few suggestions of the technology waiting to be explored.

In the Middle Ages, artists in Italy or Flanders did not limit themselves to one area of specialization. They were willing and able to participate in any visual task. Designing a tournament or a ceremony was no more outside their range than painting an altarpiece or carving a cathedral molding. They sought to complement the starkness of contemporary life, with its continual perils of disease and hunger, by an intoxicating luxuriance of visual fireworks. The Middle Ages not only needed to express, but did express, communal rejoicing in feasts of colors, in pageantry, in church windows. Our fears today, our perils, are different, but our industrial civilization nevertheless is fighting for its own heraldic embellishment. The change of seasons which throughout history has enriched our lives is now for a large fraction of urban dwellers only a rare experience. If we are to turn our cities into congenial human environments, color and light, form and texture will have to be domesticated in a creative sense.

These remarks have indicated in rough outline some of the rewards possible from collaborative endeavors as the habit of continuous give-and-take matures. We need to establish new relationships in which artistic forms will be an integral part of our man-created surroundings, not mere decorative face-lifting or prestige gestures. New technical tools and materials; new approaches to teamwork among creative individuals in the arts and in the sciences with different backgrounds and training; new awareness of the interplay of visual factors in the dynamic urban scene—these are the challenges to collaborative daring.

GYORGY KEPES

REFERENCES

1. Naum Gabo and Antoine Pevsner, *The Realistic Manifesto* (Moscow, 1920). Reprinted in part in *Gabo: Construction, Sculpture, Paintings, Drawings, Engravings* (Cambridge: The Harvard University Press, 1957), p. 151.

2. Harold Rosenberg, *The Tradition of the New* (New York: Grove Press, 1961), p. 30.

3. A. A. Michelson, *Light Waves and Their Uses* (Chicago: Chicago University Press, 1961), p. 2.

4. W. Ostwald, *Color Science* (London: Windsor and Newton, 1931-33), pp. 162–163.

MARGARET MEAD

The Future as the Basis for Establishing a Shared Culture

I *The Present Situation*

THE WORLD today is struggling with many kinds of disjuncture. Some derive from the progressive fragmentation of what was once a whole—as higher education has broken down into a mass of separate specialties. Some have come about with the development of world views that parallel and often contradict older and displaced—but not replaced—ways of viewing the world. Others result from a juxtaposition of vastly different and extremely incongruent world views within the national and also the world-wide context provided by our contemporary press and television coverage. Within the framework of the United Nations we have balloting for representatives both from countries with many hundreds of years of high civilization and from countries just emerging from a primitive way of life. Still others are the effect of changing rates in the production of knowledge, which bring about unexpected discrepancies between the young and the old. In a sense, these different kinds of disjuncture can also be seen as related to the very diverse ways in which the emergent, changing world is experienced by people of different ages—particularly young children—who are differently placed in the world, the nation, and the community.

Discussion of this tremendous fragmentation and of the agglomerations of partly dissociated, historically divergent, and conceptually incongruent patterns has been conducted, too often, in a narrow or a piecemeal fashion which takes into account only certain problems as they affect certain groups. The recent "two cultures" discussion is an example of such an approach, in which neither the arts nor the social sciences are included in what is essentially a lament about the state of communication within a small sector of the English-speaking

This paper draws on research on The Factor of Allopsychic Orientation in Mental Health, supported by a grant from the National Institutes of Health and sponsored by The American Museum of Natural History, New York.

163

world, whose members for various reasons of contemporary position or achievement think of themselves as an elite. In another context it is demanded that children's textbooks should portray "realistically" the conditions in which many American children live, because the conventional house pictured in advertisements and schoolbooks is unreal to the underprivileged children who live in cabins and cold-water flats and tenements. Even though the aim was to rectify the consequences of social and economic fragmentation at one level, a literal response to this demand would result in further fragmentation of our culture at another level. Wherever we turn, we find piecemeal statements, each of which can be regarded as a separate and partial definition of the basic problem of disjuncture, and piecemeal attempts at solution, each of which, because of the narrowness of the context in which it is made, produces new and still more complicated difficulties.

Yet these partial definitions and attempts at solution point in the same direction. We are becoming acutely aware that we need to build a culture within which there is better communication—a culture within which interrelated ideas and assumptions are sufficiently widely shared so that specialists can talk with specialists in other fields, specialists can talk with laymen, laymen can ask questions of specialists, and the least educated can participate, at the level of political choice, in decisions made necessary by scientific or philosophical processes which are new, complex, and abstruse.

Models for intercommunication of this kind—poorly documented but made vividly real through the treatment given them by historians—already exist, in the past, within our own tradition. One model, of which various uses have been made, is the Greek city, where the most erudite man and the simplest man could enjoy the same performance of a tragedy. Another, in which there has been a recent upsurge of interest, is medieval Europe, where the thinker and the knight, the churchman, the craftsman, and the serf could read a view of the world from the mosaic on the wall, the painting above the altar, or the carving in the portico, and all of them, however far apart their stations in life, could communicate within one framework of meaning. But such models are not limited to the distant past. Even much more recently, in Victorian England, a poet's words could be read and enjoyed by people of many different backgrounds, when he wrote:

Yet I doubt not thro' the ages one increasing purpose runs,
And the thoughts of men are widen'd with the process of suns.[1]

Establishing a Shared Culture

Whether or not the integration of culture which we construct retrospectively for these golden ages existed in actuality is an important question scientifically. But thinking about models, the question of actuality is less important. For the daydream and the vision, whether it was constructed by a prophet looking toward a new time or by a scholar working retrospectively, can still serve as a model of the future. Men may never, in fact, have attained the integration which some scholars believe characterized fifth-century Athens. Even so, this vision provides a challenging picture of what might be attained by modern men who have so many more possibilities for thinking about and for controlling the direction in which their culture will move.

However, all these models—as well as the simpler model of the pioneering American farmer, dressed in homespun, reared on the King James version of the Bible, and sustained by simple foods and simple virtues—share one peculiarity. In each case the means of integration is a corpus of materials from the past. The epic poems of Homer, the Confucian classics, the Jewish and the Christian Scriptures—each of these, in giving the scholar and the man in the street, the playwright and the politician access to an articulate statement of a world view, has been a source of integration. But the community of understanding of what was newly created—the poem, the play, the set of laws, the sculpture, the system of education, the style of landscape, the song—still depended on something which had been completed in the past. Today there is a continuing complaint that we have no such source of integration, and many of the measures which, it is suggested, would give a new kind of order to our thinking are designed to provide just such a body of materials. There is, for example, the proposal to teach college students the history of science as a way of giving all of them access to the scientific view of the world. Or there is the related proposal to teach all students evolution, particularly the existing body of knowledge about the evolution of man and culture, as a way of providing a kind of unity within which all specialists, no matter how specialized, would have a common set of referents.

But such suggestions place too much reliance on the past and necessarily depend on a long time span within which to build a common, shared view of the world. In the present crisis, the need to establish a shared body of assumptions is a very pressing one—too pressing to wait for the slow process of educating a small elite group in a few places in the world. The danger of nuclear disaster, which will remain with us even if all stockpiled bombs are destroyed, has created a hothouse atmosphere of crisis which forces a more rapid solution to our problems and at the same time wilts any solution which does not reflect this sense of urgency. For there is not only a genuine need for rapid solutions but also a growing restiveness among those who seek a solution. This restiveness in turn may well become a condition within which hasty, inadequate solutions are attempted—such as the substitution of slum pictures for ideal suburban middle class pictures in slum children's textbooks—within too narrow a context. Speed in working out new solutions is essential if new and more disastrous fragmentations are not to occur—but we also need an appropriate framework.

Measures taken at the college level to establish mutual understanding between the natural scientist and the humanist, the social scientist and the administrator, men trained in the law and men trained in the behavioral sciences, have a double drawback. The cumulative effect of these measures would be too slow and, in addition, they would be inadequate in that their hope lies in establishing a corpus based on something which already exists—a theory of history, a history of science, or an account of evolution as it is now known. Given the changing state of knowledge in the modern world, any such historically based body of materials becomes in part out of date before it has been well organized and widely taught. Furthermore, it would be betrayed and diluted and corrupted by those who did the teaching, as they would inevitably have to draw on their own admittedly fragmented education to convey what was to be learned. One effect of this fragmentation can be seen in attempts to express forms of new knowledge in imagery which cannot contain them, because the imagery is shaped to an earlier view of the world. In a recent sermon, for example, the Bishop of Woolwich presented a picture of dazzling contemporaneity in disavowing the possibility of belief in the corporal ascension of Christ; but then, in proclaiming a new version of the Scriptures, he used the image of the sovereignty of Christ—an outmoded image in the terms in which he was speaking.

In the last hundred years men of science have fought uneasily with the problem of their own religious belief, and men of God have hardened their earlier visions into concrete images to confront a science they have not understood. Natural scientists have elaborated their hierarchical views of "true" science into an inability to understand the nature of the sciences of human behavior, welcoming studies of fragmented aspects of human behavior, or an inappropriate reduction in the number of variables. Human scientists have destroyed the delicacy and intricacy of their subject matter in coarse-grained attempts to imitate the experimental methods of Newtonian physics instead of developing new methods of including unanalyzable components in simulations or in developing new methods of validating the analysis of unique and complex historical events. As a result we lack the capacity to teach and the capacity to learn from a corpus based on the past. The success of any such venture would be comparably endangered by the past learning of the teachers and the past learning of the students, whose minds would already be formed by eighteen years of exposure to an internally inconsistent, contradictory, half-articulated, muddled view of the world.

But there is still another serious drawback to most current proposals for establishing mutual understanding. This is, in general, their lack of inclusiveness. Whether an approach to past knowledge is narrowly limited to the English-speaking world or includes the whole Euro-American tradition, whether it begins with the Greeks or extends backward in time to include the Paleolithic, any approach through the past can begin only with one sector of the world's cultures. Inevitably, because of the historical separation of peoples and the diversity of the world's cultures throughout history, any one view of any one part of human tradition, based in the past, excludes other parts and, by emphasizing one aspect of human life, limits access to other aspects.

In the newly emerging nations we can see clearly the consequences of the efforts made by colonial educators to give to distant peoples a share in English or French or Dutch or Belgian or Spanish culture. Ironically, the more fully the colonial educators were willing to have some members at least of an African or an Asian society share in their traditions and their classics, the more keenly those who were so educated felt excluded from participation in the culture as a whole. For the classical European scholar, Africa existed mainly in very specialized historical contexts, and for centuries European students were concerned only with those parts of Africa or Asia which were ethnocentrically relevant to Greek or Roman civilization or the early Christian church. Throughout these centuries, peoples without a written tradition and peoples with a separate written tradition (the Chinese, for example, or the Javanese) lived a life to which no one in Europe was related. With the widening of the

European world in the fifteenth and sixteenth centuries, Europeans treated the peoples whom they "discovered" essentially as peoples without a past, except as the European connoisseur came to appreciate their monuments and archeological ruins, or, later, as European students selectively used the histories of other peoples to illustrate their own conceptions of human history. Consequently, the greater degree of participation felt by the member of one of these more recently contacted societies in a French or an English view of the development of civilization, the more he also felt that his own cultural history was excluded from the history of man.

It is true that some heroic attempts have been made to correct for this colonial bias. Looking at a synchronic table of events, a child anywhere in the world may sit and ponder what the Chinese or the Mayans or the ancient canoe-sailing Hawaiians were doing when William the Conqueror landed in England. But almost inevitably this carefully constructed synchrony—with parallel columns of events for different parts of the world—is undone, on the one hand, by the recognition that the New World and the Old, the Asian mainland and the Pacific islands were *not* part of a consciously connected whole in A.D. 1066, and, on the other hand, by the implications of the date and the dating form, which carry the stamp of one tradition and one religious group within that tradition. It is all but impossible to write about the human past—the movements of early man, the building of the earliest known cities, the spread of artifacts and art forms, the development of styles of prophecy or symbolism—without emphasizing how the spirit of man has flowered at different times in different places and, time and again, in splendid isolation. Even in this century, the efforts of scholars to integrate the histories of the world's great living traditions have led, in the end, to a renewed preoccupation with each of these as an entity with its own long history.

Today, however, if we are to construct the beginning of a shared culture, using every superior instrument at our command and with full consciousness both of the hazards and the possibilities, we can stipulate certain properties which this still nonexistent corpus must have.

It must be equally suitable for all peoples from whatever traditions their present ways of living spring, and it must not give undue advantage to those peoples anywhere in the world whose traditions have been carried by a longer or a more fully formulated literacy. While those who come from a culture with a Shakespeare or

Establishing a Shared Culture

a Dante will themselves be the richer, communications should not be so laden with allusions to Shakespeare or Dante that those who lack such a heritage cannot participate. Nor should the wealth of perceptual verbal detail in distinguishing colors, characteristic of the Dusun of Borneo or the Hanunóo of the Philippines, be used to make less differentiated systems seem crude. The possession of a script for a generation, a century, or a millennium must be allowed for in ways that will make it possible for all peoples to start their intercommunication on a relatively equal basis. No single geographical location, no traditional view of the universe, no special set of figures of speech, by which one tradition but not another has been informed, can provide an adequate base. It must be such that everyone, everywhere can start afresh, as a young child does, with a mind ready to meet ideas uncompromised by partial learning. It must be cast in a form that does not depend on years of previous learning—the fragmented learning already acquired by the college student or the student in the high school, the *lycée,* or the *Gymnasium.* Instead, it must be cast in a form that is appropriate for small children—for children whose fathers are shepherds, rubber tappers in jungles, forgotten sharecroppers, sailors or fishermen, miners or members of the dispossessed urban proletariat, as well as for the children whose forebears have read one of the world's scripts for many generations.

If this body of materials on which a new, shared culture is to be based is to include all the peoples of the world, then the peoples of the world must also contribute to it in ways that are qualitatively similar. If it is to escape from the weight of discrepant centuries, the products of civilization included within it must be chosen with the greatest care. The works of art must be universal in their appeal and examples of artistic endeavor whose processes are universally available—painting, drawing, carving, dancing, and singing in forms that are universally comprehensible. Only after a matrix of shared understanding has been developed will the way be prepared for the inclusion of specific, culturally separate traditions. But from the first it must have the character of a living tradition, so it will be free of the static qualities of older cultures, with texts that have become the test of truth and forms so rigid that experimentation has become impossible. And it must have the qualities of a natural language, polished and pruned and capable of expansion by the efforts of many minds of different calibres, redundant and sufficiently flexible so it will meet the needs of teacher and pupil, parent and child, friend and friend, master and apprentice, lawyer and client, statesman and audience, scientist and humanist in their different modes of communication. It is through use in all the complexity of relationships like these that a natural language is built and, given form and content by many kinds of human beings, becomes a medium of communication that can be learned by every child, however slight its natural ability. This projected corpus should not be confused with present day *popular culture,* produced commercially with contempt for its consumers. Instead, by involving the best minds, the most sensitive and gifted artists and poets and scientists, the new shared culture should have something of the quality of the periods of folk tradition out of which great art has repeatedly sprung.

A body of materials having these characteristics must bear the imprint of growth and use. Yet it is needed now, in this century, for children who are already born and for men who either will preserve the world for a new generation to grow up in or who, in failing to do so, will doom the newly interconnected peoples of the world to destruction by means of the very mechanisms which have made a world community a possibility. The most immediate problem, then, is that of producing, almost overnight, a corpus which expresses and makes possible new processes of growth.

We believe that the existing state of our knowledge about the processes of consciousness is such that it is necessary for us only to ask the right questions in order to direct our thinking toward answers. Today the technology of applied physical science has outstripped other applied sciences because in this field searching questions have been asked urgently, sharply, and insistently. This paper is an attempt to ask questions, set up a series of specifications, and illustrate the order of answer for which we should be looking. There will be better ways of formulating these questions, all of which have to do with communication, and better ways of meeting the criteria which will make answers possible. In fact, it is my assumption that the creation of a body of materials which will serve our needs will depend on the contribution and the participation of all those who will also further its growth, that is, people in every walk of life, in every part of the globe, speaking every language and seeing the universe in the wide range of forms that have been conceived by man.

II *The Future as a Setting*

I would propose that we consider the future as the appropriate

Establishing a Shared Culture

setting for our shared world-wide culture, for the future is least compromised by partial and discrepant views. And I would choose the near future over the far future, so as to avoid as completely as possible new confusions based on partial but avowedly totalistic projections born of the ideologies of certainty, like Marxism and Leninism, or the recurrent scientific dogmatisms about the possibilities of space travel, the state of the atmosphere, or the appearance of new mutations. Such divergent dreams of eternity might be left undisturbed, providing they did not include some immediate apocalyptic moment for the destruction of the world.

Looking toward the future, we would start to build from the known. In many cases, of course, this would be knowledge very newly attained. What we would build on, then, would be the known attributes of the universe, our solar system, and the place of our earth within this system; the known processes of our present knowledge, from which we shall proceed to learn more; the known treasures of man's plastic and graphic genius as a basis for experience out of which future artists may paint and carve, musicians compose, and poets speak; the known state of instrumentation, including both the kinds of instrumentation which have already been developed (for example, communication satellites) and those which are ready to be developed; the known numbers of human beings, speaking a known number of languages, and living in lands with known amounts of fertile soil, fresh water, and irreplaceable natural resources; the known forms of organizing men into functioning groups; and the known state of modern weaponry, with its known capacity to destroy all life.

These various kinds of knowledge would be viewed as beginnings, instead of as ends—as young, growing forms of knowledge, instead of as finished products to be catalogued, diagrammed, and preserved in the pages of encyclopedias. All statements would take the form: "We know that there are at least X number of stars" (or people in Asia, or developed forms of transportation, or forms of political organization). Each such statement would be phrased as a starting point—a point from which to move onward. In this sense, the great artistic productions of all civilizations could be included, not as the splendid fruit of one or another civilization, but on new terms, as points of departure for the imagination.

The frenetic, foolhardy shipping of original works of art around the world in ships and planes, however fragile they may be, can be looked upon as a precursor of this kind of change—as tales of flying saucers preceded man's first actual ventures into space. It is as if we already dimly recognize that if we are to survive, we must share all we have, at whatever cost, so that men everywhere can move toward some as yet undefined taking-off point into the future.

But if we can achieve a new kind of consciousness of what we are aiming at, it will not be necessary actually to move these priceless objects like detached figures in a dream. We can, instead, take thought how, with our modern techniques, we can make the whole of an art style available, not merely single, symbolic examples, torn from their settings. Young painters and poets and musicians, dancers and architects can, today, be given access to all that is known about color and form, perspective and rhythm, technique and the development of style, the relationships of form and style and material, and the interrelationships of art forms as these have been developed in some place, at some time. We have all the necessary techniques to do this. We can photograph in color, train magnifying cameras on the inaccessible details of domes and towers, record a poet reciting his own poetry, film an artist as he paints, and use film and sound to transport people from any one part to any other part of the world to participate in the uncovering of an ancient site or the first viewing of a new dance form. We can, in fact, come out of the "manuscript stage" for all the arts, for process as well as product, and make the whole available simultaneously to a young generation so they can move ahead together and congruently into the future. Given access to the range of the world's art, young artists can see in a new light those special activities and art objects to which they themselves are immediately related, wherever they are.

Working always within the modest limits of one generation—the next twenty-five years—and without tempting the massive consequences of miscalculation, we can include the known aspects of the universe in which our continuing experimental ventures into space will be conducted and the principles, the tools, and the materials with which these ventures are beginning. Children all over the world can be given accurate, tangible models of what we now know about the solar system, models of the earth, showing how it is affected by the large scale patterning of weather, and models showing how life on earth may be affected by events in the solar system and beyond. Presented with a clear sense of the expanding limits of our knowledge, models such as these would prepare children everywhere to participate in discoveries we know must come and to anticipate new aspects of what is as yet unknown.

Establishing a Shared Culture

Within these same limits, we can bring together our existing knowledge of the world's multitudes—beginning with those who are living now and moving out toward those who will be living twenty-five years from now. The world is now mapped, and we know, within a few millions, how many people there are, where they are, and who they are. We know—or have the means of knowing—a great deal about the world's peoples. We know about the world's food supplies and can relate our knowledge to the state of those who have been well nourished and those who have been poorly fed. We know about the world's health and can relate our knowledge to the state of those who have been exposed to ancient plagues and those who are exposed to "modern" ambiguous viruses. We can picture the ways of living of those who, as children, were reared in tents, in wattle and daub houses, in houses made of mud bricks, in tenements and apartment houses, in peasant houses that have survived unchanged through hundreds of years of occupancy and in the new small houses of modern suburbs, in the anonymity of urban housing, in isolated villages, and in the crowded shacks of refugee settlements. We can define the kinds of societies, all of them contemporary, in which human loyalties are restricted to a few hundred persons, all of them known to one another, and others in which essential loyalties are expanded to include thousands or millions or even hundreds of millions of persons, only a few of them known to one another face to face. In the past we could, at best, give children some idea of the world's multitudes through books, printed words and meager illustrations. Today we have the resources to give children everywhere living experience of the whole contemporary world. And every child, everywhere in the world, can start with that knowledge and grow into its complexity. In this way, plans for population control, flood control, control of man's inroads on nature, plans for protecting human health and for developing a world food supply, and plans for sharing a world communication system can all become plans in which citizens participate in informed decisions.

None of this knowledge will in any sense be ultimate. We do not know what form knowledge itself will take twenty-five years from now, but we do know what its sources must be in present knowledge and, ordering what we now know, we can create a ground plan for the future on which all the peoples of the earth can build.

Because it must be learned by very young children and by the children of very simple parents, this body of knowledge and experience must be expressed in clear and simple terms, using every graphic device available to us and relying more on models than on words, for in many languages appropriate words are lacking. The newer and fresher the forms of presentation are, the greater will be the possibility of success, for, as in the new mathematics teaching, all teachers—those coming out of old traditions and having long experience with special conventions and those newly aware of the possibilities of formal teaching—will have to learn what they are to teach as something new. Furthermore, parents will be caught up in the process, in one sense as the pupils of their children, discovering that they can reorder their own knowledge and keep the pace, and in another sense as supplementary teachers, widening the scope of teaching and learning. Knowledge arranged for comprehensibility by a young child is knowledge accessible to all, and the task of arranging it will necessarily fall upon the clearest minds in every field of the humanities, the sciences, the arts, engineering, and politics.

There is, however, one very immediate question. How are we to meet the problem of shared contribution? How are we to ensure that this corpus is not in the end a simplified version of modern western—essentially Euro-American—scientific and philosophic thought and of art forms and processes, however widely selected, interpreted within the western tradition? Is there any endeavor which can draw on the capacities not only of those who are specially trained but also those with untapped resources—the uneducated in Euro-American countries and the adult and wise in old, exotic cultures and newly emerging ones?

A first answer can be found, I think, in activities in which every country can have a stake and persons of every age and level of sophistication can take part. One such activity would be the fashioning of a new set of communication devices—like the visual devices used by very simple peoples to construct messages or to guide travelers on their way, but now raised to the level of world-wide intelligibility.

In recent years there has been extensive discussion of the need for a systematic development of what are now called *glyphs,* that is, graphic representations, each of which stands for an idea: male, female, water, poison, danger, stop, go, etc. Hundreds of glyphs are used in different parts of the world—as road signs, for example—but too often with ambiguous or contradictory meanings as one moves from one region to another. What is needed, internationally, is a set of glyphs which does not refer to any single phonological system or to any specific cultural system of images but will, instead,

Establishing a Shared Culture

form a system of visual signs with universally recognized referents. But up to the present no sustained effort has been made to explore the minimum number that would be needed or to make a selection that would carry clear and unequivocal meaning for the peoples of the world, speaking all languages, living in all climates, and exposed to very different symbol systems. A project for the exploration of glyph forms and for experimentation with the adequacy of different forms has been authorized by the United Nations Committee for International Cooperation Year (1965—the twentieth anniversary of the founding of the United Nations). This is designed as an activity in which adults and children, artists and engineers, logicians and semanticists, linguists and historians—all those, in fact, who have an interest in doing so—can take part. For the wider the range of persons and the larger the number of cultures included in this exploration, the richer and the more fully representative will be the harvest from which a selection of glyphs can be made for international use.

Since meaning is associated with each glyph as a unit and glyphs cannot be combined syntactically, they can be used by the speakers of any language. But considerable experimentation will be necessary to avoid ambiguity which may lead to confusion or the adoption of forms which are already culturally loaded. The variety of meanings which may already be associated with certain forms can be illustrated by the sign + (which, in different connections, can be the sign for addition or indicate a positive number, can stand for "north" or indicate a crossroad, and, very slightly modified, can indicate a deceased person in a genealogy, a specifically Christian derivation, or stand for the Christian sign of the cross) or the sign ○ (which, in different connections, may stand for circumference or for 360°, for the full moon, for an annual plant, for degrees of arc or temperature, for an individual, especially female, organism, and, very slightly modified, can stand for zero or, in our alphabet, the letter O).

Work on glyphs can lead to work on other forms of international communication. In an interconnected world we shall need a world language—a secondary language which could be learned by every people but which would in no sense replace their native tongue. Contemporary studies of natural languages have increased our understanding of the reasons why consciously constructed languages do not serve the very complex purposes of general communication. Most important is the fact that an artificial language, lacking the imprint of many different kinds of minds and differently organized capacities for response, lacks the redundancy necessary in a language all human beings can learn.

Without making any premature choice, we can state some of the criteria for such a secondary world language. It must be a natural language, chosen from among known living languages, but not from among those which are, today, politically controversial. Many nations would have to contribute to the final choice, but this choice would depend also on the outcome of systematic experiments with children's speech, machine simulation, experiments with mechanical translation, and so on. In addition, it would be essential to consider certain characteristics related to the current historical situation. Politically, it should be the language of a state too small to threaten other states. In order to allow for a rapid development of complex written styles, it must be a language with a long tradition of use in written form. To permit rapid learning, it must be a language whose phonetic system can be easily learned by speakers of other languages, and one which can be easily rendered into a phonetic script and translated without special difficulty into existing traditional scripts. It should come from the kind of population in which there is a wide diversity of roles and occupations and among whom a large number of teachers can be found, some of whom are already familiar with one or another of the great widespread languages of the world. Using modern methods of language teaching, the task of creating a world-wide body of readers and speakers could be accomplished within five years and the language itself would change in the process of this world-wide learning.

Once a secondary world language is chosen, the body of knowledge with which we shall start the next twenty-five years can be translated into it from preliminary statements in the great languages, taking the stamp of these languages as divergent subtleties of thought, present in one language and absent in another, are channeled in and new vocabulary is created to deal with new ideas.

One important effect of a secondary world language would be to protect the more localized languages from being swamped by those few which are rapidly spreading over the world. Plans have been advanced to make possible the learning and use of any one of the five or seven most widespread languages as a second language. Fully implemented, this would divide the world community into two classes of citizens—those for whom one of these languages was a mother tongue and those for whom it was a second language—and it would exacerbate already existing problems arising from differences in the quality of communication—rapid and idiomatic among native speakers and slower, more formal, and less spontaneous among those who have learned English, French, or Russian later. In contrast, one shared secondary language, used on a world-wide scale, would tend to equalize the quality of world communication and, at the same time, would protect the local diversity of all other languages.

Another important aspect of a shared culture would be the articulate inclusion of the experience of those who travel to study, work, explore, or enjoy other countries. One of the most intractable elements in our present isolating cultures is the interlocking of a landscape—a landscape with mountains or a desert, jungle or tundra, rushing cataracts or slow flowing rivers, arched over by a sky in which the Dipper or the Southern Cross dominates—and a view of man. The beauty of face and movement of those who have never left their mountains or their island is partly the imprint on the human form of a complex relationship to the scale and the proportions, the seasonal rhythms and the natural style of one special part of the world. The experiences of those who have been bred to physical environments cannot be patched together like the pieces of a patchwork quilt. But we can build on the acute and vivid experiences of those who, reared in a culture which has deeply incorporated its environment, respond intensely to some newly discovered environment—the response of the countryman to the city, the response of the city dweller to open country, the response of the immigrant to the sweep of an untouched landscape and of the traveler to a sudden vista into the past of a whole people. In the past, the visual impact of discovery was recorded retrospectively in painting and in literature. Today, films can record the more immediate response of the observer, looking with fresh eyes at the world of the nomadic Bushman or the people beneath the mountain wall of New Guinea, at the palaces in Crete or the summer palace in Peking.

We can give children a sense of movement, actually experienced or experienced only in some leap of the imagination. In the next twenty-five years we shall certainly not explore deep space, but the experience of movement can link a generation in a common sense of anticipation. As a beginning, we can give children a sense of different actual relationships to the physical environments of the whole earth, made articulate through the recorded responses of those who have moved from one environment to another. Through art, music, and film we can give children access to the ways others have experienced their own green valleys and other valleys, also green. We can develop in small children the capacity to wonder and to look through other eyes at the familiar fir trees rimming their horizon or the sea breaking on their island's shore.

In the past, these have been the experiences of those who could afford to travel and those who had access, through the arts, to the perceptions of a poet like Wordsworth in *The Prelude,* or a young scientist like Darwin on his Pacific voyage, or painters like Catlin or Gauguin. With today's technology, these need no longer be the special experiences of the privileged and the educated elite. The spur to action may be the desire for literacy in the emerging nations or a new concern for the culturally deprived in older industrialized countries. And quite different styles of motivation can give urgency to the effort to bring the experience of some to bear on the experience of all.

Looking to the future, the immediacy of motivation is itself part of the experience. It may be an assertive desire to throw off a colonial past or a remorseful attempt to atone for long neglect. It may be the ecumenical spirit in which Pope Paul can say: "No pilgrim, no matter how far, religiously and geographically, may be the country from which he comes, will be any longer a stranger to this Rome. . . ."[2] It may be the belief that it is possible to remake a society, as when Martin Luther King said:

I have a dream today . . . I have a dream that one day every valley shall be exalted, every hill and mountain shall be made low. The rough places will be made plain, and the crooked places will be made straight. And the glory of the Lord shall be revealed, and all flesh shall see it together. This is our hope. This is the faith that I go back to the South with. With this faith we will be able to hew out of the mountain of despair a stone of hope.[3]

Or it may be the belief, expressed by U Thant, that men can work toward a world society:

Let us look inward for a moment on this Human Rights Day, and recognize that no one, no individual, no nation, and indeed no ideology has a monopoly of rightness, freedom or dignity. And let us translate this recognition into action so as to sustain the fullness and freedom of simple human relations leading to ever widening areas of understanding and agreement. Let us, on this day, echo the wish which Rabindranath Tagore stated in these memorable words, so that our world may be truly a world

> Where the mind is without fear and the head is held high;
> Where knowledge is free;

Establishing a Shared Culture

> Where the world has not been broken up into fragments
>   by narrow domestic walls;
> Where words come out of the depth of truth;
> Where tireless striving stretches its arms toward
>   perfection. . . .[4]

There are also other ways in which experience can more consciously be brought to bear in developing a shared understanding. All traditions, developing slowly over centuries, are shaped by the biological nature of man—the differences in temperament and constitution among men and the processes of maturation, parenthood, and aging which are essential parts of our humanity. The conscious inclusion of the whole life process in our thinking can, in turn, alter the learning process, which in a changing world has become deeply disruptive as each elder generation has been left behind while the next has been taught an imperfect version of the new. One effect of this has been to alienate and undermine the faith of parents and grandparents as they have seen their children's minds moving away from them and as their own beliefs, unshared, have become inflexible and distorted.

The policy in most of today's world is to educate the next—the new—generation, setting aside the older generation in the mistaken hope that, as older men and women are passed over, their outmoded forms of knowledge will do no harm. Instead, we pay a double price in the alienation of the new generation from their earliest and deepest experiences as little children and in the blocking of constructive change in the world by an older generation who still exercise actual power—hoarding some resources and wasting others, building to an outmoded scale, voting against measures the necessity of which is not understood, supporting reactionary leaders, and driving an equally inflexible opposition toward violence. Yet this lamentable outcome is unnecessary, as the generation break itself is unnecessary.

In the past the transmission of the whole body of knowledge within a slowly changing society has provided for continuity. Today we need to create an educational style which will provide for continuity and openness even within rapid change. Essentially this means an educational style in which members of different generations are involved in the process of learning. One way of assuring this is through a kind of education in which new things are taught to mothers and young children together. The mothers, however schooled, usually are less affected by contemporary styles of education than the fathers. In some countries they have had no schooling; in others, girls are warned away from science and mathematics or even from looking at the stars. So they come to the task of rearing their small children fresher than those who have been trained to teach or to administer. Child rearing, in the past fifty years, has been presented as almost entirely a matter of molding the emotional life of the child, modulating the effects of demands for cleanliness and obedience to permit more spontaneity, and of preserving an environment in which there is good nutrition and low infection danger. At the same time, we have taken out of the hands of mothers the *education* even of young children. So we have no existing rationale in which mother, child, and teacher are related within the learning process. What we need now, in every part of the world, is a new kind of school for mothers and little children in which mothers learn to teach children what neither the mothers nor the children know.

At the same time, grandparents who, perforce, have learned a great deal about the world which has gone whirling past them and in which, however outmoded they are declared to be, they have had to maintain themselves, can be brought back into the teaching process. Where patience, experience, and wisdom are part of what must be incorporated, they have a special contribution to make. Mothers of young children, lacking a fixed relationship to the growing body of knowledge about the world, provide freshness of approach; but older people embody the experience that can be transformed into later learning. The meticulous respect for materials, coming from long experience with hand work, the exacting attention to detail, coming from work with a whole object rather than some incomplete part, and the patient acceptance of the nature of a task have a continuing relevance to work, whatever it may be. So also, the disciplined experience of working with human beings can be transformed to fit the new situations which arise when democracy replaces hierarchy and the discipline of political parties that of the clan and the tribe.

We have been living through a period in which the old have been recklessly discarded and disallowed, and this very disallowance resonates—as a way of life which has been repressed rather than transformed—in the movements of unaccountably stubborn reaction from which no civilization in our present world is exempt. Grandparents and great-grandparents—even those who are driven from their land to die in concentration camps and those who voluntarily settle themselves in modern, comfortable Golden Age clubs—

Establishing a Shared Culture

live on in the conceptions of the children whose parents' lives they shaped. Given an opportunity to participate meaningfully in new knowledge, new skills, and new styles of life, the elderly can embody the changing world in such a way that their grandchildren—and all children of the youngest generation—are given a mandate to be part of the new and yet maintain human ties with the past which, however phrased, is part of our humanity. The more rapid the rate of change and the newer the corpus of knowledge which the world may come to share, the more urgently necessary it is to include the old—to transform our conception of the whole process of aging so their wisdom and experience can be assets in our new relation to the future.

Then we may ask, are such plans as these sufficiently open ended? In seeking to make equally available to the peoples of the world newly organized ways of moving into the immediate future, in a universe in which our knowledge is rapidly expanding, there is always the danger that the idea of a shared body of knowledge may be transformed into some kind of universal blueprint. In allowing this to happen we would, of course, defeat our own purpose. The danger is acute enough so that we must build a continuing wariness and questioning into the planning itself; otherwise even the best plan may result in a closed instead of an open ended system.

This means that we must be open ended in our planning as well as in our plans, recognizing that this will involve certain kinds of conscious restriction as well as conscious questioning. For example, we must insist that a world language be kept as a secondary language, resolutely refusing to consider it as a first language, in order to protect and assure the diversity of thought which accompanies the use of different mother tongues. We should also guard against a too early learning of the world language, so that the language of infancy—which also becomes the language of love and poetry and religion—may be protected against acquiring a too common stamp. We must insist on the inclusion of peoples from all over the world in any specific piece of planning—as in the development of an international system of glyphs—as a way of assuring a growing and an unpredictable corpus. We must be willing to forego, in large-scale planning, some kinds of apparent efficiency. If we are willing, instead, to include numerous steps and to conceive of each step somewhat differently, we are more likely, in the end, to develop new interrelationships, unforeseeable at any early stage. A more conscious inclusion of women and of the grandparental generation in learning and teaching will carry with it the extraordinary differences in existing interrelations between the minds and in the understanding of the two sexes and different age groups.

We can also take advantage of what has been learned through the use of cybernetic models, and equip this whole forward movement of culture which we are launching with a system of multiple self-corrective devices. For example, criteria could be established for reviewing the kinds of divergences that were occurring in vocabulary and conceptualizations as an idea fanned out around the world. Similarly, the rate and type of incorporation of special developments in particular parts of the world could be monitored, and cases of dilution or distortion examined and corrected. Overemphasis on one part of knowledge, on one sensory modality, on the shelters men live in rather than the life they live there, on sanitation rather than beauty, on length of life rather than quality of life lived, could be listened for and watched for, and corrective measures taken speedily.

A special area of concern would be intercommunication among all those whose specializations tend to isolate them from one another, scientist from administrator, poet from statesman, citizen voter from the highly skilled specialist who must carry out his mandate using calculations which the voter cannot make, but within a system of values clearly enough stated so that both may share them. By attending to the origins of some new communication—whether a political, a technical, or an artistic innovation—the functioning of the communication process could be monitored. Special sensing organs could be established which would observe, record, and correct so that what otherwise might become a blundering, linear, and unmanageable avalanche could be shaped into a process delicately responsive to change in itself.

But always the surest guarantee of change and growth is the inconclusion of living persons in every stage of an activity. Their lives, their experience, and their continuing response—even their resistances—infuse with life any plan which, if living participants are excluded, lies on the drawing board and loses its reality. Plans for the future can become old before they are lived, but the future itself is always newborn and, like any newborn thing, is open to every kind of living experience.

REFERENCES

1. Alfred Lord Tennyson, "Locksley Hall" (1842).
2. *The New York Times,* May 18, 1964.
3. From the speech by the Rev. Martin Luther King at the March on Washington, *New York Post Magazine,* September 1, 1963, p. 5.
4. From the Human Rights Day Message by (then) Acting Secretary-General U Thant, December 8, 1961 (United Nations Press Release SG/1078 HRD/11 [December 6, 1961]).

OSCAR HANDLIN

Science and Technology in Popular Culture

IN OUR CULTURE, superficial links often obscure the distinction between science and technology. Popular thinking usually blurs the difference; the Cadillac and the space vehicle, the miracle drug and the computer, the H-bomb and dacron are the final products of technology that validate the enterprise of science. Research is development; and what works has a claim to credibility. The fact that two distinct types of activity are conflated in these conjunctions is rarely recognized.

Hence the deep ambivalence in popular attitudes toward science. Rarely has the man in the laboratory been so widely respected; never has he commanded so ready an access to public and private funds. One has only to recall the effects of Sputnik on American education to estimate the value set on his opinions, the esteem accorded his achievements. Yet the people who gladly vote billions for scientific research are far from understanding its inner character; and the points of view associated with it have never been altogether assimilated to the culture even of the West. The "popular delusions" which the scientist encounters with surprise upon his occasional forays outside the laboratory are the normal beliefs of a world which uses, but does not understand, the learning he develops.

Indeed, a deep underlying distrust of science runs through the accepted attitudes of people in the most advanced nations. Paradoxically, the bubbling retorts, the sparkling wires and the mysterious dials are often regarded as the source of a grave threat. Their white-coated manipulators, in the popular image, have ominously seized a power which they may use to injure mankind.

To disentangle the knotted threads of the relationships between science, technology, and popular attitudes, it is necessary to trace changes that have been almost two centuries in process. The complexities of the present are the product of a long development that has altered each of the elements involved.*

We do not have to go very far back in time to locate the prototype of the fixed man in a fixed community who supplies us with a starting point. He occupied the peasant villages of Europe fifty years ago. A century before that, in that continent and in its overseas outposts, he was the predominant figure both in the towns and in the countryside. Survivors still exist today in places that have resisted change.

The characteristic feature of the life of such persons was tradition—an understanding of the universe which passed with minor modification from generation to generation and which anticipated all the decisions the individual was called on to make. The great events of birth, marriage and death, and the lesser ones of sowing and reaping, of digging and building, of contriving and fabricating, were alike governed by a code that was self-validating in that it answered every conceivable question with conviction. The tradition also bore the sanctions of secular and sacred authority, and enjoyed the support of all communal institutions. It marked out an area of action within which man could operate with relatively little freedom but with immense security. The exceptional persons who moved beyond those limits and rejected tradition were individually important for their creativity, but they did not before the nineteenth century greatly influence the mass of men who were content to do and believe as their fathers had.

Tradition governed both the ways of doing and the ways of knowing. It set the patterns by which the artisan guided his tools, the husbandman his plow. It also gave satisfying responses on the occasions when they wondered why; for it supplied a comprehensible explanation for the affairs of the visible and invisible world. The ways of doing were not identical with the ways of knowing, but they were associated through common reference points in the traditions of the community.

The disruptive forces that broke in upon these communities already made themselves felt in the eighteenth century; they mounted in intensity in the nineteenth; and they have become the dominant factors in the social disorganization of our own time. The

* Some of the themes of this essay were treated in another context in Oscar Handlin, "Man and Magic: First Encounters with the Machine," *American Scholar*, XXXIII (1964), 408 ff.

migration of vast populations, urbanization and industrialization weakened the cohesive force of inherited institutions. The heterogeneity, impersonality, and individualism of the new social structures sapped the strength of tradition. And novel conditions demanded modes of acting and thinking for which there was no precedent. No matter how earnestly people struggled to preserve or restore the old community and its traditions, they could not stay the transformation.

Their ways of doing and their ways of knowing changed, although in different fashions. In the one case, development was continuous and controlled, in the other abrupt and unpredictable. Technology, however dangerous, had familiar features and bore the promise of service to man; science, however beneficent, was alien and threatened to overwhelm him. Ultimately when the two seemed to fuse, popular understanding failed entirely.

The ways of doing, which became technology, unfolded continuously from the experience of the past. Man the tinkerer had always sought to spare himself labor; and tradition in this respect was not entirely static. The first machines of the eighteenth and the nineteenth centuries were simply extensions of familiar techniques. Social and economic conditions imposed an ever livelier pace on these developments, but they were not altogether novel. There was no sudden severance of the essential continuity of the processes of fabrication. The machines themselves were the inventions of gifted artisans; and their use was assimilated with surprising equanimity.

The experience of factory labor was not altogether discontinuous with the past. The machines, whether of wood or iron, were not totally strange. The waterwheels, the great drive shafts and pulleys that dominated these plants, embodied no essentially new principles. To onlookers they were impressive in their ingenuity and power, but the manner of their operation was clearly visible and seemed but to extend and improve devices with which men had long been acquainted. Nor was the physical setting totally different. The earliest factories appeared in the countryside, not far removed from the familiar landscape of open fields, streams and woods. For a long time they used waterpower, and while the appearance of the mills was more complex than those familiar to every man, essentially they were not too different. It was characteristic, for instance, that one of the earliest American utopian novels to conceive of invention as a way of liberating man from labor had a thoroughly

Science and Technology

rural setting. In Mary Griffith's *Three Hundred Years Hence* (1836), great machines, moved by some internal power, did all the work of agriculture.

Now and then craftsmen displaced by new contrivances expressed their resentment—in Luddite riots and in political hostility to the growth of corporations. But the masses actually employed at the machines accepted their situation without shock. The village laborer who took a job in the mill was more sensitive to the transition from rural to urban life than to the abandonment of the plow for the loom. Often these people suffered from difficult conditions of labor and from even more difficult conditions of life. But their trials were tempered by a sense of confidence in the human capacity to master the devices that were the products of human ingenuity. They were sure that man could control and use the enormous power of the machines.

Therefore, invention could also be regarded as man's liberator, as Étienne Cabet had suggested it would be in *Voyage en Icarie*. In the series of great expositions that began at the Crystal Palace in London in 1851 and ran down through the end of the nineteenth century, the focal point was often the array of new machinery treated as symbolic of the age. The American commissioners to the Paris Universal Exposition of 1867 published six volumes of observations on the devices exhibited there. In the introduction to their report, Secretary of State William H. Seward explained that it was "through the universal language of the products of labor" that "the artisans of all countries hold communication." Industrialization was "in the interests of the mass of the people," for it promoted "an appreciation of the true dignity of labor, and its paramount claims to consideration as the basis of national wealth and power." Seward was confident that the machine would elevate man to new dignity.

The occasional intellectual observers who expressed a fear of the machine were more likely than not to attach their forebodings to the social situation of the factory. They protested against the bondage of human beings totally controlled by a routine that took no account of personality and detached man from nature. The factory enslaved those who served it by limiting their wills; and since it took no cognizance of moral considerations, it also limited their ability to make choices of good over evil. Here workers assembled in numbers that theretofore had been brought together only through some form of servitude in the military company and the ship's crew, the poorhouse and the gaol—agglomerations in which a rigid discipline that curtailed individual freedom permitted the coordination of many persons. It was no coincidence that the architecture of the early factories had much in common with that of the barracks, the military camp, and the prison. Hence the humanitarian's concern lest the power of the machine in this setting constrict personal liberties.

The factory regime detached work from nature and from all other aspects of life. The machine disregarded the alternations of the seasons and the rising and setting of the sun to operate at its own pace, winter and summer, day and night. There the laborers confronted the enterprise in a relationship that was purely economic. All those who entered the factory did so as detached individuals. Within its gates, they were not members of families or of groups, but isolated integers, each with his own line on the payroll; nothing extraneous counted. During the working hours, the laborers had no other identity than that established by the job. From being people who were parts of households, known by a whole community, they had been reduced to being servants of the machine.

By and large, nevertheless, the nineteenth century clung to its optimism about technology. Edward Bellamy, John Macnie and the utopian novelists of the 1880's and 1890's had no doubt that the machine would liberate mankind through the abundance it created. They did not deny that it would also harness man to its service. But they welcomed the consequent routine, the regularity and the order. Bellamy explained that the idea of *Looking Backward* came to him when he "recognized in the modern military system" the prototype of the Industrial Army that manned his utopia. The men of the year 2000 had "simply applied the principle of universal military service . . . to the labor question." Consequent gains in efficiency and affluence would release energies for the solution of all the problems of freedom raised by industrial regimentation.

H. G. Wells supplied a perfect encyclopedia of these hopes for the future. Beginning with his *Anticipations* (1902), a succession of roseate works showed the machine transforming and improving human life, which would evolve toward ever more centralized control. One state, one language, one ruling will would organize all men into efficient productive units. Indeed there would be no need at all for human labor as a source of energy. "Were our political and social and moral devices only as well contrived to their ends as a linotype machine . . . or an electric tram-car, there need now . . . be

Science and Technology

no appreciable toil in the world." Despite the anticipatory fears of those concerned with the future of man's spirit, in the last analysis there was faith that the machine remained a product of man and would obey his command.

Changes in the ways of knowing aroused far greater uneasiness. Traditional institutions in the solidary communities of the past had validated explanations as it had practices. Folk wisdom and the learning of the authoritative custodians of faith embraced all the accumulated knowledge of the group in a continuum that touched every aspect of experience.

Knowing was functionally related to doing. Men wished to know because they wished to be certain when they acted. The particularities of information or explanation were not critical; nor was the predictive value of any datum or concept. Minds that were not open to experiment did not seek to test the effectiveness of ideas—indeed, the very concept of doing so with reference to any of the great subjects of human concern was unthinkable. How could one verify the worth of the open-field system—or the efficacy of prayer? In these matters, men wished to know not in order to decide as between alternative courses of action, but in order to feel secure in the acts which tradition in any case dictated.

The community was aware that there were ways of knowing outside the tradition, free of its own oversight. It regarded them with suspicion as black mysteries, for they led to deviant actions and reflected the workings of strange, perhaps unholy powers. The heretics, the infidels, the Gypsies, the Jews, the witches, and the magicians shared common attributes to the extent that their abnormal behavior was connected with illicit, that is, unsanctioned, knowledge. Therefore they were at once feared and hated.

Modern scientific enterprise was from the start suspect on somewhat the same grounds. Although it was long sheltered in established clerical institutions—the universities and the church—its practitioners were detached from any community but their own and their basic goals differed from those of other men. Whatever formal obeisance the scientists made to tradition, their ultimate quest was for change rather than certainty. They unsettled rather than confirmed accepted beliefs because truth was for them an end in itself rather than a means of explaining and justifying existing habitual practices. They possessed and exercised a magic, the character and purposes of which were unknown to the uninitiate. Science smacked of the forbidden; it threatened to uncover secrets that were best left concealed. Hence the widespread dread of what might come of it in the eighteenth and nineteenth centuries when it had acquired considerable independence and had developed institutions of its own.

Even though the underlying tensions about its effects persisted, as the nineteenth century progressed, unorthodox opinions in time encountered less opposition; and even the war with theology lost its point and its bitterness. The growing tolerance of science was a factor of its utility to new, but increasingly important, social groups. Entrepreneurial types, whether among the gentry or the middle classes, who valued personal achievement above ascriptive status and who regarded inherited tradition and the entrenched community as the sources of restraints upon their desire to fulfill themselves, were likely to be experimental and calculating in their attitudes, to esteem reason above habit as a guide to action. There was likely to be a high incidence of such men in the mobile populations of the growing cities, among marginal ethnic groups and within various dissenting sects; but personalities receptive to new ideas were by no means confined within those social limits. Increasingly, such persons found attractive the kinds of knowledge that science generated.

The expanding scientific enterprise appealed to its own practitioners on abstract grounds, as a mode of progressively uncovering the truth—a good in itself. But it also drew the support of a widening circle by its utility in improving the ways of doing, demonstrable in practical results. The claims of astronomy, for instance, were long since familiar in advancing the methods of navigation. Geology and biology, by the same token, were instruments by which to develop better techniques of mining and agriculture. Discoveries in physics and chemistry would have a comparable effect upon industry. The justification by utility became a conventional tactic of the nineteenth century.

The linkage of science with practice was clearest, most dramatic, and most effective in medicine. This was a field in which ways of knowing were intimately connected with ways of doing and one in which the welfare of every man was concerned. From the mid-nineteenth century onward, the conviction grew that the way to health passed through the medical laboratory. Since in this area the scientist had access to clinical materials only through practice, he had a stake in nurturing the belief, which brought him patients,

Science and Technology

that his ministrations would yield measurable results in the cure of illness. By the end of the century the association of hospitals, universities, and laboratories in a firmly articulated complex was the visible manifestation of the union of science and technology.

By then also comparable claims were being heard from newer disciplines, including the social sciences. Political and economic systems and family and interpersonal relationships of other sorts were subject to pathologies of their own, which the proper organization of knowledge could ameliorate. Science in this broadest sense took every human concern as its province.

Common to all these assertions of the preeminence of science was the assumption that every deficiency in man's world was definable as a problem to which the correct ways of knowing would supply an appropriate solution. The staggering optimism of this article of faith endured into our own times and endowed science with the vital force to sway the opinions of the increasing numbers of its clients. Ultimately it promised that the organized use of intelligence, through its procedures, would perfect man.

The conquest of opinion was never complete. Traditional folk wisdom retained its hold in the more stable communities and among the less adaptable personalities. Familiar beliefs and practices persisted. But they became the deviations from a norm which had secured broad acceptance in the society as a whole and which by the twentieth century were buttressed by a formidable array of institutions.

Significantly, however, a subtle foreboding about the consequences disturbed even the individuals most susceptible to the claims of the beneficence of science. Again and again, a half-admitted fear creeps into the imaginative efforts to envision the future. An early nineteenth-century version of a myth gave popular form to the dread that continued to trouble even men committed to science.

Frankenstein, a dedicated young scientist who seeks knowledge to help mankind, discovers the secret of life through the study of electricity, galvanism, and chemistry, and applies his formula to create a machine-monster. The monster, however, quickly proves himself the superior. In the confrontation, the machine gives the orders: "Slave, I before reasoned with you, but you have proved yourself unworthy of my condescension. Remember that I have power. . . . I can make you so wretched that the light of day will be hateful to you. You are my creator, but I am your master;—

obey!" The monster becomes the oppressive master of man, although it was neither evil to begin with nor created out of deliberate malice.

Mary Shelley later recalled the circumstances under which the idea came to her, in 1816, while she listened to her husband and Lord Byron pass the long evenings in talk by the shores of Lake Leman. Often their conversation turned to science, and particularly to the mystery of electricity and to experiments in creating life through galvanism. And a vision suddenly came to her of the dreadful "effect of any human endeavour to mock the stupendous mechanism of the Creator of the world." The impiety inherent in the magic of which they spoke invited retribution.

Mary Shelley gave her novel a subtitle, *The Modern Prometheus*. It was a theme that her husband had also treated, and that had recurred for centuries and would continue to recur in Western imaginative writing. In another form that theme also appears in retellings of the Faust legend of a demonic personality unwilling to respect the unfathomable.

Even the most optimistic imaginations long continued to shudder with that primitive fear. "This accursed science," exclaims H. G. Wells, "is the very Devil. You tamper with it—and it offers you gifts. And directly you take them it knocks you to pieces in some unexpected way. Old passions and new weapons—now it upsets your religion, now it upsets your social ideas, now it whirls you off to desolation and misery!" The ability to work miracles leaves the world "smashed and utterly destroyed."

Within this perspective of disrupted communities and changing ways of doing and knowing, the developments of the past seventy-five years become more comprehensible. There was always a grudging acquiescence in the victory of science and technology. Now the inner changes in the new ways, despite the magnitude of the achievements to which they contributed, further alienated the mass of men, and heightened the suspicion of the power thus created.

From the middle of the nineteenth century, the structural changes that isolated science from modern life proceeded rapidly and radically. Knowledge became specialized, professionalized, and institutionalized. The three tendencies were interrelated and each had the effect of creating a closed body of skills and information. Specialization was the product of forces inside and outside science. The mere accumulation of data stored up in libraries made it in-

Science and Technology

creasingly difficult for an individual to master more than a limited sector of any field. It seemed to follow that the more limited the field the more readily could it be mastered; and that, in itself, further encouraged specialization. In addition, the emphasis upon classification as the first step in all inductive learning induced scientists to mark out, and concentrate in, a distinctive and circumscribed field of research. Finally, the growing rigor of the tests for validation required constantly improved techniques; and it was a rare individual who commanded more than one set. Science—at any rate, for most of its practitioners—became the province of the expert who excelled in the one subject he knew thoroughly.

The result was a high degree of compartmentalization, the fragmentation of knowledge into a multitude of different disciplines, each familiar only to its own initiates. A chemist was not much more able to discourse with an astronomer than with a sociologist, or an economist with an anthropologist than with a physicist. The overlapping of techniques, language, and subject matter kept some lines of communication open, but each field was really known only to those who specialized in it.

Specialization contributed to the great advances of modern science. But it also demanded such a high degree of competence that it, in fact, excluded the amateur and made the practice of science entirely professional. Learning now required a prescribed course of preparation; it imposed defined canons of judgment and validation; and it developed the *esprit de corps* of a coherent and united group.

Finally, specialization and professionalization tended to institutionalize science. Research became so expensive that no individual could buy his own telescope, computer or cyclotron; and the organization of scientific enterprise increasingly fell into forms established by government, business, universities, and foundations. These characteristics facilitated the great achievements of the past century. They were also responsible for the developing gulf that set scientists off from other men.

The accelerating pace and audacity of discovery magnified the effects of the distance between the learned expert and the rest of the population. In 1900, the graduate of a European gymnasium or lycée or of an American college could expect the knowledge acquired there to retain some currency through his whole lifetime. In 1950, anyone who wished to keep abreast had to resist desperately a mounting rate of obsolescence; although far more people were educated than formerly, their schooling now equipped them with information that could quickly lose all value. Furthermore science grew ever less inclined to replace old with new certitudes; it ceased to deal with deterministic laws and yielded instead tentative statements of probability. At the same time, it probed the most important aspects of human existence and did so with increasing confidence. Since Darwin's day it had been busily destroying the fixed universe of tradition; now it made clear that it offered no consolatory alternative of its own.

The popular response was complex; people learned to tolerate but not to assimilate science. They accepted its judgments as true, since they were now validated as authoritative. But they blocked them out as irrelevant by refusing to adapt to them the beliefs or behavior of daily life. The ability to answer correctly questions about the new astronomy or physics or psychology did not modify old views about heaven and hell or about absolute personal morality. The two kinds of knowledge co-existed in uncomfortable juxtaposition.

Technology, however, made it difficult thus to isolate science from life. As the nineteenth century drew to a close, the new knowledge invaded industry, changed the machine, and altered the nature of the factory; it then impinged directly upon the experience of the laborer who could no longer escape an awareness of its implications.

The most striking indication of the transformation was visual. In the factories built in 1900, the drive shafts and the pulleys were no longer visible. Power was transmitted through wires and tubes—often hidden—and the whole was covered up and shielded so that the machine gave the appearance of being self-contained and autonomous. The onlooker no longer saw a comprehensible apparatus; he saw an enclosed shape actuated by a hidden source of power from which the products flowed by an occult process.

Some of the changes in design were incidental to other purposes. The demands of safety, for instance, often produced the shields that concealed the mechanism of operation. Other modifications were aesthetic, although even those were related to the meaning the machine held for men. An unbroken sheet of black metal seemed more pleasing to the eye than a complex of belting and gears because it conformed to the idea of the machine as self-contained.

Science and Technology

The application to the machine and to industry of electricity was an even more important break with past human experience. Men had been experimenting with various manifestations of electricity for two hundred years, but it remained a mysterious force, somehow confused with galvanic magnetism, somehow related to the secret of life, but not popularly understood, not as comprehensible as water and steam power had been. Even after a multitude of appliances had brought it into every home, few men could grasp how a current passing through a wire created light and sound or turned the wheels of great machines. Still fewer would comprehend the processes involved in the technological application of knowledge from electrochemistry or nuclear physics to the instruments with which they worked.

The gap between the machines and their users widened steadily. In the twentieth century it was no longer the tinkerer who was inventor. The innovations were less likely to be products of industrial experience than of science; and the people who operated them understood neither the machines they served nor the technical fund of knowledge that dominated industry.

But they could not fail to be aware that their own conditions of life and labor were changing at the same time and in response to forces generated by the new technology. The factory became a new and different kind of human environment toward the end of the nineteenth century. The numbers involved were much larger than in any previous era. The plant no longer counted its employees in the scores, but in the thousands; and that increased its impersonality and rigid discipline. The analogy to the army became closer and more frightening as individual identity diminished in importance. The hordes that passed through the gates each morning had to be accounted for and their time put to a precise, measured, profitable use. Before the end of the century, Frederick W. Taylor had already outlined the principles of industrial management; and the demands of efficiency were served with increasing severity as the decades passed. Technological innovation became not only an end in itself but also a means of establishing greater control over the labor force. The more enlightened enterprises recognized the importance of human relations; but they did so as a means of increasing their efficiency, and the devices they used had the further effect of manipulating the lives of their employees.

An altered environment increased the external pressures upon personality. In the second half of the nineteenth century the factories had become urban, either through the growth in the size of the towns in which they had been located or through the shift to metropolitan centers. All the difficulties of industrial experience were therefore compounded. The machine, the factory, and the city became identified as a single entity oppressive of man.

The optimists consoled themselves with the vision of abundance of goods produced by the new regime and they hoped that the machine would compensate for the deficiencies of their own society by resolving in the future the problems with which they could not deal in the present. *The Shape of Things to Come,* as H. G. Wells saw it, was dominated by industrial plenitude that was a product of invention. Self-consciously the engineers assumed that they could not only make the machines run but manage society as well; and the technocrats envisioned a mechanical order—efficient, antiseptic and capable of dealing with any contingency.

Yet overtones of uneasiness about the mysterious new ways of knowing also persisted. In 1911, Henry James, visiting a laboratory walled with cages of white mice, exclaimed at the magnificence of the "divine power" exhibited in cancer experiments. But he also wondered about the personality of the little creatures imprisoned in the wooden cubicles. Other observers also speculated about who was making the decisions and toward what end.

Doubts therefore always offset the confidence about the results. Karel Čapek's *R. U. R.* in the 1920's created a sensation in its nightmare vision of a robot's universal which completely dominated humanity. The greatest of the popular artists, René Clair and Charlie Chaplin, in *À nous la liberté* and *Modern Times,* expressed an identical protest: the assembly line made man its slave, repressed his emotions, and crushed his individuality. He could escape to freedom only by revolt against the machine. In *Brave New World* and *1984,* Aldous Huxley and George Orwell stood utopia on its head. The necessity for mobilizing large groups along military lines, which provided Bellamy with his Industrial Army, to these writers established a terrifying engine of oppression.

Much in these protests had a familiar ring; to a considerable degree these artists repeated the criticisms of the machine already voiced in an earlier, simpler era. But the involvement of science in the technology of the more recent period diffused the concern to much wider circles which had theretofore equally accepted change in the ways of doing but which now could not readily evade the need for new ways of knowing. However routine his role, the techni-

Science and Technology

cian at the keyboard—or, for that matter, the indiscriminate television-viewer—had to wonder sometime what occurred within the box, the dials of which he turned.

Since the explanation of the scientists was remote and incomprehensible, a large part of the population satisfied its need for knowing in its own way. Side by side with the formally defined science there appeared a popular science, vague, undisciplined, unordered and yet extremely influential. It touched upon the science of the scientists, but did not accept its limits. And it more adequately met the requirements of the people because it could more easily accommodate the traditional knowledge to which they clung.

Pragmatically, the popular science was not always less correct than the official. It would be hard to assert with confidence, for instance, that faith healing, nature cures and patent medicines were always less effective than the ministrations of the graduates of recognized medical schools; or that the vision of the universe exposed in the television serial or Sunday supplement was less accurate than that of the physics textbook. By the tests of practice—of whether it worked—popular science did as well as official science.

The deficiencies of popular science were of quite another order. It formed part of no canon that marked out its boundaries or established order among its various parts. It consisted rather of discontinuous observations, often the projection of fantasy and wish fulfillment, and generally lacking coherence and consistency. Above all, it embraced no test of validity save experience. It was as easy to believe that there was another world within the crust of the earth as that there were other worlds in outer space. One took the little pills; the pain went away. One heard the knocking; the spirits were there. The observable connections between cause and result were explanation enough. It was unnecessary to seek an understanding of the links in the chain between the two.

The men and women who moved into the highly complex and technically elaborate industrial society of our times simply assimilated the phenomena about them in terms of the one comprehensible category they already knew, that of magic. And it was thus too that they understood the defined science of the laboratory and the university. The man who pressed a button and saw the light appear, who turned a switch and set the machine in motion, felt no need to understand electricity or mechanics; the operations he performed made the limited kind of sense that other mysterious events of life did. The machine, which was a product of science, was also magic, understandable only in terms of what it did, not of how or why it worked. Hence the lack of comprehension or of control; hence also the mixture of dread and anticipation.

As in the past, the new ways of knowing seem unconnected with tradition, appear to be the possession of outsiders, and are considered potentially dangerous. But for people who fly in jets and watch television, the threat has an imminence it did not have earlier. Those who blankly and passively depend upon modern technology frequently feel themselves mastered by science without knowing why.

The more useful science becomes, therefore, the more it is both respected *and* feared. That it had power at its disposal was all along known; now the machine compounds its force and creates the suspicion that it is buying men into bondage. The people who are simultaneously delighted with additional years of life expectancy and terrified by the bomb are in no position to strike the balance of their gains and losses in happiness. In their confusion, they wonder whether the price of the gadgets which delight may not be servitude to the remote and alien few who control the mystery.

The popular response to science is thus ambivalent, mingling anger and enthusiasm, lavish support and profound mistrust. Conceivably the tension can persist unresolved indefinitely into the future as it did in the past, although it would be hazardous to count on that outcome under rapidly changing modern conditions.

The profound uneasiness about the consequences of the new ways of knowing will be quieted only if science is encompassed within institutions which legitimate its purposes and connect its practitioners with the populace. Education is helpful insofar as it goes beyond the diffusion of techniques to familiarize broad segments of the population with the basic concepts and processes of science. But even those who never acquire that understanding need assurance that there is a connection between the goals of science and their own welfare, and above all that the scientist is not a man altogether apart but one who shares some of their own values.

ERIC WEIL

Science in Modern Culture

I

IF WE WANT TO DISCOVER the part science plays in our civilization, it will be useful, not to say necessary, to find out what part is attributed to science by the people—that is, all of us unless we consider ourselves specialists—who live in this civilization and according to its values.

Now, what has common opinion to say about the nature and the impact of science? Science, it proclaims, has made our life what it is, it has modeled and is constantly remodeling our civilization, it dominates our world. But if we ask a cultivated representative of this opinion whether that is the whole truth, he will readily admit that it is not. It is not just science that acts in this way, it is our particular form of science. Although the cultivated man may not give much thought to it, he knows that every cultural system, even the most primitive, transmits to its members knowledge, truth, true rules of practical, moral and technical content, and considers itself the bearer and distributor of "science." But that "science," our imaginary interlocutor would continue, is not science in our meaning of the word. It does not analyze its objects, it classifies them according to their qualities into families, clans, and tribes; it is qualitative science and, applied, it becomes magic. And though magic may make magnificent promises, it is only we and our science that are able to keep them. We, not they, are able to fly through the air, to live under the waters, to hear the voice of the dead. And we have succeeded because our science is objective and does not look for anything but knowledge pure and disinterested, whereas they have failed because their goal was success.

Up to this point, it would be difficult not to agree with popular opinion. It is a fact that we in our civilization have become, as Descartes said, the owners and masters of nature. We have achieved this because we renounced "understanding" nature—attributing to her traits that belong only to us, qualities that depend on our physiological and psychological constitution, intentions, ends, aversions. We have tried to study her as she is and to read her great book in the language she used—the language of mathematics—instead of writing texts in our human language on pages we ourselves fit in. We carried the day, not although, but because we were not pursuing victory. It would be erroneous and unjust to suppose that the common opinion has neglected this side of the facts, and that people look only at results. It is commonly known that men of science are, at least ideally, "disinterested," that research is "pure," that those who do research do not necessarily strive for results that would be inconceivable without their work. But it is precisely this split appreciation, this contradictory view that ought to preoccupy us. Science is good because it is useful and gives riches, power, and comfort; and at the same time it is the noblest of human pursuits. Science is the mainstay of our economic, social, and political life; and the man of science is the successor to the sages of old to whom popular opinion applies, often in a most touching manner, for answers to questions that have nothing to do with his special competence, simply because he is considered objective, disinterested, unpartisan, and wise.

II

The situation is paradoxical enough to justify a, necessarily sketchy, historical inquiry: it will not solve the problem, because history, correctly understood, does not even pretend to be able to do so, but it may help to bring it better into focus.

The root of the matter is that our double-faced idea of science stems from two different origins. There was, to start with, a "disinterested" science, which was not conceived as an instrument to master and appropriate nature; it refused every intervention in the course of nature; it did not want to dominate, it was in pursuit of understanding. It even rejected experimentation, in our sense, i.e., the search of measurable, and thus mathematically describable, underlying factors (though it knew of course experimentation in the form of trial and error). Its analysis was conceptual, in other words metaphysical; it did not subject nature, as Kant proclaimed modern classical physics does, to questioning under conditions forced upon her by the questioner in order that he may receive measurable indications. So it is not surprising that the most respected figures in science kept clear of technology. Archimedes, who was a great engineer as well as a great scientist, did not publicize his inventions, because he feared for his honor. Science was *theoria*, pure *view*, not *praxis*.

It would be a mistake to believe that this attitude died with the aristocratic civilization that gave birth to it. It did not change much when modern science was born—or rather, reborn from Greek sources. Galilei's fame rested not on his remarkable engineering performances, which brought him jobs and money, but on discoveries whose practical value in the eyes of his contemporaries was at first practically nil: in 1600 astronomy and the theory of free fall did not promise usefulness. Galilei built instruments for precise observation, not machines—it has been the great merit of A. Koyré to have insisted upon this fundamental and often neglected distinction. Leonardo da Vinci's history is different: he was not shy of being an engineer, but he was not a man of mathematical science. When Leonardo spoke of mechanics as the "noblest and the most useful of sciences," he was not in possession of a mathematical theory of mechanics nor did he seem to seek one. When he wrote, "Mechanics is the paradise of mathematical sciences, because with it we reach the fruit of mathematics," it is his reason that is important, not his appreciation. Descartes and Newton built instruments, as did many other natural philosophers, but though some of their creations may have been of great technical utility, witness Huyghens' clocks, they were not conceived and executed with a view toward their extra-scientific utility.

But there was another strand at the dawn of modern science, which derived from the revolutionary discoveries of the Middle Ages. During that period of the eclipse of pure, theoretical science, men whose names will forever remain unknown had created things of decisive importance: ways to harness non-human energy, and methods of employing animal forces, with an efficiency antiquity had never attained. Transport had been transformed and industries were created that relied on sources of energy the Greeks and Romans had certainly known but had not learned to domesticate effectively. On the other hand during the later Middle Ages cities in the most developed parts of Europe had become autonomous in two senses: they had grown relatively independent of both central authority and their powerful neighbors, and they had ceased to be important only as residences and capitals of princes and bishops. The new bourgeois society, which was throwing off the values of its natural enemy, feudal aristocracy, gave empirical engineering a chance to become respectable.

These two tendencies began to act on one another at the time of the Renaissance.* Scientists took cognizance of inventions, even though they neither were nor wanted to be inventors, and engines became objects of study for them. It is no accident, for instance, that Galilei so often chooses the cannon as an example or that ballistics is one of the main subjects of early research. To the "modern" philosophers, these new devices deserved scientific analysis quite as much as did natural objects. The situation remained the same for a long time: the steam engine had worked well for more than a generation before the corresponding mathematical theory was created. But as soon as that stage was reached, the two streams began to flow together. Practice began to act on theory by building what then became problems for science, and science, by solving the problems so born, offered the engineer the possibility of calculating, before he built his machines, their effects and the conditions for their safe and remunerative operation.

This fusion, which began during the seventeenth century in some fields, became a universal phenomenon toward the end of the eighteenth century. Modern industry and the science that it both presupposes and fosters have realized Descartes' dream—which was an old one even in his time. Here a new question arises: why did this fusion not happen earlier, since both technicians and scientists were present in the towns? A realistic answer is that if the intellectual conditions were already in existence, the new relation between mathematical theory and empirical practice became an historically

* Not to make complex things even more complicated, I have omitted intentionally one other strand of the utmost importance, but which in the history of ideas has played its part mainly in furnishing justifications for new attitudes it would probably not have produced by itself. The Bible considers the world, natural and historical, as a *cosmos,* but as one that is not understandable directly, as it is for Greek *theoria:* it is consistent and meaningful as the result of divine planning, which planning is essentially hidden from human eyes and intellect. The world is meaningful, but only for a *faith* that *believes* in a meaning it cannot *discover* in this earthly existence. On the other hand, Adam, while depending for his understanding on God, is the master, under God, of the whole creation. When the divine mediation between fact and meaning is negated or even doubted, the modern situation (which will be analyzed in the following pages) results quite naturally. The importance of these remarks for the present topic will appear later, although I shall not take them up again. They are put here to avoid the reproach of overlooking a decisive factor.

Science in Modern Culture

important factor because the political situation prevailing first in Italy, and later over all of Western Europe, was unique. Europe comprised a number of independent states, similar in wealth and power, each of which had as its paramount interest the defense of its frontiers and/or the aggrandizement of its territory. Now technical questions would play a decisive part in this uninterrupted struggle among equals: communications, artillery, money flowing from industry and commerce, these were the factors upon which power came to depend even more than on territory and population. No wonder, then, that the first technical schools, all of them fostered by government, either turned out mining engineers, as in Germany, or were conceived as schools for future officers of artillery and technical troops, as in France. It is interesting to note that the first definition of *engineer* in the Concise OED still reads: "One who designs and constructs military engines or works." Technology, unlike empirical techniques, came into being because princes needed technicians and money—under Louis XIV Colbert's mercantilistic system imported whole industries—siege machines, roads, and canals. Princes wanted power, and they came to understand that knowledge procures it. Unlike the oriental despots who were free to exploit their subjects because the outer barbarians and conquered peoples had no possibility of going over to a better master, the western powers had need of experts and specialists to help them compete with powers equal to their own.

The science that they used and depended on was, however, an existing science, and it is worthwhile to ask why this science had arisen in Europe during the sixteenth and seventeenth centuries— this disinterested science, pure, mathematical, non-qualitative, non-explicative. When Newton said that he did not invent hypotheses, he meant that he did not pretend to know what gravitation was in itself, which would have been the natural question for a metaphysician; he wanted only to describe how it worked and to give an adequate mathematical account of observed phenomena. The same attitude is present in the thinking of all the great creators of modern physics, although one can observe how difficult and even impossible it was for men like Kepler and Galilei to eliminate every trace of anthropocentrism or anthropomorphism from their thinking. Disinterested or what Max Weber has called "value free" science became the idea and the ideal, in a sense—the difference is decisive—which was unknown to antiquity, for according to the philosophers science led to a world-view that satisfied the human needs of human beings, were it only by allowing them to accede to the beautiful, to the absolutely beautiful spectacle of the *cosmos*. The change is revolutionary: how did it happen?

It seems to have grown out of the changing attitude toward religion; at a time when religion was discredited in the eyes of many people or, through a reaction against this attitude, became the center of theological and political strife, "value-free" science remained as the sole refuge for people with purely intellectual interests and no vocation for martyrdom—this science that had nothing to do with what had up to that moment been considered the fundamental values. It was a return to the Greek *theoria* of the *cosmos,* which Kepler among many others endeavored to maintain, but which the new "philosophy" of Bruno and the new "cosmology" of Descartes were to destroy replacing it with the silent infinity of homogenous unoriented space and innumerable interchangeable particles of matter. In Galilei's famous trial, behind all the misunderstandings and worse, there may well have been on the part of his persecutors an unconscious fear, not of his particular cosmology, but of any science that eliminated all values foreign to mathematical science.

Such hypotheses have more than historical importance. They enable us to understand how our present situation originated, and how was born what we may call the common attitudes of our day, with their contradictory, though historically complementary, aspects. Nothing, the common opinion holds, can be done without disinterested science, but what we are really interested in is the results. The ideal of precision, which is often called rationalism, and that of helping men, nations, the whole of humanity, are fused, as they were already for Descartes, who saw clearly that "the fruits of the tree of science" could advance medical knowledge.

III

Physics has become the archetype of true science, followed by all the sciences (and technologies). Precision through mathematical analysis may not yet prevail in all of science, for the biological, social, and historical sciences have not yet overcome their methodological troubles, but they all strive to become "exact," objective, value-free.* They aspire to objectivity because only in this way can they attain power, as physics has attained it in its field. But the

* One of the first and always best analyses of this situation has been given by Max Weber in his famous lecture *Wissenschaft als Beruf.*

power they seek is the control of history; we are becoming progressively better able to analyze economical, social, strategic situations and to predict results and discover the necessary conditions of success, in a word, to direct events.

Thus it is no wonder that popular opinion is struck by present and foreseeable results. Men of science may well wonder whether the public is not over-optimistic in its confidence that everything can be bettered, all evils eradicated, poverty vanquished, illness overcome, perhaps even death pushed out of the perfect world to come. But their skepticism should not persuade them that the great majority of humanity does not hold these views. The debates of the United Nations and their agencies on underdeveloped countries and ways to help them, to give only one illustration, may be considered largely propaganda by many self-styled realists, hard-headed in perhaps more than one sense; but this propaganda would fail if it did not appeal to deep and widespread attitudes, convictions, and even mythologies, and if it did not therefore command very real and serious reactions. Men of science may think that the explicit and implicit promises of progress made by communism, for instance—and what it offers is just mastery over nature and over history—cannot be fulfilled in the near future and for the whole of humanity; but it can scarcely be denied that about half the population of the earth has accepted that system, be it only passively (and that is open to doubt), and that another fraction may be ready to join them unless they receive from some other source what communism holds out to them. It may even be asked whether the skeptic does not contradict himself. What he says is not that the enterprise is impossible; he maintains that it is extremely complex, that poor nations will not get rich overnight, that profound transformations will be required in their religious convictions, their family system, their social organization. But he seems to forget that precisely by raising these objections he accepts the principle: there will be progress, he says, if the conditions enumerated by social science are fulfilled—which signifies that, according to him, these prerequisites are known or can be elucidated and that, in principle, science can do the job *if* it is allowed to direct the operation; he does not doubt of science, but rather of the intelligence of the people and their leaders.

Pure objective value-free science and the idea of man's universal domination over nature and history have come together, and it is not probable that this alliance will be broken. But it remains an alliance, it has not become a unity of fundamental values and outlook.

ERIC WEIL

Science stays pure, while technology uses and very often inspires disinterested research but keeps its basic interest in results. The scientist is not an engineer, the engineer is not a scientist, although they collaborate; they have been brought together. And that is precisely the source of the problem: is our civilization rent by this duality of outlook and purpose, or is it unified by the interdependence that history has introduced? Is the rift between knowledge and power—if these two terms may be allowed to designate the ideals of the two sides—equivalent to disruption, or is their coming together the fundamental unity of our culture? Was Plato right in affirming that only pure knowledge of eternal truth deserves to be pursued? Or was Saint-Simon's perspective the correct one when he wanted for humanity mastery over history through mastery over nature and through scientific organization? Or is it possible that the rift, if it is one, was characteristic of an earlier stage of our civilization and is gradually being bridged? It is said that there is more disinterested science in our day than there has ever been before; but it can be answered that the proportion of pure to applied science has dropped constantly since the day when all science was disinterested. More money and time are being expended on fundamental research now than during any period of the known past; but those who allot the money and so give other people the leisure and means to do research—the governments, business concerns, foundations—may simply have discovered that this kind of work leads, in a way that no one can foresee, to very profitable results, if input and output are compared. Disinterested science is paying dividends, as the Russians found when they learned that the A-bomb was built with the help of the "idealistic" physics which, judging from a metaphysical viewpoint, they had looked upon as antithetical to "class interest" and unforgivably "objectivistic." So it might seem that there was once a problem of opposition between knowledge and power, between pure science and technology: is the conflict still with us? Has the fusion between them already occurred, or has it at least begun? Is science to become a tool, necessary and highly respected, for acquiring total mastery over nature and history? It would look as if it were to play exactly that part, and as if the philosophical interpretations of science offered by pragmatism and instrumentalism were justified—if there did not remain a lingering doubt, though of quite another order. We can still ask whether our civilization is to grow more meaningful or whether, left to itself, it will become more schizophrenic if it goes the way that observed facts are indicating, toward mastery for mastery's sake, with nothing to tell us with scientific, value free objectivity which values are to guide us in the use of this mastery. The fears and the unrest of our day are there to show that this is not just an intellectual's empty problem.

IV

The preceding considerations and questions have shown at the very least that facts will not lead us any further. We are faced with a choice and a decision. And although only fools take their decisions without looking at the facts, nobody has ever made up his mind by looking at them exclusively unless he had made his choice unconsciously like the pragmatist who knows in his bones that success, whatever that may be, is good and that the proof of the pudding is in the eating (which is quite true of puddings and pudding eaters, i.e., people who know that puddings are good).

Modern science is objective and, considered in itself, pure theory. It has thrown out anthropomorphism and anthropocentrism. It has inherited the Greek idea of scientific truth as a system of consistent discourse, but with one important modification. It has not retained the idea that knowledge of the world leads man to knowledge about himself by indicating the best way of life, because modern science does not admit of a meaningful world that can be understood the way Plato and all the Greek philosophers thought they understood the *cosmos*. Nature for modern physics and "cosmology" is just what it is, or rather it is what science says it is, exactly as "human" sciences describe historical worlds whose factual structures can be discovered, without conveying any meaning valid for the historian, the economist, or the social anthropologist in their own lives. Any meaning that these structures held for the participants is a mere *fact* to the social sciences. That is one aspect of modern science. The other is that this science has rendered possible human action upon conditions that have never before been considered modifiable. Not that science sought this result—although many men of science had been looking for it. Science was not pursuing anything but pure knowledge. Nevertheless, the combination of certain people and certain situations caused science to become "interesting"— as an instrument of power over nature, history, natural resources, and human beings. Probably it was no accident. When science renounces anthropocentrism, it is bound to be at the service of the most primitive interest, the acquisition of power. Our culture has developed a split personality, rent between its thirst for objective truth and its desire for power. And curiously enough, this schism results not through any fault of technology and applied social science, but through the fact that the most disinterested and purest form of science refuses to pronounce on questions which by their very nature are not "objective" because they concern ways of life.

V

It is a problem of good and bad, of the desirable and its opposite. Facts cannot solve it, and science cannot even formulate it in its own language. So it will be necessary to go back to fundamentals and to introduce some classical philosophical distinctions.

What does it mean when we say that science is value-free, disinterested? The expression is evidently unsatisfactory, for it is precisely the pure researcher who finds his work supremely interesting and of the greatest value. The underlying equivocation is easy to clear up: interest may be attached either to something valuable in itself, or to something useful toward attaining a valuable end. The difference is the old one between facts and values. To say that a thing is interesting or desirable in itself is a value judgment, but to say that some given factor is necessary in order to obtain a desirable end is a judgment of fact, or a judgment concerning the factual relations among facts. I cannot offer scientific proof of my value-judgments, but I can and must do so when I speak of facts and their relations.

Now, it has been common knowledge, at least since Hume's days, that there is no path from fact to value. Science is concerned with facts exclusively, and science alone is qualified to distinguish what is a fact from what is not. Value judgments are not scientific nor can they become so. The theory has often been presented, and G. E. Moore has given it a particularly influential form with his criticism of the "naturalistic fallacy": According to Moore, from the fact that a thing is done, it does not follow logically (though it could easily follow pragmatically) that it ought to be done. But it may well be asked whether this purely negative statement is sufficient to elucidate the relations between facts and values.

It would be only an apparent objection to say that certain sciences are concerned with values, for example, sociology and psychology. For these sciences the values become objects of observation and enquiry, they are analyzed as facts and studied the way constitutions are or the change in price of basic commodities or military techniques or rituals, though there may be specific difficulties in finding out which values certain people at a given time regard as decisive and central to their way of life. In principle the science of value facts is value free.

Mistaken though it is, the objection leads nevertheless to a point of positive importance. Values, it is said, are being studied as facts. True, but they interest us not in isolation but as value systems, as more or less consistent rules, sometimes explicit, sometimes to be discovered through long and complex analyses. The different values of a culture, or of a religion or a political party, cannot be unrelated among themselves. If these values are to offer direction and meaning to a group's life, they ought to permit not so much survival (for groups have sacrificed their lives at the feet of their values) as guidance, i.e. consistency: coordination between values is indispensable to the formation of the decisions of the group and its members. Unrelated values lead not to justified but to arbitrary choices. Values form value systems, and that signifies that in each value field a logical, and thus decidable, discussion is possible and that rules can be elaborated for it (though there is no necessity for doing it). People who adhere to the same set of values may not only formulate problems concerning choices, they may even solve them, simply by pointing out that this or that action would be inconsistent with this or that part of the system, or that introducing new values would disrupt its consistency. Value systems in this way establish the possibility of rational discourse and discussion. But they do so only for those who accept the fundamental value axioms of a given civilization, or given morals or esthetics. There is no discussion between systems that have no common axioms. Thus science, even in its most formal definition as consistent discourse, cannot do the job of choosing between different sets.

That is not all, for we are now bound to apply this result to objective science itself, and to its principal exigency, consistency. Disinterestedness, objectivity, and so forth are values; science has no way of proving that they ought to be values, because the very idea of proof—the appeal to consistency of discourse—presupposes that these values have been acknowledged beforehand. We shall have to say, since there is no other possibility, that these values are basic to our civilization. But that admission reverses, and completes, the thesis of absolute separation between facts and values in a highly surprising manner. Facts depend upon science and on the questions asked by the scientist, because it is he who decides which facts are relevant, i.e., are scientific facts; thus facts depend upon the spirit in which these questions are formulated, on the scientist's axioms; and the choice of these axioms is actually a choice, in other words, a value judgment. It is certainly true that values do not follow from facts, but it now appears that facts become relevant only through values. No facts in our sense of the word exist where there is no objective, disinterested science. Every attempt to prove scientifically the value of science is nothing but a *circulus in probando*.

It is tempting at this point to fall back on the idea of mastery over nature and history as a justification, though pragmatic, of the value of consistency. And that is actually what popular thought and instrumentalist philosophy are trying to do. It is to no avail, for two different and equally strong reasons. First, the idea of power on which such a demonstration would be founded could not lead to any result, unless power were already considered desirable. In this way power would constitute one of the basic, axiomatic values, the validity of which is precisely the object of scrutiny. Secondly, if this justification presents itself as *valid*, it presupposes that the value of consistency, without which no valid proof can be conceived, has been acknowledged at the outset—and this is precisely the value to be justified. That does not imply that power cannot be accepted as a fundamental value, or that science can never be treated as instrumental. Examples of such a choice are abundant, even among philosophers.

All we can say then is that consistency is a fundamental value in our civilization. It is not *the* fundamental value, for if it were, the present problem of possible disruption would not exist. But it is fundamental at least for every "reasonable" discussion of disruption, since without it decidable discussion becomes impossible. Nevertheless, and this also is a fact and therefore contingent, other people have made other choices and we too can always decide in favor of another option. Reason (or consistency) can be considered as a negative value: Nietzsche and Heidegger, not to mention older and greater men such as Luther, or more unpleasant ones like Hitler and his "thinkers," have done so. Here, however, we are *thinking* about our civilization in a consistent manner i.e. scientifically, or we are at least trying to do so. What we discover is that science and consistency are unable to justify fundamental values, and particularly themselves, as necessary. Could that be the real reason for our envisaging science as a disruptive factor in our culture? One thing at least is evident: no civilization could worry about its consistency and unity unless it adhered to the values of consistency and fact. Scientifically (or, if the term is preferred, logically), we can show that there is no justification for values, that, as Dostoyevsky said, everything is possible when no transcendental value is acknowledged as irrefutable and undisputable. And so, logically, scientific thought seems to have undermined its own basis.

VI

Max Weber, who has already been quoted, had the rare and admirable courage to accept the consequences of this analysis, and not much has been added to his declaration that values belong in the realm of preachers and prophets, not in that of science. His own option, he declared, was for science, because science gave him the possibility of being honest with himself (he referred, of course, to the social sciences and especially of his own pursuits, sociology and history). He thought he could explain what this option included as presuppositions on one hand, as exigencies on the other, but he considered quite illegitimate any attempt to prove that his choice was the only good one. Such intellectual honesty and courage—qualities even rarer than his stupendous learning—certainly deserve respect. But even great men are fallible, and the problem is so serious that we must consider the possibility of his being in error.

Weber had started by separating in the Kantian manner the fields of values ("freedom") and facts ("nature"), though actually he had taken over this distinction not from Kant himself, but from certain neo-Kantians. This is not just a pedantic point of learning: Kant himself, in his last writings, had insisted upon the moral necessity (*sollen*) of a union or reunion of the two realms: life, action, science itself, he had come to think, would be inconceivable if meaning, i.e. values, did not *exist* and if reality were value free, and therefore *meaningless*. The result of his complex, and often confusing but probably never confused, thinking was that, since value free science is a human pursuit, it is possible only in a structured and meaningful world, not a "world of values" but a real world, full of sense for man if he chooses to look for it. No choice would be imaginable in a magma of facts, nor could there be choice under conditions of total value entropy.

This is the point that Weber did not see, nor is it discerned by many scholars of philosophy, such as the positivists and most adherents of linguistic analysis. We are born into a world, not into a disconnected multiplicity of facts and values. Only existing values may be rejected, transformed, or re-evaluated, because every action against old, and in favor of new, values starts from existing values (and those who fight given values are often more dominated by them than is the lax believer). Science, considered as human activity founded on certain values, does not *give* us a world, it originates in a world that has become what it is in history or, if more philosophical language is preferred, through successive self-interpretations of men, which in their turn can be understood. Weber, great historian though he was, in his reflections on history had become a historicist, regarding all value systems as equivalent, and projecting all of them on the same plane. Consistent value systems ("ideal types") are indispensable for a consistent, and understanding, interpretation of history and human attitudes.* But the human attitudes present in history are no more consistent than fall is free in nature, although real fall is understood by reference to "ideal" fall. We do not choose our values before we start living. The world is always understood before it becomes questionable; it can become dubious only if we start from an anterior orientation. Understanding precedes science.

VII

Let us sum up. Science is value-free, though it is based on values, among which, paradoxically enough, freedom from value judgments is one of the first; and life is directed by values. Science has shaped our natural and social surroundings and goes on doing so; without disinterested science, mastery over nature and history would be impossible. And science has no means to tell us what we are to do with this mastery, nor whether it is good or bad in itself. If there were an answer, it would establish unity; but it would not be given by science. Popular opinion is wrong when it looks upon scientists as the successors of the sages of old. To consider science as the universal measuring rod for values is an unscientific ideology: when a scientist answers a question in the field of values, he is speaking not as a man of science, but as an ordinary believer, citizen, moral subject, although his schooling may—sometimes—help him to be more consistent and clearheaded than his neighbors.

But refutations, as a rule, destroy neither ideologies nor the

* The constitution of such pure value systems becomes in its turn a fact and a factor in history.

feelings that find expression in rationalizations. The opposition between facts and values is itself a fact, and a very important one. Until it is clearly and critically stated, it prevents us from asking the only questions that could possibly lead out of a situation in which power is no guide, science refuses to be one, and the important things in life—choices, decisions, in a word values—are considered completely arbitrary, since everything not arbitrary belongs to the realm of science, the scientifically arbitrary character of whose foundations is conveniently forgotten. The fundamental attitude can be called *scientism:* only what can be established scientifically is true, objective, and valid everywhere and for everybody (madmen excepted), whereas the remainder of human discourse has nothing to do with truth, although this remainder is in fact the greater part and the more important one for human beings as such (scientists not excepted). It is this scientism that leads to *historicism,* not chronologically since historicism is far older, but logically: values are contingent facts in history, which is itself contingent since it cannot be deduced in the manner of a law of mathematical physics. The surprising thing is that science itself has no pretensions to directing choices and decisions, whereas scientism, before taking seriously what essentially preoccupies man, exacts the kind of proof and justification that, according to its own interpretation, science has no way of offering. In the terminology of psychoanalysis, scientism is fighting a superego of its own creation, but which it considers as a dominating reality, independent of us and our options. The answer, already outlined, is that science is a human activity in a world that man *understands* and *understood* before he tried to *know* it scientifically, a world he has lived in before, and while, creating sciences and methods. There are questions about this world, but our wonder (the first step toward science and universally valid knowledge, according to Plato and Aristotle) begins only when, in a world that is familiarly understood and trusted, something "goes wrong." We understand the world before we question it: understanding, in an *anthropocentric* manner, is older than science and more profound. It is an absurd wish to reduce understanding to science.

Science as interpreted by scientism—and we have seen that this interpretation is no accident—has become a disruptive factor in our culture on a profound, probably the profoundest, level. If an illustration were needed, it could be found in that divorce of classical "humanities" and "artistic" history from "science" which, in extreme though not rare cases, leads to distrust, contempt, and voluntary isolation on both sides. Preaching is not serious, and research is in no way qualified to influence our lives, so run the feelings of the interested parties: of what good is poetry, art, history, philosophy, or a pure physics that culminates in A-bombs and theories understandable and satisfying only to specialists? This is not to imply that these convictions are universal, even less that they are justified; but they exist, and scientism, which is their ignored root, is unable to fight them even if among the proponents of scientism there are probably few who do not deplore the absence of more positive relations between the two fields. The underlying fact is that the exact natural and social sciences have everything to do with knowing, and nothing to do with understanding the world we live in, and thus they cannot give us the means to justify our fundamental decisions. These natural and social sciences, no doubt, are doing an admirable job of pointing out both the conditions for success and the consequences of possible decisions, but even this falls short of a solution of the real problem, since we might always be willing to accept the consequences, however dire, or the prerequisites, however hard they may be to realize: consequences and conditions belong to the realm of facts, while options depend on values.

This is not to recommend a return to old, and presumably better, times. Rousseau overlooked the fact that his ideal had meaning only in and for the world he opposed; and Thoreau withdrew to his (relative) wilderness because he was civilized. Science and its offspring, technology, have come to stay, and we shall have to live with them. The question is, first, how we are to do so without producing more and more split personalities, particularly among the best educated and most serious people, and, second, how we are to prevent those drunk with this new power from exercising in our name the acquired mastery over nature and history in order to dominate us for domination's sake. Not that power in itself is bad. Lord Acton in his famous saying saw only one side. Indeed, absolute power corrupts absolutely; but the slave's ethic of absolute impotence is not healthier.

VIII

What then is required? The answer comes to this: we must think our world and our condition as human beings. We must relegate science and mastery to their proper place, which will always be an important place, or, to put it somewhat paradoxically, we must learn to consider the problem of science instead of thinking only in the framework of science, and we must consider the problem of power, and not only think in the categories of power.

From the time when Socrates brought philosophy from heaven down to earth, as the old saying goes, and, instead of studying astronomy and Ionian physics, began to seek an understanding of human problems and relations, until Kant's and Hegel's days, that has been the work of philosophy. Plato admired science (he even fathered our idea of pure theory) and no one who ignored geometry was allowed into his Academy—which signifies that mathematics and consistent thinking were in his eyes prerequisites to be acquired outside his school, where his students were to learn something very different from science in the narrow sense. For Plato the essential questions centered on values or rather (to avoid the current confusion of values with things appreciated) on the question of *good* and *evil*. It was no secret for Plato that we make choices, that the world he lived in (and where we live as well) offers many "values"—ways of life, objects and situations that qualify as desirable or detestable—and that the choice is free if we are prepared to take the consequences. But he saw at the same time that this world in which we make choices is not just a sum of disconnected data of fact and value, nor even of isolated or isolable value systems. Men are fighting over values, but not in a meaningless struggle; they do so in a living and meaningful history. And *if* they have decided, not so much in favor of *good* against *evil* as such, but in favor of declaring this thing *good* and that *bad*, they may come to terms, provided they want to do so. There is no demonstration that Socrates can use against Callicles in the *Gorgias:* he can only tell a myth and explain that Callicles, if he persists in his ways, will destroy human relations as well as all possibility of understanding the world. Science was supremely important in Plato's view, but only because it gave the individual the indispensable schooling in consistent thinking, not because it was good in itself.

What has happened is that modern science has become autonomous, a value in itself. The result is that we have a sort of bad methodological conscience as soon as we are faced with questions concerning the meaning of our lives. It is no longer a simple question of finding out which things are good or bad: *good* and *bad* have themselves become suspect or, if one prefers less old-fashioned words, *meaningful* and *meaningless* have suffered this destiny. If a feeling of insecurity is so visible when people leave their special field, and their unpreparedness so obvious when they dare to wander—

which is a risk taken by the best—then the old task of philosophy ought, once again, to become urgent. Has it in fact done so?

One may well doubt it. Philosophy, particularly in the English speaking world, has become scientific, whereas on the continent it prefers more and more to ignore science and the problems it has given birth to. "Serious" philosophers renounce the very idea of justifying values: at most, they are interested in the formal consistency of existing value systems, among which they declare themselves unable to establish differences in value. It is a second-level activity, a reflection on differences in speech and meanings, when it is not turning into mathematical logic. That is not a small or negligible enterprise: most of the things said here are being said by this philosophy, which has most effectively pursued the necessary work of eliminating ambiguous statements and, even more usefully, ambiguous and meaningless questions and pseudo-problems. Everybody who wants to think straight, and not waste time and energy on quests which *a priori* cannot succeed, owes that school a debt of deep gratitude. But it has bought its positive results at too high a price. It has become scientist itself, in accepting as its only criteria the formal ones of science. Life, fortunately or unfortunately, and choices and decisions are not always logically consistent, nor can they always be. Analytical philosophy has thrown to the wolves of arbitrariness all that cannot be seized with the only method it considers legitimate, although it admits that the remainder that lies outside scientific thought plays a very great role in life. It has taken up Max Weber's theses, but in quite another spirit, seeing liberation where Max Weber discovered reasons for, at best, hope against all the motives for despair. It is able to throw out "metaphysical" questions and discover the structure of scientific discourse in the exact sciences and—in principle, though the work is far less advanced—in the historical, social and anthropological sciences, but it has not been able to discover or even to ask what it means to live, as we do after all, in a meaningful world, in a living and lived nature and history, and not in those consciously abstract worlds of the physicist and the professional historian and anthropologist. Above all, analytical philosophy is not able and does not desire to discover what we beings are who live in this world and in it have built sciences, technologies, and analytical or pragmatic philosophy.

The evident objection will be that such a desire—some will call it a dream, others a program—cannot be fulfilled without opening the door for every kind of arbitrariness and handing over philosophy to the very people we are all afraid of, irresponsible announcers of imaginary salvations and absurd panaceas. The danger is real. But that danger does not come from man's wish to understand himself and his world. It is always with us, and it has been with us more than ever since science renounced meaning and chose the ideal of exact knowledge. This choice is in itself unimpeachable, as long as its axioms are not applied in a field where they become inoperative. There they become even destructive, not because they ask for consistency, but because their means are appropriate only to their particular field and produce inconsistency when civilization as a whole becomes the problem. The danger would not be greater, it would be less, if the question of meaning were put clearly and if its urgency were considered; it would be great indeed—and will always be so, as long as human beings are born violent, and may remain so—but it would be seen and not hidden as it is so often in present-day thought.

There may even be hope for a more positive answer, if it is true that we live in a *world*, and not among a stream of electrons, and that we are beings with feelings and thoughts, and not just objects for psychology, physiology, economics, and social sciences. The answer would not be *scientific*, if that means incontrovertible; it would have to be pursued—and to be found—in historical life where consistency is never given nor presupposed but is only an end to be realized, where the different conceptions of man and world do not exist side by side, as historicism sees them, but are in constant interaction, interfere with one another, fight and become reconciled. It could be found in an analysis of the structure of world and man, or more precisely, in an analysis of man's actions and discourses which would reveal what is his world and what he is for himself. And it might be possible that such an analysis, an understanding analysis of understanding, would give us an opening toward the discovery of what is good for man.

It is, I should like to repeat, a program, or at best a promise. But the program might itself be necessary, unless we are decided to give in to arbitrariness in the things that are the most important ones for us, not as scientists and technicians of nature and society, but for us in our lives. Of course, to choose such a program would again be an arbitrary option: no one can prove its necessity to those who reject consistency and understanding. But it would be an ultimate choice, between violence and reason, if such old-fashioned terms can be printed nowadays; and it would not be a negligible result if it were shown that there is an ultimate choice.

HERBERT MARCUSE

Remarks on a Redefinition of Culture

I TAKE AS STARTING POINT the definition of culture given by Webster, namely, culture as the complex of distinctive beliefs, attainments, traditions, etc., constituting the "background" of a society. In the traditional usage of the term, "attainments" such as destruction and crime, and "traditions" such as cruelty and fanaticism have usually been excluded; I shall follow this usage, although it may prove necessary to re-introduce these qualities into the definition. My discussion will be focused on the relationship between the "background" (culture) and the "ground": culture thus appears as the complex of moral, intellectual, aesthetic goals (values) which a society considers the purpose of the organization, division, and direction of its labor—"the good" that is supposed to be achieved by the way of life it has established. For example, increase in personal and public freedom, reduction of inequalities which prevent the development of the "individual" or "personality," and an efficient and rational administration may be taken as the "cultural values" representative of advanced industrial society (their denial is officially condemned in the East as well as in the West).

We speak of an existing culture (past or present) only if the representative goals and values were (or are) somehow translated into the social reality. There may be considerable variations in the extent and adequacy of the translation, but the prevailing institutions and the relationships among the members of the respective society must show a demonstrable affinity to the proclaimed values: they must provide a basis for their *possible* realization. In other words, culture is more than a mere ideology. Looking at the professed goals of Western civilization and at the claims of their realization, we should define culture as a process of *humanization*, characterized by the collective effort to protect human life, to pacify the

A Redefinition of Culture

struggle for existence by keeping it within manageable bounds, to stabilize a productive organization of society, to develop the intellectual faculties of man, to reduce and sublimate aggressions, violence, and misery.

Two qualifications must be made at the outset: (1) the "validity" of culture has always been confined to a *specific* universe, constituted by tribal, national, religious, or other identity. Ideas such as equality and liberty have rarely been translated into reality for the benefit of all members of the society—some groups (and large groups) have always been excluded from the blessings and advantages of culture. There has always been a "foreign" universe to which the cultural goals were not applied: the Enemy, the Other, the Alien, the Outcast—terms referring not primarily to individuals but to groups, religions, "ways of life," social systems. In meeting the Enemy (who has his epiphany also within one's own universe) culture is suspended or even prohibited, and inhumanity can often run its course. (2) It is very questionable, especially if we look at the contemporary situation, whether aggression, violence, cruelty, and misery have really been reduced in the development of civilization. Culture is the social process of sublimation, and today violence and aggression seem to be less sublimated than in previous periods of history; their prevalence on such a large scale invalidates the notion of progress in humanization. Moreover, violence and aggression and their institution may well be an integral part of culture, so that the attainment or approximation of the cultural goals takes place *through* the practice of cruelty and violence. This may explain the paradox that so much of the higher culture of the West, of its art and literature, has been protest, critique, and indictment of culture—not only of its miserable translation into reality, but of its very principles and content.

Under the preceding assumptions, the re-examination of a given culture involves the relation of values to facts, not as a logical or epistemological problem, but as a problem of social structure: how are the means of society related to its self-professed ends? The ends are supposedly those defined by the (socially accepted) "higher culture"; thus they are values to be embodied, more or less adequately, in the social institutions and relations. The question can therefore be formulated more concretely: *how are the literature, arts, philosophy, science, religion of a society related to its actual behavior?* The vastness of this problem precludes any discussion here other than in terms of some hypotheses referring to present-day trends.

It is generally admitted that the cultural values (humanization) and the existing institutions and policies of society are rarely, if ever, in harmony. This opinion has found expression in the distinction between *culture* and *civilization,* according to which "culture" refers to some higher dimension of human autonomy and fulfillment, while "civilization" designates the realm of necessity, of socially necessary work and behavior, where man is not really himself and in his own element but is subject to heteronomy, to external conditions and needs. The realm of necessity can be (and has been) reduced and alleviated. Indeed, the concept of progress is applicable only to this realm (technical progress), to the advance in *civilization;* but such advance has not eliminated the tension between *culture* and civilization. It may even have aggravated the dichotomy to the degree to which the immense potentialities opened by technical progress appear in sharpening contrast with their limited and distorted realization. At the same time, however, the conflict between the material and intellectual capabilities of advanced industrial society, on the one hand, and their repressive utilization, on the other, is itself being suppressed by the systematic preconditioning of individual needs and by the systematic administration of satisfaction. The incorporation of higher culture into daily work and leisure, the organized consumption of beauty, joy, and sorrow has become an integral part of the social administration of the individual—necessary items in the reproduction of the "affluent society." The tension between culture and society, between intellectual and material production, has been suppressed so effectively that the question arises whether, in view of the tendencies prevalent in advanced industrial society, the distinction between culture and civilization can still be maintained. More exactly, has not the tension between means and ends, cultural values and social facts been resolved in the absorption of the ends by the means—has not a "premature," repressive, and even violent coordination of culture with civilization occurred by virtue of which the latter is freed from some effective brakes on its destructive tendencies? With this integration of culture into society, the society tends to become totalitarian even where it preserves democratic forms and institutions.

Some of the implications in the distinction between culture and civilization may be tabulated as follows:

A Redefinition of Culture

Civilization	Culture
manual work	intellectual work
working day	holiday
labor	leisure
realm of necessity	realm of freedom
nature	spirit (*Geist*)
operational thought	nonoperational thought

In the academic tradition, these dichotomies once found their parallel in the distinction between the natural sciences on the one hand, and all others on the other, the social sciences, humanities, etc. This distinction between the sciences has now become entirely obsolete: natural science, the social sciences, and even the humanities are being assimilated to each other in their methods and concepts, as exemplified by the spread of positivist empiricism, the struggle against whatever may be called "metaphysics," the direct application of "pure" theory, the susceptibility of all disciplines to organization in the national or corporate interest. This change within the educational establishment is in accord with the fundamental changes in contemporary society which affect the entire dichotomy tabulated above: technological civilization tends to eliminate the transcendent goals of culture (transcendent with respect to the socially *established* goals), thereby eliminating or reducing those factors and elements of culture which were antagonistic and alien to the given forms of civilization. There is no need here to repeat the familiar proposition that the facile assimilation of work and relaxation, of frustration and fun, of art and the household, of psychology and corporate management alters the traditional function of these elements of culture: they become affirmative, that is to say, they serve to fortify the hold of the Establishment over the mind—that Establishment which has made the goods of culture available to the people—and they help to strengthen the sweep of what *is* over what *can be* and *ought to be*, ought to be if there is truth in the cultural values. This proposition is not condemnation: wide access to the traditional culture, and especially to its authentic oeuvres, is better than the retention of cultural privileges for a limited circle on the basis of wealth and birth. But in order to preserve the cognitive content of these oeuvres, intellectual faculties and an intellectual awareness are required which are not exactly congenial to the modes of thought and behavior required by the prevailing civilization in advanced industrial countries.

In its prevailing form and direction, progress of this civilization calls for operational and behavioral modes of thought, for acceptance of the productive rationality of the given social systems, for their defense and improvement, but not for their negation. And the content (and mostly hidden content) of the higher culture was to a great extent precisely this negation: indictment of the institutionalized destruction of human potentialities, commitment to a hope which the established civilization denounced as "utopian." To be sure, the higher culture always had an affirmative character inasmuch as it was divorced from the toil and misery of those who by their labor reproduced the society whose culture it was—and to that degree it became the ideology of the society. But as ideology, it was also dissociated from the society, and in this dissociation it was free to communicate the contradiction, the indictment, and the refusal. Now the communication is technically multiplied, vastly facilitated, much rewarded, but the content is changed because the mental and even physical space in which effective dissociation can develop is closed.

As to the elimination of the former antagonistic content of culture, I shall try to show that what is involved here is not the fate of some romantic ideal succumbing to technological progress, nor the progressive democratization of culture, nor the equalization of social classes, but rather the closing of a vital space for the development of autonomy and opposition, the destruction of a refuge, of a barrier to totalitarianism. Here I can indicate only some aspects of the problem, starting again with the situation in the academic establishment.

The division into natural sciences, social, or behavioral, sciences, and humanities appears as a highly extraneous division, since the distribution of subject matter, at least between the last two, is more than questionable—the academic quandary reflects the general condition! There is indeed a noticeable divorce of the social sciences from the humanities, at least from what the humanities were supposed to be: experience of the dimension of *humanitas* not yet translated into reality; modes of thought, imagination, expression essentially nonoperational and transcendent, transcending the established universe of behavior not toward a realm of ghosts and illusions, but toward historical possibilities. In our present situation, does the analysis of society, of social and even of individual behavior, demand *abstraction from humanitas?* Does our cultural situation, our universe of social behavior repudiate and invalidate the humanities and make them truly *nonbehavioral* and thus "nonscientific" sciences, concerned mainly with personal, emotional, metaphysical, poetic values unless they translate themselves into behavioral terms? But in so doing, the humanities would cease to be what they are. They would surrender their essentially nonoperational truths to the rules governing the established society, for the standards of the behavioral sciences are those of the society to whose behavior they are committed.

Now, the expelled nonoperational dimension was the core of the traditional culture, the "background" of modern society until the end of its liberalist period; roughly, the era between the two world wars marks the terminal stage of this period. By virtue of its remoteness from the world of socially necessary labor, of socially useful needs and behavior, because of its separation from the daily struggle for existence, culture could create and preserve the mental space in which critical transgression, opposition, and denial could develop—a space of privacy and autonomy in which the mind could find an Archimedean point outside the Establishment from which to view it in a different light, comprehend it in different concepts, discover tabooed images and possibilities. This Archimedean point seems to have disappeared.

To avoid any romantic misinterpretation, let me repeat: culture has always been the privilege of a small minority, a matter of wealth, time, good luck. For the underprivileged populace, the "higher values" of culture have always been mere words or empty exhortations, illusions, deceptions; at best they were hopes and aspirations that remained unfulfilled. However, the privileged position of culture, the gap between the material civilization and the intellectual culture, between necessity and freedom, was also the gap which protected the realm of non-scientific culture as a "reservation." There literature and the arts could attain and communicate truths which were denied and repressed in the established reality, or transformed into socially useful concepts and standards. Similarly, philosophy—and religion—could formulate and communicate moral imperatives of universal human validity—often in radical contradiction to the socially useful morality. In this sense, I dare say that the nonscientific culture was less sublimated than the form in which it became translated into actual social values and behavior—and it was certainly less sublimated than the uninhibited novels of our days—less sublimated because the inhibited, mediated style of the higher culture evoked, as the "negative," the uncompromised needs and hopes of man, which present-day literature presents in their socially prevalent realization, permeated with the prevalent repression.

The higher culture still exists. It is more available than ever before; it is more widely read and seen and heard than ever before; but society has been closing the mental and physical space in which this culture could be understood in its *cognitive* substance, in its exact *truth*. Operationalism, in thought and behavior, relegates these truths to the personal, subjective, emotional dimension; in this form they can easily be fitted into the Establishment—the critical, qualitative transcendence of culture is being eliminated and the negative is integrated into the positive. The oppositional elements of culture are thus being reduced: civilization takes over, organizes, buys and sells culture; substantially nonoperational, nonbehavioral ideas are translated into operational, behavioral terms; and this translation is not merely a methodological but a social, even political process. After the preceding remarks, we may now express the main effect of this process in one formula: the integration of cultural values into the established society *cancels the alienation of culture from civilization,* thereby flattening out the tension between the "ought" and the "is" (which is a real, historical tension), between the potential and the actual, future and present, freedom and necessity.

The result: the autonomous, critical contents of culture become educational, elevating, relaxing—a vehicle of adjustment.

Every authentic oeuvre of literature, art, music, philosophy speaks a metalanguage which communicates facts and conditions other than those accessible in behavioral language—this is their irreducible, untranslatable substance. It seems that their untranslatable substance now dissolves in a process of translation which affects not only the suprahuman and supranatural (religion) but also the human and natural contents of culture (literature, the arts, philosophy): the radical, irreconcilable conflicts of love and hate, hope and fear, freedom and necessity, subject and object, good and evil become more manageable, comprehensible, normal—in one word, behavioral. Not only the gods, heroes, kings, and knights have disappeared whose world was that of tragedy, romance, song, and festival, but also many of the riddles they could not solve, many of the struggles with which they were concerned, many of the forces and fears with which they had to cope. An ever increasing dimension of unconquered (and unconquerable) forces is being conquered by technological rationality and by physical and social science. And

A Redefinition of Culture

many archetypal problems become susceptible to diagnosis and treatment by the psychologist, social worker, scientist, politician. The fact that they are badly diagnosed and treated, that their still valid content is distorted, reduced, or repressed should not conceal the radically progressive potentialities of this development. They can be summed up in the proposition that mankind has reached the historical stage where it is *technically* capable of creating a world of peace—a world without exploitation, misery, and toil. This would be a civilization which has become culture.

The technological corrosion of the transcendent substance of higher culture invalidates the medium in which it found adequate expression and communication, bringing about the collapse of the traditional literary and artistic forms, the operational redefinition of philosophy, the transformation of religion into status symbol. Culture is redefined by the existing state of affairs: the words, tones, colors, shapes of the perennial works remain the same, but that which they expressed is losing its truth, its validity; the works which previously stood shockingly apart from and against the established reality have been neutralized as classics; thus they no longer preserve their alienation from the alienated society. In philosophy, psychology, and sociology, a pseudo-empiricism predominates which refers its concepts and methods to the restricted and repressed experience of people in the administered world and devalues nonbehavioral concepts as metaphysical confusions. Thus the historical validity of ideas like Freedom, Equality, Justice, Individual was precisely in their yet unfulfilled content—in that they could not be referred to the established reality, which did not and could not validate them because they were denied by the functioning of the very institutions that were supposed to realize these ideas. They were normative ideas—nonoperational, not by virtue of their metaphysical, unscientific character, but by virtue of the servitude, inequality, injustice, and domination institutionalized in society. The modes of thought and research which dominate in advanced industrial culture tend to identify the normative concepts with their prevailing social realization, or rather they take as norm the way in which society is translating these concepts into reality, at best trying to improve the translation; the untranslated residue is considered obsolete speculation.

To be sure, the contrast between the original and the translation is obvious and part of the daily experience; moreover, the conflict between the potential and the actual sharpens with technical progress, with society's increasing capacity to conquer scarcity, fear, and toil. However, it is also this progress and this capacity which block comprehension of the causes of the conflict and of the chances of its solution—the chances of a pacification of the struggle for existence, individual and social, within the nation and on the international scale. In the most highly developed areas of industrial civilization, which provide the model of culture in the contemporary period, the overwhelming productivity of the established system augments and satisfies the needs of the populace through a total administration which sees to it that the needs of the individual are those which perpetuate and fortify the system. The rationale for qualitative change thus evaporates, and with it the rationale for the alienation of culture from civilization.

If the changing relation between culture and civilization is the work of the new technological *society* and if it is constantly sustained by it, then a theoretical "redefinition," no matter how justified, must remain academic inasmuch as it goes *against* the predominant trend. But here too the very remoteness and "purity" of the theoretical effort, its apparent weakness in the face of realities may turn into a position of strength if it does not sacrifice its abstractness by accommodating to a fallacious positivism and empiricism, fallacious inasmuch as these modes of thought are oriented to an experience which, in reality, is only a mutilated sector of experience, isolated from the factors and forces which determine experience. The administrative absorption of culture by civilization is the result of the established direction of scientific and technical progress, of the expanding conquest of man and nature by the powers which organize this conquest and which utilize the rising standard of living for perpetuating their organization of the struggle for existence.

Today this organization operates through the permanent mobilization of the people for the eventuality of nuclear war, and through the continued mobilization of socially necessary aggression, hostility, frustration, and resentment generated by the struggle for existence in the "affluent society." This is the universe which, in the most advanced areas of industrial civilization, determines and confines experience—confines it by repressing the real, nonutopian alternatives. They are *qualitative* alternatives, for the pacification of the struggle for existence, the redefinition of work in terms of a free realization of human needs and faculties presuppose not only essentially different institutions but also essentially different men—men who no longer have to earn a living in alienated labor. This differ-

A Redefinition of Culture

ence cannot emerge within the tightening framework of institutions essentially designed to organize alienated labor. Under these circumstances, altering the established direction of progress would mean fundamental social change. But social change presupposes the vital *need* for it, the experience of intolerable conditions and of their alternatives—and it is this need and this experience which are barred from developing in the established culture. Their liberation is preconditioned on the restoration of the lost cultural dimension which was (no matter how precariously) protected from the totalitarian power of society: it was the mental dimension of autonomy.

Education for intellectual and emotional independence—this sounds like setting a goal which is generally recognized. In reality it is an all but subversive program which involves violation of some of the strongest democratic taboos. For the prevailing democratic culture fosters heteronomy in the guise of autonomy, arrests the development of needs in the guise of their promotion, and restricts thought and experience in the guise of extending them everywhere and to all. The people enjoy a considerable range of freedom in buying and selling, in looking for jobs and in choosing jobs, in expressing their opinion, in moving about—but their liberties nowhere transcend the established social system which determines their needs, their choice, and their opinions. Freedom itself operates as the vehicle of adjustment and confinement. These repressive (and regressive) tendencies accompany the transformation of industrial society into technological society under the total administration of men, and the simultaneous changes in the occupation, mentality, and political function of the "people" affect the very foundations of democracy. An enumeration of some of the familiar phenomena must here suffice.

We may note first a growing passivity of the people vis-à-vis the omnipresent political and economic apparatus; submission to its affluent productivity and to its use "from above"; divorce of the individuals from the sources of power and information, which makes the recipients into objects of administration. The needs of the established society are introjected and become individual needs; required behavior and desirable aspirations become spontaneous. At the higher stages of development, this total coordination proceeds without terror and without abrogation of the democratic process.

On the contrary, there is at the same time a growing dependence of the elected leaders on the electorate which is constituted by a public opinion shaped by the predominant political and economic interests. Their dominion appears as that of productive and technological rationality. As such, the dominion is accepted and defended, and the people make it their own. The result is a state of general interdependence which obfuscates the real hierarchy. Behind the veil of technological rationality, universal heteronomy is accepted as liberties and comforts offered by the "affluent society."

Under such conditions, the creation (or re-creation) of a refuge of mental independence (practical, political independence is effectively blocked by the concentrated power and coordination in advanced industrial society) must assume the form of withdrawal, willful isolation, intellectual "elitism." And indeed, a redefinition of culture would run counter to the most powerful trends. It would mean the liberation of thought, research, teaching, and learning from the established universe of application and behavior, and the elaboration of methods and concepts capable of rationally surmounting the limits of the established facts and "values." In terms of the academic disciplines, this would mean shifting the main emphasis to "pure" theory, that is, *theoretical* sociology, political science, and psychology; to speculative philosophy, etc. More important would be the consequences for the *organization* of education: the shift would lead to the establishment of "elite" universities, separated from colleges that would retain and strengthen their character as vocational schools in the largest sense. Complete financial independence would be a prerequisite for the former: today more than ever before, this is a matter of the source of material support. No individual private patron would be capable of financing an education which might prepare the mental ground for a qualitatively different hierarchy of values and powers. Such an education could possibly be imagined as the concern of a government willing and capable of counteracting the prevailing political and popular trend—a condition which has only to be formulated in order to reveal its utopian character.

The very notion of intellectual-elite universities is today denounced as antidemocratic bias—even if the emphasis is on "intellectual," and if the term "elite" designates selection made from the school and college population as a whole, a selection solely according to merit, that is to say, according to the inclination and ability for theoretical thought. The notion is antidemocratic indeed if the established mass democracy and its education are assumed to be the realization of a democracy corresponding exactly to the histori-

A Redefinition of Culture

cally possible forms of freedom and equality. I do not believe that this is the case. The prevailing positivistic and behavioral trend serves all too often to cut the roots of self-determination in the mind of man—a self-determination which today (as in the past) requires critical dissociation from the given universe of experience. Without this *critique of experience,* the student is deprived of the intellectual methods and tools which would enable him to comprehend and evaluate his society and its culture as a whole, in the historical continuum in which this society fulfills, distorts, or denies its own possibilities and promises. Instead, the student is trained for comprehending and evaluating the established conditions and possibilities only *in terms of* the established conditions and possibilities: his thinking, his ideas, his goals are programmatically and scientifically restricted—not by logic, experience, and facts, but by a purged logic, a mutilated experience, incomplete facts.

The protest against this stifling behaviorism finds an irrational outlet in the numerous existentialist, metapsychological, and neo-theological philosophies which oppose the positivistic trend. The opposition is faulty—and even illusory. They too contribute to the decline of critical reason inasmuch as they abstract from the real stuff of experience without ever returning to it after the abstraction has attained the conceptual level. The existential experience to which they refer is also a restricted, mutilated experience, but in contrast to positivism, experience is distorted not only by the nexus of the established social universe of experience but also by the insistence that the existential decision or choice can break through this universe and reach the dimension of individual freedom. To be sure, no effort of thought, no mode of thought can do so, but they can help or hinder the development of that consciousness which is a precondition for accomplishing the task.

The concepts of critical reason are philosophical, sociological, and historical in one. In this interrelation, and linked to the growing mastery of nature and society, they are the intellectual catalysts of culture: they open the mental space and faculties for the emergence of new historical projects, new possibilities of existence. This theoretical dimension of thought is today severely reduced. The emphasis here placed on its extension and restoration may appear less irrelevant if we recall that our culture (and not only our intellectual culture) was projected and predefined, even in its most practical aspects, by science, philosophy, and literature before it became a fully developed and organized reality: the new astronomy and physics, the new political theory anticipated (in affirmation and negation) the subsequent historical experience. The liberation of theoretical thought from its commitments to a repressive practice was a precondition of progress.

The reorganization of culture I have suggested above would also violate the taboo placed on the position of *science* today. (I use intentionally the frightful term "organization" in this context because culture has become an object of organization; to "abstract" culture from its prevailing administration means first to reorganize and disorganize it.) The role of science in an established culture must be evaluated not only with respect to the scientific truths (nobody in his right mind would deny them or minimize their "value") but also with respect to their ascertainable impact on the human condition. Science is responsible for this impact—and this is not the moral and personal responsibility of the scientist but the function of the scientific method and concepts themselves. No teleology, no extraneous ends have to be superimposed on science: it has its inherent historical ends from which no scientism and no repression can separate it.

Science as intellectual activity is, prior to all practical application, an instrument in the struggle for existence, in man's struggle with nature and with man: its guiding hypotheses, projections, and abstractions emerge in this struggle and anticipate, preserve, or change the conditions under which this struggle develops. To say that the very rationale of science is to improve these conditions may be a value judgment, but it is a value judgment no more and no less than that which makes science itself a value, which makes truth a value. We have accepted this value, "civilization" has been its gradual and painful realization; it has been a determining factor in the relation between science and society, and even the purest theoretical achievements have entered into this relation, regardless of the scientist's own consciousness and intentions. The very elimination of "ends" from science tightened the relation between science and society and increased immensely the instrumentalist capabilities of science in the struggle for existence. The Galilean projection of Nature without an objective Telos, the shift of the scientific quest from *Why* to *How*, the translation of quality into quantity, and the expulsion from science of the nonquantifiable subjectivity—this method has been the prerequisite of whatever technical and mate-

A Redefinition of Culture

rial progress has been made since the Middle Ages. It has guided the rational concepts of man and nature, and it has served to create the preconditions for a rational society—preconditions for *humanity*. It has done so while at the same time increasing the rational means of destruction and domination, that is, the means for *preventing* the realization of humanity. From the beginning, construction was bound up with destruction, productivity with its repressive utilization, pacification with aggression. This dual responsibility of science is not contingent: quantified science, and nature as mathematized quantity, as mathematical universe, are "neutral," susceptible to whatever utilization and transformation, limited only by the limits of scientific knowledge and by the resistance of brute matter. In this neutrality, science becomes susceptible and subject to the objectives which predominate in the society in which science develops. It is still a society in which the conquest of nature takes place through the conquest of man, the exploitation of natural and intellectual resources through the exploitation of man, and the struggle with nature through the struggle for existence in aggressive and repressive forms, on the personal as well as on the national and international levels. But science itself has attained a level of comprehension and productivity which places it in *contradiction* to this state of affairs: "pure" scientific rationality involves the real possibility of abolishing scarcity, toil, and injustice the world over—the possibility of pacifying the struggle for existence. What is at stake is not the undoing or the curtailing of science, but its liberation from the masters whom science itself has helped to set up. And this liberation would not be an external event which would leave the scientific enterprise in its structure intact: it may well affect the scientific method itself, the scientific experience and projection of nature. In a rational and humane society, science would have a new function, and this function might well necessitate a reconstruction of scientific method—not a return to pre-Galilean qualitative science-philosophy, but rather the scientific quantification of new goals, derived from a new experience of man and nature—the goals of pacification.

Today the question must be asked whether, in the "affluent societies," science has not ceased to be a vehicle of liberation, whether it does not (via destruction research and planned obsolescence) perpetuate and intensify the struggle for existence instead of alleviating it. The traditional distinction between science and technology becomes questionable. When the most abstract achievements of mathematics and theoretical physics satisfy so adequately the needs of IBM and of the Atomic Energy Commission, it is time to ask whether such applicability is not inherent in the concepts of science itself.* I suggest that the question cannot be pushed aside by separating pure science from its applications and putting the blame on the latter only: the specific "purity" of science facilitated the union of construction and destruction, humanity and inhumanity in the progressive mastery of nature. In any case it is impossible to measure the destructive against the constructive efforts of science; nor is it possible to distinguish, within the whole of scientific research, between life-preserving and life-impairing fields, methods, and concepts—they seem to be internally linked. Science has created its own culture, and this culture is absorbing an ever larger part of civilization. The notion of the "two cultures" is misleading, but even more misleading, under the prevailing conditions, is the plea for their reunion.

The non-scientific culture (I shall confine myself here to literature as its representative) speaks a language of its own, substantially different from that of science. The language of literature is a *meta*language inasmuch as it does not pertain to the established universe of discourse which communicates the existing state of affairs. It communicates "a different world," governed by different standards, values, and principles. This different world appears *in* the established one; it ingresses into the daily business of life, into the experience of one's self and of others, into the social and natural environment. However this difference may be constituted, it makes the world of literature an essentially *other* one—a negation of the given reality. And to the degree to which science has become an integral part, or even a driving power behind the given reality, literature is also the negation of science. There is no such thing as (scientific) realism in the authentic literature of the West, not even in Zola's oeuvre: his society of the Second Empire is the negation of that society in its reality.

The gap between scientific and nonscientific culture *today* may be a very promising circumstance. The neutrality of pure science has made it impure, incapable or unwilling to refuse collaboration with the theoreticians and practitioners of legalized destruction and

* I have discussed this question in my *One-Dimensional Man* (Boston: Beacon Press, 1964), Chapters 6 and 7.

A Redefinition of Culture

exploitation. The aloofness of nonscientific culture may preserve the much needed refuge and reservation in which forgotten or suppressed truths and images are sustained. When society tends toward total coordination and administration (through scientific means), the alienation of nonscientific culture becomes a prerequisite of opposition and refusal. Whether or not a poet or writer or classicist knows the Second Law of Thermodynamics or the "overthrow of parity" is his personal business: it certainly would not do him any harm (nor would it be harmful if such knowledge were to become part of the general education). It may also be entirely irrelevant for what he has to say. For the "natural order" which the quantifying sciences define and master is not *the* natural order, and the "scientific edifice of the physical world" is *not*, "in its intellectual depth, complexity and articulation, the most beautiful and wonderful collective work of the mind of man."* It seems to me that the edifice of literature, art, and music is infinitely more beautiful, wonderful, deep, complex, and articulate, and I believe that this is not simply a matter of preference. The world of nonscientific culture is a multidimensional world in which "secondary qualities" are irreducible, and in which all objectivity is qualitatively related to the human subject. Scientific modesty often conceals a frightening absolutism, a happy rejection of nonscientific but rational modes of thought into the realm of fiction, poetry, preference.

I have referred to *The Two Cultures* because the message of the book seems to me merely another exhortation to conformity in the guise of scientific rationality. The union or reunion of the scientific and nonscientific culture may be prerequisite to progress beyond the society of total mobilization and permanent defense or deterrent, but such progress cannot be accomplished within the established culture of defense and deterrent which science so efficiently sustains. In order to make this progress, science must liberate itself from the fatal dialectic of Master and Servant which transforms the conquest of nature into the tool of exploitation, and into the technology of their perpetuation in "higher" forms. Prior to this liberation of science, the nonscientific culture preserves the images of the ends which science by itself cannot and does not define, namely, the ends of humanity. Evidently the redirection of science involves social and political changes, that is to say, the emergence of an essentially different society whose continuation can dispense

* C. P. Snow, *The Two Cultures: And a Second Look* (The New American Library 1964), p. 20.

with the institutions of aggressive defense and deterrent. Within the established institutions, preparation for such an eventuality will be primarily a negative one, namely, reduction of the overwhelming pressure on nonconformist, critical-transcendent modes of thought, to counteract the oligopoly of behavioral pseudo-empiricism.

If there is still any meaning in Kant's statement that education should be not for the present but for a better society, education would also (and perhaps foremost) alter the place of science in the universities and in the area of "research and development" as a whole. The overwhelmingly generous financial support which the physical sciences enjoy today is support not only for research and development in the interest of humanity but also in the opposite interest. Since this fusion of opposites cannot be dissolved within the framework of the existing social system, a modicum of progress may perhaps be attained by a policy of discrimination with respect to support and priority. However, such a policy would presuppose the existence of governments, foundations, and corporations which are willing and powerful enough to reduce rigorously the military establishment—a rather unrealistic assumption. One can envisage the establishment of an academic reservation where scientific research is undertaken entirely free of any military connections, where the inauguration, continuation, and publication of research is left entirely to an independent group of scientists committed to a humanist pursuit. Granted that there are many universities and colleges that today refuse to engage in any government-sponsored research which involves military projects: one might still advocate some establishment that would not merely exercise such restraint but would actively further publication of documents on abuses of science for inhumane ends.

Today, even these modest-sensible ideas are scorned as naive and romantic, are heaped with ridicule. The fact that they are condemned before the omnipotent technical and political apparatus of our society does not necessarily demolish the value which they may possibly have. By virtue of the impenetrable union between political and technological rationality today, ideas not bent to this union appear as irrational and detrimental to progress—as reactionary. For example, one hears comparison of the protest against the ever growing programs of outer space with the opposition of medieval Aristotelianism against Copernicus and Galileo. However, there is nothing regressive in the insistence that all energy and money devoted to outer space is wasted so long as it is withdrawn

A Redefinition of Culture

from use for the humanization of the earth. The undeniable technical discoveries and improvements resulting from the conquest of outer space must be evaluated in terms of priority: the possibility of staying (perhaps even living) in outer space should have lower priority than that of abolishing intolerable living conditions on earth. The notion that both projects can be effectively carried out at the same time and by the same society is ideological. The conquest of outer space may accelerate and extend communication and information, but the question must be asked whether they are not already fast and extensive enough, or even too fast and too extensive for much of what is communicated and done. The ancient concept of *hubris* makes good non-metaphysical sense when applied to destruction wrought, not by the gods but by man. The rationality of global military and political competition (or rather conflict) is not necessarily synonymous with human progress. When the latter is bound to the former, protest against this bondage is made to appear as a form of irrational regression; but this perversion is itself the work of politics. Evidently the notion of an education within the existing society for a better future society is a contradiction, but a contradiction that must be solved if progress is to take place.

DANIEL BELL

The Disjunction of Culture and Social Structure: Some Notes on the Meaning of Social Reality

> ". . . social forces always find expression in culture, even when they work unseen, and the problem is stated falsely if culture and society are torn apart from one another and are regarded as fully independent spheres which, as such, react upon one another. The social process is contained in the very structure of cultural life itself so that it is never for one moment free from its influence."
>
> Karl Mannheim—*Man and Society in an Age of Reconstruction.*

THE THESIS of these notes is that one of the sources of our difficulty in comprehending contemporary "culture" (that is, giving it a stylistic definition other than the ambiguous term "modernity") is the disjunction between the social structure and the culture. By social structure I mean the system of social relationships between persons, institutionalized in norms and rules. By culture I mean the symbolic expressions in the realms of ideas and art of the experience of individuals in those relationships. The disjunction arises because of difficulties involved in finding appropriate symbolic expression for efforts to grasp the meaning of experiences in contemporary society.

In one sense, none of this is new. Man, seemingly, has had the recurrent feeling—call it alienation, forlornness or existentialist despair—of being lost, or cast out of the world. In Christian sensibility there is the agonized theme of the separateness of man from God. In the esthetic humanism of Schiller there is the lament that the "zoon condition" of Greek life, where man was a perfect whole, has given way to the differentiation of function, resulting in an estrangement of the intuitive and speculative minds and the dissociation of sensibility. In Hegel, there is the cosmic drama of

This essay was originally given as the Sigmund Falk Memorial Lecture at Hebrew Union College in Cincinnati on November 12, 1964.

The Disjunction of Culture and Social Structure

the movement of the world from a pre-existent unity through the dualities of nature and history, thought and experience, man and spirit, to the re-unification of the Absolute in the "realization" of philosophy. For Marx, in a more naturalistic mode, it was the division of labor (of mental and physical labor, of town and country) which was generally responsible for alienation in work, plus the specific fact that in a commodity-exchange society a man becomes "reified" in his labor so that his personality becomes dissolved in his function.

Contemporary experience, in its effort to articulate its own disorientation, draws from all these speculative and philosophical reflections. But at times excessively so, for musings about "the human condition" only blur the distinctiveness of modern times or the distinctive ways in which some of these larger truths become expressed in concrete fashion. Yet modes of experience do vary radically in time and place. Lucien Febvre once pointed out that the age of Rabelais had little *visual* sense, that hearing in particular seemed to precede and remain more important than sight, a primacy which was reflected in the imagery of the prose and poetry of the time. Or Marcel Granet has attempted to show how particular conceptions of number (but not quantity), space and time played a distinct role in the formulation of classic Chinese political philosophy and classic Chinese art.

Contemporary social science, however, has tended to eschew this form of analysis. It deals with formal organizations or social processes (for example, industrialization) but rarely with the modes of experience themselves, modes which mediate between social structure and culture. These notes, an exploration in sociological analysis, seek to illustrate the ways in which social perceptions are shaped, often unconsciously, by modes of experience.

I. *The Revolution in Sensibility*

Our technical civilization is not only a revolution in production (and in communication); it is a revolution in sensibility as well. The distinctiveness of this civilization—call it "mass society" or "industrial society"—can be understood in a number of ways; I choose to define it (not exhaustively) within these dimensions: number, interaction, self-consciousness, and future-time orientation. In effect, the way in which we confront the world is conditioned by these elements.

Number. In 1789, when George Washington was inaugurated as the first president of the United States (and the Constitution had just been ratified), American society comprised fewer than four million persons, of whom 750,000 were Negroes. Few persons lived in cities; New York, then the capital, had a population of 33,000 persons. In all, 200,000 individuals lived in what was then defined as "urban areas"—meaning, places with more than 2500 inhabitants. It was a young population: the median age was sixteen, and there were only 800,000 males above that age.

Because it was a small country, members of the political elite knew each other, as did the thin stratum of leading families. But for most persons, living in isolated clumps or in sparsely inhabited areas, life was vastly different. People rarely traveled great distances; a visitor from afar was a rarity. News meant local gossip, and the few news sheets concentrated on parochial events. The ordinary person's image of the world and its politics was extremely limited.

Today, the United States numbers well over 180,000,000 persons, more than a hundred million of whom live in metropolitan areas (that is, within a county containing at least one city of 50,000 residents). The median age is over thirty and 130,000,000 persons are over fourteen years of age. Few persons live or work in social isolation. Even those who work on the farms are tied to the national society by the mass media and the popular culture.

In the way in which we "perceive" the world today, as against 1789, two aspects are striking: the difference in the number of persons each of us *knows,* and the number each of us *knows of.* On the job, in school, in the neighborhood, in a profession, in a social milieu, an individual today knows literally hundreds if not thousands of other persons; and with the multiplication of the mass media—with the enlargement of the political world, and the enormous multiplication of entertainment figures and public personalities—the number of persons one *knows of* accelerates at a steeply increasing rate.

Simply, then, the number of encounters each of us has, and the range of names, events and knowledge we have to master—this is the most obvious fact about the world which today confronts us as a "given."

Interaction. The "mass society," however, is not composed of numbers alone. Czarist Russia and Imperial China were large land-mass societies, with huge numbers of persons. But these societies

The Disjunction of Culture and Social Structure

were essentially segmented, each village largely recapitulating the features of the other. It was Emile Durkheim in his *Division of Labor* who gave us the clue to what is distinctive about the mass society. It is when segmentation breaks down and people come into interaction with each other—where ensuing competition leads not necessarily to conflict but to more complex divisions of labor, of complementary relationships and of increased structural differentiation—that new social forms emerge.

What is distinctive, then, about contemporary society is not only its size and number, but the increased interaction—physical (through travel, through larger work units, through larger housing densities) and psychic (through the mass media)—which ties us to so many other persons, directly and symbolically. Increased interaction leads not only to social differentiations, but as a mode of experience to psychic differentiation as well—to the desire for change and novelty, to the search for sensation, to the syncretism of culture, all of which mark so distinctively the rhythm of contemporary life.

Self-consciousness. To the classic question of identity, "who are you," a "traditional" person would say: "I am the son of my father."[1] A person today says, "I am I, I come out of myself, and in choice and action I make myself."

This change of identity is the hallmark of our own modernity. For us, experience—rather than tradition, authority, revealed utterance or even reason—has become the source of understanding and of identity. Experience is the great source of self-consciousness, the confrontation of self with diverse others.

Insofar as one makes one's *own* experience the touchstone of truth, one seeks out those with whom one has common experience in order to find common meanings. To this extent, the rise of generations, and the sense of generation, is the distinct focus of modern identity.[2] But this change is, also, the source of an "identity crisis." The idea of reality, sociologically, is a fairly simple one. Reality is a confirmation by "significant others." Traditionally, a *bar-mitzvah* is a confirmation by the Jewish community, a marking out of a new status (the acceptance of the responsibility for the covenant) in a ceremonial act. Graduation from school is a confirmation in a new role and a new status. When a person is confirmed by others, there has to be some sign of recognition.

Reality breaks down when the confirming "others" have lost their meaning for the person seeking to locate himself or to find a place in the society. The sociological problem of reality in our time —in terms of social location and identity—arises because individuals have left old anchorages, no longer follow inherited ways, are constantly faced with the problems of choice (the ability to choose—to choose careers, styles of life, friends, political representatives— is, for the mass of people, something new in social history), and find no longer authoritative standards or critics to guide them. The change from family and class to generation as the "structural" source of confirmation thus creates new strains in identity.

Time-orientation. Ours is a society that has become "future-oriented" in all its dimensions: a government has to plan for future growth; a corporation has to plan for future needs (capital sources, market and product changes, etc.); the individual has to think in terms of a career. In effect, society no longer goes on in crescive fashion; it becomes mobilized for specific ends.

The greatest pressures today devolve upon the young person. At an early age he is under pressure to make firm choices; to get good grades in school, to enter a good college, to choose a vocation. At all stages he is rated, and the performance ratings now become a card of identity that he carries throughout his life.

The failure to provide adequate mechanisms during the transitional period (that is, school guidance, vocational counselling) leads to obvious strains—it invites "beat" behavior and other forms of opting out of the system. In this respect, the "beat fad" parallels the behavior of the early industrial worker when the machine harness was slipped over him as he came off the farm. In both instances one finds wild outbursts (the machine-breaking of the early industrial revolution is matched, perhaps, by drop-out rates in high schools and colleges), the pastoral romance (which in the case of the "beats" becomes slum romance), and similar forms of unorganized class struggle.

The new emphasis on the future in terms of social as well as individual planning—and the resistance to this emphasis because of the new kinds of pressures which such an emphasis entails—becomes a new dimension of our experience in American society.

These four elements, as I have sought to indicate, shape the way in which individuals respond to the world. Two of them—number and interaction—are features of the social environment which "structure" our responses, unconsciously, in the way in which

The Disjunction of Culture and Social Structure

the balancing of mass and size of type on the front-page of a newspaper tends to direct our eye in a determinate sequence. They are responsible, primarily, for the emphasis in modern sensibility on *immediacy, impact, novelty, sensation* and *simultaneity*. These rhythms also tend to shape (as I have sought to show in an essay in *Encounter*, May, 1963) the technical forms of painting, music and literature as well. The emergence of self-consciousness (or the "cult of experience") and the pressures of a mobilized society—particularly where the social mechanisms have been inadequate to handle the problems of innovation and adaptation—have led to the more open and conscious modes of ideological response to the society—to rebellion, alienation, retreatism, apathy or conformity,* modes that are sharply etched on the surface of the culture.

II. *The Diremption of Culture*

These modes of experience—together with some more formal aspects of industrial society, principally functional specialization, and the requirements of the new "intellectual technology"—are reflected in certain disjunctions between the social structure and the culture.

I single out for illustration three realms in which these disjunctions have occurred: 1) The disjunction of "role" and "person"; 2) Functional specialization: the disjunction between "role" and "symbolic expression"; 3) The change in vocabulary: from metaphor to mathematics.

1. *The Disjunction of Role and Person*

In contemporary sociology—as in the intellectual world as a whole—there rages a debate as to whether modern society is one of increasing depersonalization or of increasing freedom. It seems strange that views so diametrically opposite are held by intellectually responsible persons with little effort either to mediate, reconcile, or even establish the terms upon which the debate is conducted.

In a theoretical sense, the roots of the two positions (as expressed in modern sociology) go back contrastingly to Max Weber and Emile Durkheim. For Weber, the drift of society was one of increasing bureaucratization (or functonal rationality) in which the greater specialization of function meant the increasing separation

---

* I am adopting here, for only slightly different purposes, Robert Merton's well-known paradigm in his essay "Social Structure and Anomie."

241

of the individual from the control over the enterprises of which he was a part.* Regulated by the norms of efficiency, calculability, and specialization, man is seen as an appendage to "the clattering process of the bureaucratic machinery."

Durkheim had an almost contrary perspective. In the way he dichotomized social change, the shift from "mechanical solidarity" was, in effect, a movement from homogeneity to heterogeneity, from uniformity to diversity. Societies of the first kind had little division of labor; the collective spirit was so strong that violations of rules were dealt with in a retributive way. Societies of the second type featured a complex division of labor, a separation of sacred from secular elements, a greater choice of occupations, and a loyalty to one's profession rather than to the parochial group as the source of identity or belonging. Sharing some elements of nineteenth-century evolutionary beliefs, though not the unilinearity of a Maine or a Spencer, Durkheim saw social development as inherently "progressive" in its unfolding, though precipitating new kinds of problems. (In one sense, the emphasis of a Weber is on *rationalization,* of a Durkheim on the *rational.*)

This bifurcation continues in contemporary sociology and in intellectual life generally. Those adhering to the Marxist or an existentialist position emphasize the depersonalization inherent in modern bureaucratic life—*vide,* Marcuse, Fromm, Tillich. Others, such as Talcott Parsons or Edward Shils, emphasize the way in which modern society allows for greater variety of choice, the emphasis on achievement, the up-grading of occupations and a greater individualism.

How does one thread one's way through this debate? As William James once said, whenever you meet a contradiction, make a distinction, for people often use the same words to mean two different things. In a curious way, both theories are correct, largely because each is talking about a different dimension. If one makes the distinction between *roles* and *persons,* one can perhaps see the way each theory talks past the other.

I think it is quite evident, following Weber, that modern society increasingly forces a narrow specialization of roles. Broad as-

---

* In Hans Gerth's formulation: "Marx's emphasis upon the wage worker as being 'separated' from the means of production becomes in Weber's perspective merely one special case of a universal trend. The modern soldier is equally 'separated' from the means of violence; the scientist from the means of enquiry, and the civil servant from the means of administration."

The Disjunction of Culture and Social Structure

pects of life which were once centered in the family (namely, work, play, education, welfare, health) are increasingly taken over by specialized institutions (enterprises, schools, trade unions, social clubs, the state). Role definitions (the many different hats we wear) become sharper, and in the crucial area of work, where in the nineteenth-century *mythos* a man found his identity, tasks and roles become minutely specialized. (*The Dictionary of Occupational Titles* lists over 20,000 different specialized jobs in its analysis of vocational outlooks. We even see this in intellectual tasks. The National Register of Scientific and Specialized Personnel, in compiling lists of intellectual talents in the country, now lists about 900 fields in the sciences.)

Within organizations the creation of hierarchies, job specifications, minute definition of responsibilities, rating systems, escalator promotions, and the like, all give emphasis to this sense of fragmentation of self—as it is defined through the *role*.

At the same time it is also clear that, as a *person*, one now has a wider range and variety of choices than ever before. There are many more different kinds of jobs and professions. One can travel to many different places and live in different cities. In the area of consumption (and in using culture as a form of consumption), there is a wider provenance for creating a personal, or a chosen, style of life. All of this is summed up in the phrase, which is distinctive in its modern application, "social mobility."

Modern life creates a bifurcation of *role* and *person* which for a sentient individual becomes a strain.[3]

2. Functional Specialization: The Disjunction of Role and Symbolic Expression

A characteristic of science, as of almost all organized human activity, is the increasing segmentation, differentiation and specialization—sub-division and sub-specialization—of each field of knowledge. Natural philosophy, which was an inclusive term in the seventeenth century, sub-divided into the natural sciences of physics, chemistry, botany, zoology, and so forth. Speculative philosophy of the nineteenth century gave rise to sociology, psychology, mathematical logic, symbolic logic, analytical philosophy, and so forth. In any of the fields today, new problems give rise to further specializations: chemistry, which was once divided into analytical, organic, inorganic, and physical, is in one accounting sub-divided into carbohydrate, steroid, silicone, nuclear, petroleum, and solid state.

One sees this process not only in the fields of knowledge, but in the character of organizations, as new problems give rise to new functions and to new specializations to deal with them. Thus a business corporation which once had a simple staff-and-line organization now finds itself confounded with the problems of coordinating a dozen broad functions such as research, marketing, advertising, quality control, personnel, public relations, design, finance, production, let alone the dozens of sub-specializations within each of the functions (so that personnel, for example, would include labor relations, internal communications, job training, plant security, safety, time records, welfare and medical benefits, and the like.) And one finds similar divisions in *every* formal organization, whether it be a business enterprise, a university, a hospital, or a governmental agency.

The point in all this is that the high degree of specialization—both in the fields of knowledge as well as in the structures of organizations—inevitably creates an almost unbearable strain between "the culture" and the social structure. In fact, it becomes quite difficult to speak even of "the" culture, for not only do specializations create "sub-cultures" or private worlds—in the anthropological sense—but these in turn create private languages and private signs and symbols which often (the case of the jazz musician is the most obvious) infiltrate the "public" world of culture.

Today, the culture can hardly, if at all, reflect the society in which people live. The system of social relations is so complex and differentiated, and experiences so specialized, complicated or incomprehensible, that it is difficult to find common symbols of meaning to relate one experience to another.

In the nineteenth century, the "agency" of expression was the novel. The function of fiction, paradoxically, was to report fact. When social classes began to confront each other in the nineteenth century in the comedy of manners and morals, there was great curiosity as to how each class lived, or as to how individuals who moved up the social ladders took on, or failed to take on, new class styles and modes. There was equally an interest in the nature of work.

The extraordinarily differentiated social structure which has come into being today makes it difficult for a novelist—and even a sociologist—to probe the nature of the worlds of work. Thus

The Disjunction of Culture and Social Structure

fiction, as well as social criticism, tends to deal with consumption styles, or reflect in the themes of alienation and bureaucratization the sentiment against the honeycomb complexity of social structure.

Insofar as experiences in the society are no longer generalizable into the culture, culture itself becomes private, and the individual arts either technical or hermetic. At the turn of the century, the function of the critic was to "mediate" between the creative new experiments being conducted in painting and music, and to find a common esthetic to explain them. Today there is no critic who can assimilate music to painting or painting to music—and it is probably not the fault of the critic. Even the arts have become highly technical: the "new criticism" in literature as a parallel to the technical innovations of the great novelist-masters; the complex intentions of abstract-expressionist painting, with its new emphasis on surface and space.

The real difficulties in the appreciation of the "modern" (both in literature and painting) have been masked by the fact that they have become modish, and, through their popularizers and imitators, common coin for the consumption culture. The only genuine avant-garde movement today is in music, and it remains so because the new electronic music, or post-Webern tonalities, or the new mathematics of serial music, are so technical that even a critic finds it difficult to act as intermediary to other arts, let alone the general public.

The rise of pop art, the introduction of "chance" elements in music, the appreciation of "junk" as esthetic, and the vogue of "happenings" in which paint, sculpture (posture), music and dance are fused into one, all reflect the reaction against the technical and hermetic elements in art. It is not only a new way to "shock" even a blasé public, but it poses a threat to the traditional (and formal) conceptions of genre in a new way. If John Dewey could say that "Art is Experience," what these practitioners are saying is that all "experience is Art." It is, in effect, a denial of specialization by an insistence on the fusion of all arts but one. It is an erasure of all boundaries between the arts, and between art and experience.

3. The Disjunction of Vocabulary: From Metaphor to Mathematics

Reality is always inferential (who has seen custom?) and we employ concepts to describe reality. In the history of "culture" one or another mode of experience has always been dominant as the source of concepts. It is the change in language—the expansion of the abstract mode of thought—which enlarges the disjunction of our experience.

In the primitive world-view—and in such sophisticated primitivism as Zen Buddhism—the world is presented in its immediacy. One did not say "hard" or "soft," for even these terms pre-suppose philosophical ontologies (for example, the nature of substance, or the problem of relative degree); something was "stone" rather than "hard," or "grass" rather than "soft."

Greek cosmogony gave us a vocabulary of first-level abstraction. The pre-Socratics introduced metaphor; Plato, with the idea of the demiurge, the symbol; Aristotle, the idea of analogy. (Our traditional modes of thought here employed all three. Imagery can be visual, aural or tactile, but employs the techniques of metaphor, symbol or analogy in "picturing" the world.)

Theological speech, as derived from Christian thought, is deeply soaked in symbols—the Cross, the Messiah, the Epiphanies, the Sacraments—and the language emphasizes mystery and personality: grace, charisma, kairos, passion or suffering, ritual.

The breakdown of theological beliefs and the rise of a scientific world-view, leading to the enthronement of physics and the natural sciences, gave us in the eighteenth and nineteenth centuries a mechanical cosmology—the image of the world as a machine, or as a celestial clock. (This ordered world reached its apogee in two images: the beauty and precision of Laplace's *Mécanique Céleste*, in which the universe functioned as a jewel, and the idea of the "great chain of being" in which all creatures were united in one perfect strand. In Alexander Pope's words: "Vast chain of Being! which from God began,/Natures ethereal, human, angel, man,/Beast, bird, fish, insect, what no eye can see,/No glass can reach, from Infinite to thee.")

The language of analysis, once derived from theology, was now wrested from the early physical sciences. (Poetry, driven, as Whitehead put it, from the world of fact by science, resorted to ambiguity as its mode of expression, while modern existentialist theology finds its mode in paradox.) In the social sciences the key terms were Force, Motion, Energy, Power (and while these terms have specific referents in physics, they have few operational specificities in social analysis). But as the natural sciences progressed, the social sciences added new biological analogies to the metaphors

The Disjunction of Culture and Social Structure

derived from physics: evolution, growth, organic structure and function, and these terms, until most recently, were the language of sociology.

Even when, in the nineteenth century, social science sought to find a language of its own—"economic man," "psychological man," "capitalism," etc.—this led to a conceptual realism or what Whitehead called "the fallacy of misplaced concreteness." The search for "a language of one's own" in order to avoid the trap of reification has led (as exemplified in Talcott Parsons' *Structure of Social Action*) to "analytical abstraction." Thus, theory construction in sociology, for one, has become a highly deductive system derived from a few basic axioms, or really analytical concepts such as the patterned variables in the action schema of Parsons, in which the empirical referents no longer stand for concrete entities (the individual, society, etc.).

But in the more general sweep of knowledge, the dominant mode of intellectual experience today is mathematical, and especially in our new "intellectual technology" (linear programming, decision theory, simulation) we have the "new" language of variables, parameters, models, stochastic processes, algorithms, hueristics, minimax, and other terms which are being adopted by the social sciences.

Yet the type of mathematics that is influential here is not the deterministic calculus of classical mechanics, but a calculus of probabilities. Life is a "game"—a game against nature, a game of man against man, and one follows rational strategies which can provide maximum pay-offs at maximum risks, minimax pay-offs at minimax risks, and that most lovely of terms in utility preference theory, a pay-off which is provided by a "criterion of regret."

But all of this leads to a paradox: the modern vocabulary is purely rational, with no referent other than its self-contained mathematical formulae. In a modern cosmology (as in physics, and now in the other sciences as well), pictures have gone, words have gone; what remains—apart from elegance, but the elegance of formal ingenuity—is abstract formulae. And underneath these formulae there is no law of nature as we knew it before, eternal, universal, immutable, and readily discernible. Underneath are uncertainty and the break-up of temporal and spatial sequence.[4]

Thus our vocabulary reinforces the dominance of an abstract world conception. And this is the penultimate disjunction between culture and social structure.

III. *The Eclipse of Distance*

The underlying social reality, the stylistic unity of the culture of the past hundred years, lies, I would argue—though its explication is far beyond the scope of this essay—in a structural form of expression that I have called "the eclipse of distance," of psychic, social and esthetic distance.[5] Modern culture began as an effort to annihilate the contemplative mode of experience by emphasizing *immediacy, impact, simultaneity,* and *sensation.* It is today at the point of breaking up all fixed points of reference in formal genres.

The esthetic intention, from the mid-sixteenth to the mid-nineteenth century, was to establish certain formal principles of art around the rational organization of space and time. The painting of the Renaissance—say the painting of Uccello—was "rational" in that it not only applied formal mathematical principles to the depiction of a scene, but also sought to translate into art a rational cosmography of space as depth and time as sequence. In music, as Max Weber pointed out, the diatonic scale was the basis for a rational organization of chords. The fundamental intention of the neo-classical critics, such as Lessing, was to set forth "laws" of esthetic perception: literature and painting, working through different sensuous media, differ in the fundamental laws governing their creation. But underneath all this was a notion of rational organization: depth, the projection of three-dimensional space, gave objects a time value, a simulation of the real world; narrative and sequence were chronological chains which provide a sense of progression.

The diverse movements of modern art have acted to break up this rational construction. Modern painting, eliminating interior distance, thrusts itself on the viewer, emphasizing a sense of immediacy and impact, seeking to capture a simultaneity of planes on a single canvas. Modern poetry, beginning with the theory of "verbal recklessness" as formulated by Rimbaud, breaks up fixed rules of syntax and grammar and, with Mallarmé, abandons referential brute reality to concentrate on the words themselves and their internal relationships within phrase and sentence. The modern novel becomes associative in thought, stream of consciousness in structure, phenomenological in its surfaces, and destructive of sequence and temporality. Modern music, taking Schoenberg as the turning point, denies the necessity of any structural harmonic background and becomes obsessed with sound alone. The remarkable fact is that in

The Disjunction of Culture and Social Structure

all the arts—painting, poetry, the novel, and music (and the cinema *par excellence*)—one can discern a *common* structure of expression, despite the conscious intentions of the artists. This common structure is the "eclipse of distance."

In the loss of "psychic distance," there is the suspension of time, a substitution of moment and event for sequence. In the modern novel, the consequence is to bring the "primary process," the dream sense, to the fore; and the spectator is pulled into the work. In the loss of "esthetic distance," the work "imposes" itself on the spectator; and one must respond, in one's feelings, immediately to the experience. At root, what this has meant is the overturning of the "rational cosmography"—the orderly sequence of time, of beginning, middle, and end; the interior conception of space, of foreground and background, of figure and ground—which shaped Western thought from the sixteenth to the mid-nineteenth century.

The search of the modern was a search for the heightening of experiences in all dimensions and to make those experiences immediate to the senses of people. Yet some cultural signs indicate that we may have come to the end of that phase, a movement which reached its apogee in the esthetic rebellion of 1890–1930. The aimlessness of Camus' *L'Étranger,* the anti-novels of Robbe-Grillet and Butor with their denial of introspection, the vogue of Zen, with its efforts to deny self-consciousness, the static, decaying worlds of Beckett, the hallucinogenic cults fostered by the drug-takers, all express a nihilism or a gnosticism which is subversive of society itself. The literature of modernity—the literature of Yeats, Lawrence, Joyce, and Kafka—was a literature which, as Lionel Trilling put it, took "to itself the dark power which certain aspects of religion once exercised over the human mind." But it was, in its private way, concerned with spiritual salvation. Its successors seem to have lost concern with salvation itself. In this sense, it has become "post-modern" or "post-Christian."

For Ortega y Gasset, art was the freest activity of the human imagination, the least dependent of human actions on social constraints and conditions; and, for this reason, the first signs of change in collective sensibility became noticeable there. The agonized fantasies of a Rimbaud a hundred years ago prefigure the cruder cult of adolescence today. But what does the anti-art of the post-modernist cults foreshadow for the morrow? In the disjunction of culture and social structure it is becoming increasingly more difficult to tell.

DANIEL BELL

REFERENCES

1. One sees this, of course, in the traditional Russian patronymic, or the usual Arab form of naming, such as Ali ben Achmed, or in the residues of old English names such as John/son, Thom/son, and the like.

2. In more traditional societies, or in the early phases of contemporary society, *social class* was usually the main source of identity. The rise and fall of families, as Schumpeter noted, was the rise and fall of social classes. In the earlier quest for position and power in society one sought to rise with one's class, or, as more open mobility became possible, to rise out of one's class (cf. Trilling's "Young Man from the Provinces"). Social class is still today a potent shaper of identity, but it decreases in importance with the rise of education as the chief route to "place" in society. Both in the literary sphere (where the process has a long history) and now in the political realm, the generation assumes a great importance. For the immigrant worlds—and America has been equally a land of many such worlds—the generation has been the chief source of psychic identity.

3. This distinction between *role* and *person* is somewhat different from the distinction between *office* and *person*. Any society, in order to enforce authority, emphasizes a distinction (most notably in an army) between a *rank* and the person bearing the rank. One obeys the rank, not the person.

4. Whether it is pure fancy or genuine speculation, it is interesting that a writer in the *Times Literary Supplement,* in commenting on the influence of computers on the organization of knowledge, sees it as breaking up "linearity" (and introducing "simultaneity") in the organization of prose and in the production of effects. The discussion of this would take us, for the moment, far afield. (See "Poetry, Prose, and the Machine" in the *Times Literary Supplement,* May 4, 1962. This is reproduced in the pamphlet, published by the T. L. S., *Freeing the Mind.*)

5. I can provide only the barest outlines—and forgo the necessary examples and illustrations—of what the reader will recognize is a very complex argument. But this is a sketch, from a work in progress, and I leave it in chiaroscuro outline.

RENÉ DUBOS

Science and Man's Nature

The Shaping of Modern Culture by Science

WORDS HAVE dictionary meanings, but more importantly they have undertones which are determined by the history, beliefs and hopes of the people who use them. The word culture, for example, denotes very different attitudes and contents depending upon the kind of civilization to which it is applied. For civilizations of the Arcadian type, based on the belief that life was happy in the past, the role of culture is to preserve and transmit experience and traditions as faithfully as possible. In contrast, civilizations of the Utopian type, which believe that happiness can be realized only in New Jerusalem, demand that culture prepare man for the mastery of nature and for the creation of a better world.

Most men, in any period of history, have been at times Arcadians and at times Utopians. There is no doubt, however, that the world as a whole is now losing its belief in Arcadia and that the concept of culture is changing accordingly. Whereas traditional civilizations put a premium on the transfer of beliefs and customs from one generation to another, modern societies tend to regard the heritage of the past as but a matter of entertainment for leisure time, and to consider that the forces which are creating the world of tomorrow are the really serious concern of culture. One of the consequences of this shift of emphasis has been the progressive recognition that the natural sciences constitute as legitimate a component of culture as the traditional knowledge of man, of his history, and of his artistic creations.

It goes without saying that many varied social forces other than science have played and continue to play an immense role in shaping modern life. The invention of tools and of agriculture by prehistoric man, the emergence of social groups and especially of large cities, the development of laws and of the various religions, are but a few among the non-scientific forces which have determined the evolution of human nature and of the ways of life. Today, however, science and the technologies derived from it constitute the forces which affect most profoundly the environment in which men have to function and to evolve. Either by choice or from necessity, the cultural evolution of man will be molded in the future by scientific concepts and technological forces. Even more important probably is the fact that science is accelerating the rate of environmental and conceptual changes.

The horse remained the most rapid means of locomotion until the invention of the railroad, but we have moved from the propeller to the supersonic aircraft in one generation. All civilizations have until recently considered the earth as the center of the universe and man as the highest form of life, but we now seriously think about ways of communicating with other thinking and highly evolved creatures that we assume to exist in many parts of the universe. Science is the most characteristic aspect of our civilization precisely because it provides the mental and physical apparatus for rapid changes in our ways of life and even more perhaps in our conceptual views of creation. Indeed, the tempo at which man changes the environment and his views of himself is now so rapid that the rules of conduct for the good life must be changed from one generation to the other. In many fields, the wisdom of the father is now of little use to his son.

The immense role of science in the practical affairs of the modern world is recognized by all, even by its detractors, but surprisingly its influence on culture is often questioned, even by its champions. The following statement is typical of this skeptical attitude concerning the modern mind as it confronts science: "Our lives are changed by its handiwork, but the population of the West is as far from understanding the nature of this strange power as a remote peasant of the Middle Ages may have been from understanding the theology of Thomas Aquinas."[1] I shall attempt later in this essay to consider some of the factors which contribute to the estrangement of the scientific enterprise from the human condition. But it may be useful to emphasize first that science has influenced modern thought and culture much more profoundly than is usually admitted. In fact, it is probable that most educated men have now incorporated concepts derived from theoretical science in their daily thoughts even

Science and Man's Nature

more effectively than medieval or Renaissance Europeans ever incorporated Thomas Aquinas in their cosmologies or their ethics.

The rate of acquisition of new knowledge was so slow in the distant past, and indeed until the advent of experimental science, that ancient civilizations found it difficult to conceive of the possibility of progress. Men whose lives depended entirely on the course of natural events were bound to be more aware of the recurrence of daily and seasonal phenomena, year after year, than of the continuous process of change which we now take for granted. Seeing that natural events repeat themselves endlessly, they tended to extrapolate from these cosmic cycles to human history. For them, the myth of eternal return seemed to apply to the affairs of man just as it did to the cycles of nature and the motions of stars. The known conditions of the present seemed to them but one stage in the endless ebb and flow of events.

It is difficult, of course, to determine with precision at what time the myth of eternal return was displaced in the Western mind by the concept of progress, namely, by the belief in a continuous process of change toward a new state different not only from the present, but also from anything in the past, and hopefully better. The philosophical teachings of the Renaissance and of the Enlightenment certainly helped to formulate the concept and make it intellectually acceptable. But there is no doubt that the philosophy of progress became part of collective consciousness in the Western world approximately at the time when experimental science first began to prosper. Men like Condorcet or Franklin wrote of progress as a theoretical possibility, and placed their hopes for its realization in the future developments of science. However, it was the doctrine of biological evolution which eventually provided the theoretical basis for the concept of progressive historical change. The doctrine of evolution therefore provides one of the most striking examples of the influence of scientific knowledge on modern culture.

Few laymen, it is true, have an exact understanding of the scientific mechanisms involved in biological evolution. Nevertheless, practically all of them now accept as a fact that everything in the cosmos—heavenly bodies as well as living organisms—has developed and continues to develop through a process of historical change. In the Western world, most great religions have come to accept a progressive historical view of creation.

Enlightened laymen tacitly apply evolutionary concepts not only to living organisms and to man, but also to his social institutions, his customs, and his arts. Yet the general acceptance of this evolutionary view is rather recent, dating only from the post Darwinian era. Evolutionary concepts were still either ignored, ridiculed, or almost universally opposed less than one hundred years ago. In contrast, they appear so obvious today that most orthodox churches, political parties, and schools of sociology, history, or art, teach them and indeed make them the basis of their doctrines. It can be said without exaggeration that theoretical biology has thus introduced into human thought a new element which pervades all aspects of traditional culture.

Cosmology, or the physicochemical sciences, could probably be used just as well as the theory of evolution to illustrate how much modern thought is being influenced by scientific knowledge. But since I am a biologist ignorant of these fields, I must act here as a representative of the lay public whose views concerning the cosmos and the structure of matter are progressively being transformed by a kind of knowledge that I do not really understand. Like every human being, for example, I have been puzzled by the concept of the divisibility of matter. I cannot imagine that the division of matter into smaller and smaller fragments can go on indefinitely, but neither can I imagine how this division can come to an end since I can always carry out one further dividing operation in my mind. Fortunately, I begin to sense that this paradox is not entirely beyond human comprehension. Although I know nothing of the theories or practices of elementary particle physics, I can apprehend that when sufficient energy is applied to elementary particles in the big accelerators, the particles are changed not by a process of true division but by a transmutation of energy into matter; every particle can be transformed into any other if the energy applied is sufficiently great.

In the preceding paragraph, I have mentioned on purpose a kind of phenomenon completely foreign to my knowledge in order to illustrate the manner in which science becomes incorporated into the cultural tradition. Science shapes culture not necessarily through its technical aspects, but rather by providing new points of views and by facilitating new attitudes. That the earth is round, and that all living creatures that we know have a common ancestry, is not obvious either to my senses or my common sense, yet these concepts have become integrated in my daily thoughts and thus constitute part of the fabric of my culture. It would be surprising if the general concepts of elementary particle physics and of relativity theory did not in some way become integrated in the general culture of the next generation.

The integration of scientific knowledge into general culture will probably be accelerated by the fact that there is a wide public awareness of some of the basic assumptions of science. Many lay persons have come to realize that each particular field of science develops as if it were a self-contained structure, with its own body of facts and its own inner logic. Students of matter investigate elementary particles and the laws which govern the primordial stuff of which these particles might be but the transient manifestations; their information is derived from recent experiments in high energy physics carried out with the aid of complex hardware. Students of human evolution trace the origin of man, step by step, to some small creature which lived in trees at the beginning of the Paleocene period; their conclusions are derived from the comparative study of ancient fossils found here and there in many parts of the world. It is obvious enough that the structure of matter and the evolution of man constitute two fields of science which have developed independently, each with its own techniques, points of view and goals. In this light, it would appear as if there were no such thing as science, but only a multiplicity of unrelated fields of knowledge. But while it is a fact that each field of science has its own characteristics and displays its own pattern of development, it is also true, and probably far more important, that no incompatibility has ever been found between one field of science and another; the laws of one do not violate the laws of the other.

The remarkable compatibility between all fields of science, whether they deal with inanimate objects or with living things, has implications which affect deeply the culture of our times. The validity of these implications is supported by the fact that the various scientific disciplines strengthen each other when, perchance, they can establish contact. Despite the immense diversity of creation, we all accept that there exists in nature a profound underlying unity. The search for this unity provides the motivation for the lives of many different men, some who like Einstein search for it in general natural laws, and others who like Teilhard de Chardin would trace cosmic evolution to a divine origin.

So general is the belief in the unity of nature, and in the power of the scientific approach, that this method is now applied to most areas of human concern, from the natural sciences to the historical sciences, from the analysis of the human fabric to the appreciation of human arts, naive as it may be to hope that methods developed for the study of inanimate objects can be applied to the much more complex and qualitatively different problems of social human life. But despite their premature character, the attempts to apply the scientific method as used by the natural sciences to problems for which it is not suited are of interest because they reveal a general awareness that we have under cultivation only a small area of the fields which can be exploited by science.

The Antiscience Movement

Since the various scientific fields include all the subjects on which reasonable men can converse objectively and exchange verifiable information, it is difficult if not impossible to state in words where science ends and where the humanities begin. The paradox, however, is that this semantic difficulty hardly ever causes any confusion in human behavior. The immense majority of the lay public shows by its reading habits that it sharply differentiates between science and non-science; this differentiation also appears in the fact that concert halls and art museums have more popular appeal than science exhibits. The "two cultures" may be an illusion, but in practice science is still regarded in our communities as a kind of foreign god, powerful and useful, yes, but so mysterious that it is feared rather than known and loved.

It is healthy to acknowledge that scientists themselves generally behave like the lay public when they function outside their areas of professional specialization. The student of plasma physics or of plasma proteins is not likely to select books on marsupials for his bedside reading, nor is the organic chemist inclined to become familiar with problems of population genetics. Most scientists, it is true, are interested at present in radiation fallout and in the hidden surface of the moon, but so are many members of the Rotary Club. Winston Churchill, Pablo Picasso and Ernest Hemingway are much more frequently discussed at the luncheon tables of scientific research institutes than are the Nobel prize winners in physics, chemistry, or biology of the same generation. And if Linus Pauling or Robert Oppenheimer is mentioned, it is less likely with regard to either's achievements as chemist or physicist than because their behavior makes them interesting and vital human beings. In brief, while scientists are deeply committed to their own specialized fields, they generally turn to non-scientific topics when they move outside their professional spheres.

Science and Man's Nature

The priority of general "human" concerns over purely scientific interests acquires particular importance in education. Whatever historians and philosophers of science may say concerning the fundamental similarities between science and the humanities as intellectual and creative pursuits, the high school or college student soon discovers from his personal experience that the two kinds of learning and activities are different as far as he is concerned. He will probably like one and despise the other; and science commonly loses in the comparison. A recent study of high school students selected for extremely high scholastic aptitude (only one per cent of the total student population!) revealed that the percentage of those selecting science decreased from 37.77 per cent in 1958 to 28.87 per cent in 1963.[2] Even more serious was the finding that among those who had originally selected science 55.2 per cent of the males and 58.9 per cent of the females changed to other fields during their college years. The significance of these figures becomes the greater when it is realized that the trend away from science occurred during a period when great social pressure was being exerted on young people to induce them to go into scientific careers.

The difficulty of scientific courses, and the shortage of gifted scientific teachers devoted to the training of undergraduates, may account in part for this disturbing rejection of science. But to be satisfied with such obvious explanations seems to be unwarranted, and unwise. At the risk of oversimplifying the problem and exaggerating its gravity, I incline to the view that the attitude of the lay public and of many young people toward science is at bottom one of hostility arising from anxiety. In my opinion, this anxiety is in part the result of a breakdown in the system of relationships between human nature and the scientific creations of man.

Throughout this essay, the expression human nature is used in the French sense of *nature humaine,* which encompasses much more than does the English phrase. By human nature I mean not only the instinctive, psychological and moral attributes which are characteristic of man, but also all the physiological needs and urges which are woven into his very fabric, and which he has retained from his evolutionary past. In other words, I shall have in mind man's total nature rather than the limited aspects of it usually denoted by the expression human nature. In the light of this larger view of man's nature, it may be easier to understand how scientific knowledge, although it enables man to manipulate his environment, paradoxically leaves him an outsider in the world he is creating.

While man is progressively mastering nature, his own nature has not so far surrendered to the scientific and technological onslaught.

Mankind has, of course, always known anxiety. The doctrine of original sin may well be merely a symbol for the uneasiness man experienced when he first realized that he was alienating himself from the rest of creation. From ancient times many have been those who believed that the world is out of joint, and it is not at all certain that their percentage numbers are larger than in the past. What is beyond doubt is that the gap between man's nature and the rest of nature is constantly becoming wider, hence the ambivalent attitude of modern man toward science. He wants the benefits of scientific technology, but he feels uneasy and indeed apprehensive about scientific knowledge *per se*. Despite much writing on the miracles of science, public fear and mistrust of scientists is probably on the increase and is certainly becoming more vocal. More and more frequently the emphasis is on the potential dangers of technological innovations, and even on horror stories concerning them.

The attitude of uneasiness has been increased, of course, by the fear of nuclear warfare, and of certain technologies which threaten the health of man. Popular articles entitled "The truth about . . ." almost uniformly refer to the dangers of medical and technological procedures, and hint at the social irresponsibility of scientists. However, the origins of the antiscience movement are more complex and more profound than would appear from recent developments. There was already much talk of the "bankruptcy" of science during the 19th century. Science was then accused of destroying religious and philosophic values without substituting for them any other guide to behavior, or any convincing picture of the universe and of human destiny. This dissatisfaction is pungently expressed in Dewey's warning that "a culture which permits science to destroy traditional values, but which distrusts its power to create new ones, is destroying itself." The malaise has now extended to the scientific community itself, as recently acknowledged in a public lecture by a distinguished professor of chemistry in the United States. "Science is only one branch of philosophy . . . if we do make claims for support because of our rather immediate relation to industrial technology, we may well be making value-judgments concerning technology that we are, by virtue of our training, ill-equipped to make."[3]

Admittedly, the meaning of the word "value" is so poorly defined that most scientists would probably deny that it has any usefulness as a basis either for discussion or for action. Yet, the word is so charged with the hopes of mankind, its impact on the relationships between the world of science and the rest of society is so great, that it must be recognized as a real force. I would not presume to formulate values or propose a solution to the dilemma stated by Dewey. I shall instead limit myself to a consideration of several aspects of the scientific enterprise which contribute to its progressive estrangement from the human condition, and thereby to incoherence in modern life.

Man and his Future

A symposium entitled "Man and His Future" was held in London in 1963. Its purpose was to examine the consequences of the fact that "research is creating and promising methods of interference with natural processes which could destroy or could transform every aspect of human life which we value."[4]

The participants in the symposium found it rather easy to discuss the role of science in several current problems, such as: how to feed the billions of hungry people in the world; how to maintain an adequate supply of raw materials and of energy; how to accelerate the process of learning; how to prepare man for space travel. There was a tacit agreement among them that by using the proper scientific approach "almost everything one can imagine possible will in fact be done, if it is thought to be desirable." In contrast, the participants found no basis for common discourse when the discussions turned to the physical, psychological, emotional, cultural, or ethical traits which are desirable for human betterment. Indeed, the sheer diversity of views concerning what constitutes the good life led one of them to conclude that the only possible social policy for science as well as for human institutions was "piecemeal social engineering," that scientists must forego ambitious social plans and dedicate themselves instead to limited goals.

History shows, however, that human institutions cannot merely drift if they are to survive. Each civilization is characterized by the special kind of problems which it elects to emphasize. Furthermore, all societies operate on certain assumptions, and move toward certain goals. Despite our pathetic attempt at objectivity, we as scientists are in fact highly subjective in the selection of our activities, and we have goals in mind when we plan our work. We make *a priori* decisions concerning the kind of facts worth looking for; we arrange these facts according to certain patterns of thought which we find congenial; and we develop them in such a manner as to promote social purposes which we deem important. The most sweeping assumption in our communities at the present time is that the good life will automatically emerge if we focus our scientific efforts on the production of things and on the manipulation of the body machine, even though a large percentage of scientists probably believe that such an attitude is responsible for incoherence in technological civilization.

One might argue, of course, that incoherence is not objectionable *per se*, that incoherence may even be a symbol of intellectual integrity, and a necessary condition for the evolutionary development of mankind, since no one knows how to formulate either the ultimate truth, or the good life, or even the intermediary goals on the way to these ideals. In practice, however, there are limits to the amount of incoherence that man and his societies can tolerate; the popular success of anti-utopian and anti-scientific literature at the present time may indicate that we are approaching the breaking point.

I shall attempt in the following pages to discuss several disturbing aspects of the interplay between man's nature and the environment created by scientific knowledge. First to be considered will be the fact that, while the external environment and the ways of life are being revolutionized by technology, biological man remains fundamentally the same as he was when he emerged from his animal past. Outwardly, man makes adjustments to the new conditions of life; inwardly, however, he has so far failed to make true adaptations to them, and this discrepancy creates physiological and psychological conflicts which threaten to become increasingly traumatic.

Another cause of incoherence in our societies is that modern knowledge, especially scientific knowledge, relates less and less to human experience. In many cases, the technical apparatus of knowledge reaches into aspects of reality which are beyond human grasp. There is a disjunction between scientific knowledge and direct human experience.

Because science and technology are now advancing without the guidance of a well thought out philosophy of natural and social values, they achieve results and produce effects which in many cases no longer correspond to real human needs. Man, through science, has released disruptive forces which he has not yet learned to control. In front of his eyes, these forces are undermining the relation-

Science and Man's Nature

ships slowly built through evolutionary processes between nature, the works of reason, and the hidden aspects of man's nature.

H. G. Wells pointed out in *A Modern Utopia* that ours is an adaptive civilization, incompatible with static social structures. Since we transform the external world through technology, we must also change our societies and ways of life because the maintenance of adaptive fitness is as essential for the survival of institutions as it is for the survival of living things. As presently formulated, however, evolutionary and social concepts give but an inadequate picture of man's relation to his environment. Their inadequacy comes from the fact that human societies and ways of life are rapidly changing while certain fundamental components of man's nature remain essentially unaltered.

Ever since the Neolithic revolution, man has become increasingly proficient in controlling the external world—beasts, forests, floods, climate, and many other natural forces. He has also developed enough knowledge of his own body and behavior to exercise some measure of control over certain obvious aspects of his life. Indeed, his confidence that he can modify and improve not only external nature, but also his own nature, constitutes the rationalistic basis for modern technological civilization. In Western countries, at least, technology has transformed the external world, medicine is learning to manipulate the body and the mind, social institutions are striving to establish universal respect for human dignity. Thus, ways of life are undergoing profound adaptive changes in an attempt to keep *social* man in tune with the rapid changes in the environment which are brought about by technological innovations.

In contrast, many important aspects of man's fundamental nature are not changing at all, or change so slowly that they are out of phase with the modern world. Biological evolutionary mechanisms are far too slow to keep pace with social evolution. For example, most functions of the body continue to exhibit diurnal and seasonal cycles, as well perhaps as cycles of other periodicities. Even though the ideal of technology is to create a constant and uniform environment, physiological functions still undergo cyclic changes because they are linked to the cosmic forces under which human evolution took place. When modern life carries the day into the night, maintains the same temperature and food supply throughout the year, and imposes rapid changes of latitude in a jet aircraft, it creates physiological conflicts because man's body machine continues to function according to the cosmic order. Anyone who travels by jet aircraft has a direct perception of the physiological disturbances caused in his body by the change of latitude. The immediate effects of the conflict between the paleolithic constitution of man and the exigencies of modern life can be documented by chemical, physiological and psychological measurements, but little is known of their long range consequences. There is no doubt, however, that many physiological disturbances have their origin in the conflict between the modern environment and the paleolithic ordering of physiological functions.

The so-called fight and flight response constitutes another manifestation of very ancient hidden forces which are still operating in modern man. It consists in a series of physiological and chemical processes which are rapidly mobilized in the body under conditions of threat, and which were certainly useful in the past. When prehistoric man encountered an enemy or a wild beast, a variety of hormonal processes placed his body in readiness either for combat or for running away. Today, the same processes are still set in motion under circumstances which modern man symbolizes as a threat, for example during social conflicts at the office or at a cocktail party. The physiological consequences of the fight and flight response, however, are no longer useful and indeed are probably noxious, since the proprieties of civilized life require the subjugation of the direct, physical response, and thus prevent the expenditure of physical energy.

Many other ancestral mechanisms which persist in modern man must find some outlet, even though they no longer correspond to a necessity of life. Just as a kind of hunting activity remains a need for the house cat even when it is well fed at home, similarly man has retained from his evolutionary past certain needs which no longer have a place in the world he has created, yet which must be satisfied.[5] Ancient civilizations were aware of the profound effects that hidden physiological and psychological forces exert on human behavior and they commonly symbolized these forces by a ferocious bull struggling against reason. In fact, most people have developed empirical procedures to let these occult forces manifest themselves under somewhat controlled conditions. As shown by Dodds in *The Greeks and the Irrational,* the Dionysian celebrations, the Eleusinian mysteries, and many other myths and rituals, served as release mechanisms for fundamental human urges which did not find adequate expression in the rational and classical aspects of Greek life; even Socrates found it wise to participate in the Corybantic rites.[6] Many such ancient traditions still persist in the advanced countries of Western culture, even though in a distorted form. In the most modern city, as among the hills of Arcadia three thousand years ago, men and women perceive in springtime that nature is awakening and at work in their bodies, just as it is in the beasts and trees. Carnival is still celebrated when the sap starts running.

Scientific knowledge of the persisting ancestral aspects of man's nature hardly goes beyond a vague awareness of their existence. Limited though it is, this knowledge is nevertheless sufficient to make it clear that medical and social philosophies are based on assumptions which should be reexamined. Some of these assumptions have come to light in their simplest and perhaps crudest forms during discussions on the medical problems posed by the necessity to make man more effective in the technological age, and also to prepare astronauts for life in space capsules.

At the London symposium mentioned above,[7] the participating scientists each had his own formula for modifying man by mechanical protheses, organ grafting, drug action, or eugenic control. But they hardly concerned themselves with the effects of these alterations on the aspects of man's nature which Dodds grouped under the adjective "irrational." A similar indifference appears in a recent article by a physician specialized in problems of space medicine. According to him, the sensible solution of these problems is to drastically modify man; the easiest approach being, in his view, to replace certain organs by mechanical parts more efficient for dial reading and better suited to electronic control. Natural, ordinary man could thus be converted into an "optiman."

Needless to say, the efficiency that biotechnologists aim at fostering in the various forms of "optiman" has little to do with the ancient but still vigorous biological human urges. Commentators in the daily press and in magazines have pointed out in many humorous or scornful articles that some scientists appear to be unaware of these fundamental needs of man's nature. The lay public has pragmatically recognized that man retains from his ancestral past certain needs and drives which, even though scientifically ill defined, nevertheless cry out for some form of expression.

There are also many tacit assumptions in the belief that the goal of technology, including medicine, should be to provide man with a sheltered environment in which he is protected as completely as possible from traumatic experiences. This assumption is dangerous because of the fact that many important traits of man's nature cannot develop normally, or remain in a healthy state, without constant stimulation and challenge.[8] Life at constant temperature through air conditioning, learning made effortless through mechanical aids, avoidance of conflicts through social adjustment, are examples of the means by which modern life eliminates or minimizes physiological or psychological effort, but by the same token causes an atrophy of man's adaptive mechanisms. Thus, while protection from stresses and effort may add to the pleasure or at least comfort of the moment, and while emotional neutrality minimizes social conflicts, the consequences of an excessively sheltered life are certainly unfavorable in the long run. They are even dangerous in that the human jelly fish becomes adjusted to a particular place and time, but loses his ability to readjust as surroundings change.

Scientific Knowledge and Human Experience

In contrast with the arts, science is usually identified with logic and reason. Indeed, a large part of scientific history obviously consists in the progressive unfolding of a logical process; each particular field of science has its own inner logic, which makes one fact derive from another. It is also true, on the other hand, that the growth of science presents many aspects which are essentially independent of logic. At any given period, scientists are profoundly influenced by the assumptions which they accept as a basis for their work, and by the goals which they pursue consciously or more often unconsciously. To a large extent, these assumptions and these goals are those of the social community as a whole.

The most influential assumption of modern science is that the best and indeed the only scientific approach to the study of natural phenomena and of living organisms is to divide them into fragments and to investigate elementary structures and properties in greater and greater detail. While it is repeatedly, and properly, pointed out that this analytical approach has been immensely fruitful in discoveries, there is far too little recognition of the disturbing fact that it has led to the neglect of other fields of science. Although everyone recognizes that the very existence of natural phenomena and of living organisms is the manifestation of the interplay between their constituent parts under the influence of environmental factors, hardly anything is known of the mechanisms through which natural systems function in an integrated manner.

Science and Man's Nature

In the course of reductionist analysis, the scientist tends to become so much involved intellectually and emotionally in the elementary fragments of the system, and in the analytical process itself, that he loses interest in the organism or the phenomenon which had been his first concern. For example, the student of man who starts from a question singled out because of its relevance to human life is likely to progress seriatim to the organ or function involved, then to the single cell, then to the cellular fragments, then to the molecular groupings or reactions, then to the individual molecules and atoms; and he would happily proceed if he knew enough to the elementary particles where matter and energy become indistinguishable. Problems of great interest obviously arise at each step in the disintegration of the original phenomenon. But in practically all cases the phenomenon itself is lost on the way, and the knowledge acquired in the course of its analysis usually throws little light on its determinants and modalities—let alone on the approach to its control. Scientists might find it useful now and then to evaluate their professional activities in the light of Kant's admonition, "To yield to every whim of curiosity, and to allow our passion for inquiry to be restrained by nothing but the limits of our ability, this shows an eagerness of mind not unbecoming to scholarship. But it is wisdom that has the merit of selecting from among the innumerable problems which present themselves, those whose solution is important to mankind."

Loss of interest in phenomena as they occur in Nature is found in practically all fields of science. It would be out of place to discuss here the consequences of this aspect of scientific professionalism for the advancement of knowledge. But it is relevant to the present theme to suggest that therein lies in part the cause of the estrangement of the general public from science. The primary interest of the public is in the phenomena of nature or in the living organisms, whereas the deepest commitment of the professional scientist is to the results of his analytical processes. In consequence, the scientist generally loses his public as he loses sight of the original problem.

Furthermore, whereas science was at first a method to deal with the world of matter and of life as man perceives it through his senses, much of the scientist's knowledge is now acquired through technical and mental processes which operate outside the range of immediate human experience. Emile Gilson stated in his William James Lectures at Harvard that "Every scientist naturally has the temper and the tastes of a specialist . . . . the natural tendency of science is not towards unity, but towards an ever more complete disintegration." This statement certainly describes a state of affairs which is increasingly prevalent, but it does not, in my opinion, deal with the most important aspect of the problem. A more disturbing aspect of modern science is that the specialist himself commonly loses contact with the aspect of reality which was his primary concern, whether it was matter, life or man.

In his own experience of the physical world, the physicist does not use his specialized knowledge for a richer or more subtle contact with reality; nor is the biologist rendered capable of perceiving the living experience more acutely because he is familiar with intermediate metabolism or x-ray diffraction patterns of contractile fibers. The theoretical physicist apparently finds it difficult to convert the mathematical formulae on which he depends into experiences or thoughts meaningful to his own senses and reason. The general biologist finds no trace of the creativeness of life in the macromolecules he isolates from the cell. The student of consciousness cannot relate the operations of the sense organs or of the nerve impulse to the emotion elicited by a fragrant rose or a romantic sunset.

There has been much talk during recent years of the lack of communication between the humanistic and the scientific aspects of knowledge. In reality, however, this disjunction is not so critical as is often suggested. Each and every one of us can and does learn many facts and concepts pertaining to areas of knowledge totally different from the one in which he is a specialist. The breakdown in communication is complete only when the concepts cannot be related to human experience. The physicist, the biologist, the humanist, and the layman can all find a common ground for discourse if they talk about matter, life, or man as perceived by the senses, or as apprehended in the form of images, analogies, and responses. But discussions of matter in terms of mathematical symbolism, or of life and man in terms of disintegrated components, cannot be related to any form of direct experience. Specialists must return to the original human basis of their work if they want to converse with mankind.[9]

Science and Technology as Independent Forces

Just as scientific knowledge is becoming alienated from human experience, so are its technological applications becoming increasingly alienated from human needs. Although modern technology appears at first sight but a spectacular extension of what it started out to be in the 18th and 19th centuries, in reality it is moving toward other goals. This change of focus is contributing to the disjunction between science and mankind.

The natural philosophers and sociologists of the Age of Reason were concerned with a few well defined problems of obvious importance for the welfare of the human race. Everywhere they saw misery and disease caused by acute shortages of food and of elementary conveniences; they observed that ignorance of the natural forces generates terror, superstitions and often acts of cruelty. The task they set for science was therefore to abolish the threat of scarcity, and to gain enough knowledge to help man face the natural world without fear. These goals were within the range of human experience. By making it possible to reach them, science was truly acting as a servant of mankind.

In contrast, science and the technologies derived from it now often function as forces independent of human goals. In many cases, as we have seen, knowledge creates concepts that man cannot restate in terms of his experience; and increasingly technology creates services and products that man does not really need. All too often, knowledge and technology pursue a course which is not guided by a pre-determined social philosophy. The knowledge of ionizing radiations and of atomic structure was developed by men with the highest ideals who can be regarded as saints of science, yet immense harm has come from their creations. The guilt for this harm cannot be placed on villains with selfish interests or bent on hurting mankind; it results rather from a political and social process which allows science to move blindly in the social arena.

Even though dangers are also inherent in the knowledge concerning automation, synthetic chemicals, or almost any other new technology, surprisingly little is done to evaluate the possible social consequences of these innovations. One dramatic illustration of this negligence is the research budget of the State Department. Science, lavishly endowed by public funds, produced nuclear weapons—the means by which man can now destroy himself. The problem of preventing this catastrophe is primarily the State Department's responsibility. Yet its total budget for policy research studies is negligible. Indeed, there is very little federal support for any kind of scholarly work on the explosive international issues now facing the world. Nor is there much recognition of the fact that the recent advances in medicine have created vast new problems which are essentially social, political, and economic rather than scientific. As E. M. Forster predicted in "The Machine Stops," technology moves on, but not on our lines; it proceeds, but not to our goals. It is urgent that science and technology be given goals of significance and value to man lest the sorcerer's apprentice be converted from a literary symbol into a terrifying reality.

The Industrial Revolution, with mass production of energy and its rapid injection into all aspects of social life, is everywhere beginning to disrupt the great dynamic processes which have so far maintained the earth in a state compatible with human life. Disruption of the water cycle is speeding water on its way to the sea and increasing its destructive action on land surfaces; denudation of the soil is creating dust bowls all over the earth; pollution of the air and of water is beginning to upset the biological balance and to damage human health. The medical sciences themselves are becoming so effective that they can affect unfavorably the fate of immense numbers of people and of their descendants, often creating new pathological processes as they control old diseases. Their greatest impact, probably, will be not so much on the size of the world population as on its genetic qualities, and on its other qualitative characteristics.

Needless to say, there is nothing fundamentally new in the fact that technology alters the relationship between man and nature. For many thousand years, man has modified his environment by using fire, farming the land, building houses, opening roads, and even controlling his reproduction. The all important difference, however, is that many modern applications of science have nothing to do with human biological needs and aim only at creating new demands, even though these be inimical to health, to happiness, or to the aspirations of mankind. Technology allowed to develop for its own sake often acts as a disruptive force which upsets the precarious relationships upon which civilizations have been built in the past. It creates new environmental conditions to which man finds it difficult to adapt, and which destroy some of the most valuable human attributes.

A process of adaptation is of course going on continuously between man and the new world he is creating. As we have seen, however, some important traits which are built into the fabric of man's nature are not likely to be eliminated, or significantly modified, despite all the changes which occur in his societies and ways of life. Even when man becomes an automated and urbane city dweller, his physiological processes remain geared to the daily rotation of the earth around its axis and to its annual rotation around the sun; the paleolithic bull which survives in his inner self still paws the earth whenever a threatening gesture is made on the social scene. The tragic paradox is that science fosters ways of life and manners of response which are often determined by technological expediency, whereas it hardly concerns itself with the fundamental characteristics and needs of man's nature.

While most human beings believe that the proper study of mankind is man, the scientific establishment has not tooled itself for this task. The great scientific institutions are geared for the analytical description of the body machine, which they approach in much the same spirit as they do simple inanimate objects. They pay little heed to the scientific study of man as a functioning entity, exhibiting all the complex responses that living entails. Nor do they pay much attention to the environmental factors which condition the manifestations of human life.

The disjunction between man's nature and the creations of science and technology inevitably manifests itself in social disturbances. In principle, these disturbances are not beyond the scope of scientific study; in practice, however, they have a low order of priority in the world of learning. The study of man as an integrated unit, and of the ecosystems in which he functions, is grossly neglected because it is not in the tradition which has dominated experimental science since the 17th century. Such a study would demand an intellectual approach, as well as research techniques and facilities, different from those which are fashionable and professionally profitable in the academic establishment.

Two historical reasons account for the tendency of scientists to neglect the problems posed by the complex situations found in the real world. One is that the simpler problems are more likely to yield clear results and rapid professional advance. The other reason is that until recently, the applications of science were direct and on the whole beneficial. Only during the past few decades has science become such a powerful force that any technological intervention affects simultaneously many aspects of human life.

Land conservation, water resources, urban development, the physiological and mental qualities of the human race are but a few among the immense problems created by the impact of scientific technology. It is therefore a moral obligation for the scientific establishment to devote itself in earnest to the study of ecosystems, both those of nature and those created by man. But ecosystems cannot be studied by the use of the oversimplified models which constitute the stock in trade of orthodox experimental science.

The urgency to escape from shackles of the scientific past is particularly apparent when attention turns to man himself. One of the strangest assumptions of present day biology is that knowledge of living man will automatically follow from so called "fundamental" studies of the elementary structures and reactions of fragments derived from living things. In reality, a very different kind of knowledge is needed to understand the nature of the cohesive forces which maintain man in an integrated state, physically, psychologically, and socially, and enable him to relate successfully to his environment. Hardly anything is known of man's adaptive potentialities, of the manner in which he responds to the stimuli which impinge on him early in his development and throughout his life, of the long range consequences of these responses not only for himself but for his descendants. There are countless problems ranging from those posed by the earlier sexual maturity of children to those involved in urban planning, which should and could be studied scientifically, yet have hardly any place in the curriculum of universities or research institutes.

Science for Man

Incoherence implies the breakdown of integrative relationships. One remedial measure is of course to establish better understanding and communication within the scientific community itself and between it and the public. But there is no knowledge of how this can be done effectively. At most, it is known that a few scientific books of distinction have been widely read, or at least have had a wide influence and are often quoted. A study of the reason for their success might provide some insight into the determinants of the public response to science, and indirectly into the aspects of science which have human values.

There are good reasons to believe that conceptual views of the world, even if purely theoretical, can have as much general appeal as utilitarian applications, and it is obvious of course that the appeal is even greater when the facts have some relevance to the problems which have always preoccupied mankind, whether these be concerned with the place of man in the cosmos or with his survival and welfare. But in any case, scientific communication demands more than the description of facts or the reporting of news. In science, just as in any other field, man can communicate with man only through the channels of shared experiences, or still better, through mutual hopes.

Through its emphasis on over-simplified models, the scientific community is betraying the very spirit of its vocation—namely, its professed concern with reality. Nature exists only in the form of complex ecosystems, and these constitute the environment which man perceives, and to which he responds. As human life becomes more dependent on technology, it will become more vulnerable to the slightest miscarriage or unforeseen consequence of innovations, hence the need for studies directed to the problems of interrelationships within complex ecosystems. Science will remain an effective method for the acquisition of knowledge meaningful to man, and consequently for social service only if its orthodox techniques can be supplemented by others which come closer to the human experience of reality, and to a kind of social action designed for fundamental human needs.

The study of natural and man-made ecosystems, as well as of man's responses to environmental forces, has as much intellectual dignity and deserves as much academic support as the study of isolated particles and elementary reactions. Only through a scientific knowledge of man's nature and of the ecosystems in which he functions can technology be usefully and safely woven into the fabric of society. Indeed, a truly human concept of technology might well constitute the force which will make science once more part of the universal human discourse, because technology at its highest level must integrate knowledge of the external world and of man's nature.

Since each particular field of science has its inner logic of growth, the scientific enterprise can long continue to move on its own momentum even though it becomes increasingly indifferent to man. Lacking worthwhile social goals, however, science may soon find itself floundering in a sea of irrelevancies. Eventually, it might even be rejected by ordinary men if they were to decide that its values are irrelevant and dangerous. "It seems to me entirely possible," stated recently a Sigma Xi lecturer, "that our society, which, for whatever motives, has invested not only immense sums of money but large amounts of spiritual faith in what it uninformedly conceives science to be, may become as thoroughly disillusioned and rebellious toward scientific and technological authoritarianism as early societies became rebellious towards regal authoritarianism."[10]

Despite its spectacular successes, science is not yet firmly established in the human mind. Its increasing alienation from the problems which are of deepest concern for mankind might well transform the anti-utopian outbursts so characteristic of our time from a literary exercise into an antiscience crusade. In its mildest form, such a crusade will at least continue to clamor for a moratorium on science, under the pretext that knowledge is accumulating faster than it can be digested and therefore is becoming dangerous. In reality, of course, there cannot be any retreat from science. Rather, public apprehension and hostility point to the need for an enlargement of science. Scientists must take more to heart the questions which deeply concern human beings; they must learn to give greater prominence to large human values when formulating their problems and their results. Fortunately, this is probably easier than is commonly believed because, as emphasized earlier, history shows that the broad implications of science can become integrated in the intellectual fabric of modern societies. Human cultures, like organisms and societies, depend for survival on their internal integration, an integration which can be achieved only to the extent that science remains meaningful to the living experience of man.

REFERENCES

1. Toulmin, Stephen, *Foresight and Understanding*, Indiana University Press, 1961.
2. Nichols, Robert C., "Career Decisions of Very Able Students," *Science*, 1964, *144*, 1315-19.
3. Hutchison, E., "Science and Responsibility," *American Scientist*, 1964, 52, 40A-49A.
4. Wolstenholme, G., *Man and His Future,* Boston: Little, Brown & Co., 1963.
5. An extended discussion of these aspects of human nature which survive from man's paleolithic origins will be found in a forthcoming book by R. Dubos, *Man Adapting,* to be published by Yale University Press (Silliman lectures).
6. Dodds, E. R., *The Greeks and the Irrational,* Berkeley: University of California Press, 1951.
7. Wolstenholme, G., *op. cit.*
8. Dubos, R., *op. cit.*
9. Barfield, O., *Worlds Apart, A Dialogue of the 1960's,* London: Faber and Faber, 1963.
10. Hutchison, E., *op. cit.*

ROBERT S. MORISON

Toward a Common Scale of Measurement

IT IS the purpose of this essay to show that in its pursuit of increasingly refined observation of the material world, of the greatest agreement among observers, and of the highest degree of repeatability, science has resorted to methods which present a picture of that world alien in many ways to immediate experience. The old-fashioned, immediately perceived world still largely determines the motivation of individuals and of whole societies, but it is the inferred world of science that helps us reach the objectives toward which we are motivated. In less cumbersome language, subjective perception makes us feel where we want to go, while objective inference tells us how to get there.

There are many other differences between the subjective and the objective attitudes, between science and the humanities, or between scientists and artists. These are dealt with in other articles in this collection. We shall consider some of the disjunctions and paradoxes which arise directly from the two different ways of knowing represented by direct, immediately given perceptions on the one hand, and the objective inferences of science on the other. One's final hope is, of course, that scientists and humanists (and especially creative artists) will recognize that they are in fact observing and talking about the same world and that they have a duty to translate their findings into each other's languages.

In its beginnings science did not seem to differ except in unimportant degree from ordinary or common-sense knowledge. The earliest men who would now be thought of as scientists described the world around them in familiar everyday terms. Bodies were warm or cold, heavy or light, and red, yellow or green. To put the matter a little differently, the words the earliest scientist used were those which described the world in the way it was directly revealed by the process known as perception. Some philosophers, it is true, worried about the status of perception as a means of knowing the physical world, and Plato came to the conclusion that perceived knowledge was distinctly inferior to knowledge inferred by the process of right reason. This feeling that there is a purer, more perfect world accessible to reason, one that was later to become even more accessible to the complicated and indefinable process known as science, has persisted with varying intensity ever since. It derived originally from the beauty and apparent perfection of the mathematical formulations which could be developed to describe the relations between natural phenomena.

Until the development of instruments and scales for measuring qualities other than spacial position and extension, mathematical expressions of observable events were largely limited to matters of geometrical form and motion. Aristotle, who, as Bertrand Russell says, diluted Plato by common sense, kept the world described by science in close touch with the world as perceived by most men through their senses. He managed to do this, it seems to me, in two rather different ways: First, by giving a much more confusing account of the status of universals and abstract ideas than Plato did, he made it more difficult for the average man to become preoccupied with the "ideal." Secondly, he provided a large number of interesting and surprisingly accurate descriptions of the material world of living things in terms of how it looks and feels to the unaided senses.

It was Aristotle who dominated the thinking of the medieval world; and the schoolmen, highly abstract though they were, continued to provide the general public with a view of nature which seemed familiar to their senses. In the words of Professor E. A. Burtt, "The entire world of nature was held not only to exist for man's sake, but to be likewise immediately present and fully intelligible to his mind. Hence the categories in terms of which it was interpreted were not those of time, space, mass, energy, and the like, but substance, essence, matter, form, quality, quantity—categories developed in the attempt to throw into scientific form the facts and relations observed in man's unaided sense experience."[1]

These views on the problem of knowledge were combined with rather different views from those we have on the nature of causality —much more importance being given to the "natural tendency" of both inanimate and living things to fulfill certain essentially predestined roles. Clues to the future behavior of such objects were sought in careful observations of the perceived qualities that supposedly revealed their inherent nature. Although most of us now have some difficulty in understanding motion as a property or quality, significant remnants of the Aristotelian view have survived to this day in casual references to "human nature" and more thoughtful and systematic discussions of the Natural Law.

The medieval reliance on perceived qualities and natural tendencies first showed itself inadequate when men sought a more precise understanding of motion. It played an important role for centuries later in other branches of science, and traces of the attitude still may be detected in biology today. The pathologist, for example, usually begins his discussion of the changes brought about by disease with a careful description of the size, color, and consistency of the organ in question. In physics, reference to qualities of this sort has almost entirely disappeared, although the chemist may, out of respect for tradition, speak briefly about a "pure white powder" or a "bright yellow crystal" before getting down to the business of melting points and spectral absorptions.

So long as science contented itself with making observations largely by the unaided hand and eye and recorded its findings in the everyday language of an essentially qualitative terminology, there was very little tendency towards a disjunction between science and everyday life or between science and scholarship in general. The scientist might be a more careful observer than most men, and certainly he recorded his observations more systematically. But there was nothing about the world described by science that struck either the man in the street or the philosopher in his study as very different from the world presented directly to the senses.

Most students of the subject seem to agree that our modern troubles began with Descartes, who had the courage to explore the implications for philosophy of renaissance physics. For it was he who made it fashionable to think in terms of two different worlds (or cultures). In the first place he revived in much more exact and compelling form the Pythagorean-Platonic idea of the universe as a vast, mathematically governed machine. His conception differed from the ancient one, however, in being material and mechanistic rather than primarily spiritual and teleologic. Most important for our present purposes, Descartes started the modern trend toward putting man in a peripheral, almost accidental position in the scheme of things. Man's characteristic way of perceiving the world in terms of sensory qualities seemed so obviously defective to Descartes that he was even led to underrate the empirical method which was then making modern science possible. Properties such as color, consistency, and weight, which previously had been thought to reside in external objects, became to him mere "secondary" qualities which "In truth . . . represent nothing to us out of our mind."[2] So began the famous dualism which has troubled philosophers ever since.

Scientists have on the whole been less troubled than the philosophers since they chose simply to circumvent the problem by enlarging as much as possible the world that can be objectively measured and relying as little as possible on "the senses, that is, [on] the judgments formed without consideration in childhood."[3] Thus the perception of color as a qualitative judgment is converted by science into a pointer reading on a spectrophotometer; the pitch, intensity, and quality of audible sounds emerge as numbers from an audio analyzer, while the qualities named hot and cold were long ago reduced to readings on a thermometer. No esoteric philosophical purpose consciously prompted these successful attempts to reduce subjective perceptions to objective pointer readings. For the most part they were the simple results of a wish to see objects too small or too far away to be seen by the naked eye, to hear more than can be heard with the unaided ear, and to see, hear, and feel all things with greater reproducibility and agreement among multiple observers. Most important of all perhaps was the desire to render the physical world in terms that could be conveniently inserted into mathematical formulae.

All these purposes have been triumphantly advanced so that now there are few physical phenomena that cannot be described in such a way as to command a high degree of agreement among observers at different times and places. Certain biological phenomena like the differentiation of cells and tissues are still rather difficult to express in mathematical terms, but here too there is reasonable agreement among observers about the events as described in verbal symbols and diagrams. At the higher biological levels the objective is the same, but there is much yet to be done in devising appropriate scales for measuring such psychological phenomena as anxiety, hostility, and frustration, or the elusive elements which go to make up personality.

Thus as a first approximation we may say that our knowledge of the mechanical-mathematical machine described by Descartes has been greatly increased in both quantity and quality. Some phenomena which in his day seemed wrapped in an enigma inside the mind have been shown to be in principle reducible to the same terms as those used in discussing the outside or "extended" world, though the essential nature of consciousness still escapes us.

Everyone is so well aware of the power scientific knowledge has given us that there is no point in reviewing it here. Most men have in fact come to believe that science is fully capable of abolishing or at least controlling such age-old impediments to happiness as hunger, disease, and premature death. Somewhat more optimistically, a smaller number of people look to science to control or eliminate the sorrows and tragedies which grow out of the relations of human beings with one another or with the condition in which they find themselves. This school of thought is relatively recent, and perhaps finds its most extreme expression among the dialectical materialists.

In part the hope for improving human existence is based on the thought that much of what we think of as bad behavior, crime, delinquency, and the like is traceable to bad living conditions, poor housing, malnutrition, and inadequate education, all of which could obviously be alleviated by appropriate applications of science. Increasingly the hope is also based on a belief that a scientific analysis of human behavior per se will allow us to mold such behavior in more satisfactory directions.

Systematic study of the world outside the individual with a view to its systematic alteration closer to the heart's desire is a relatively recent development. Important changes in the conditions of living have of course occurred throughout recorded history, but until some two centuries ago they occurred in an unpredictable and episodic way and at widely separated intervals. Certainly the shifts from hunting to agriculture, or from an agriculture dependent on rainfall to an irrigation economy brought with them enormous shifts in the condition of man. But no one seriously sought solutions to the basic problem of human existence by means of deliberate manipulation of the environment. On the contrary, guidance in achieving the good life was sought in direct transactions between man and the supernatural. It mattered little whether these transactions were carried on by the mysterious process of divine revelation or by the more laborious exercise of right reason. The point in either case was how to adjust one's individual soul to the universal soul.

For example, Job clearly felt that his only problem was how to come to terms with, accept, or believe in a God who rather capriciously gave and took away the blessings of the material world. It never occurred to him that he might approach the problem by developing insecticides to control the locusts, better medical care for his boils, or by devising a comprehensive insurance system to compensate for the losses which could not be prevented by existing technologies.

It is clear that for most of recorded history, culture, whether it is defined as the "best that has been thought and known" or as "an acquired or learned system of shared and transmittable ways of adjusting to life situations," was regarded primarily from the point of view of its effect on man himself. In short, it concentrated on the inculcation of correct attitudes and appropriate responses to outside stresses. The existence of the stresses themselves was for the most part accepted as inevitable. Cultures differed from one another primarily in their concept of the relationship between man and the supernatural and in the expression of this relationship in moral codes, religious rituals, and artistic creation. Culture as an accumulation of techniques for controlling the environment and increasing production attracted less conscious attention, changed only very slowly over time, and was on the whole less variable from place to place. The great majority of men lived everywhere as poverty-stricken peasants on the bare margin of subsistence.

The results of the change to a scientific approach now crowd around us for everyone to see. Not only does everyone see the results; it is becoming harder and harder to see anything else. In distinguishing cultures from one another, less attention is paid to the ceremonies for worshiping God, the number and type of relationships which exist between men and women, or the way three dimensions are represented in a two-dimensional drawing. Crucial cultural distinctions are instead measured in terms of Gross National Product, optional per capita expenditures, infant mortality rates, and numbers of years of schooling available to the average child. Thus for many purposes Latin America, India, and tropical Africa are all more or less lumped together in our minds. Their artistic achievements and religious outlooks could scarcely differ more from one another, but they all three seem much alike in their need for capital, the largely agricultural nature of their economies, their illiteracy, their high infant mortality rates, and their even higher birth rates. At the other end of the developmental scale, few people would argue with the contention that the United States seems in many important respects more like atheistic Russia or Buddhist-Shintoist Japan than it is like certain Western Christian countries which are only now entering the industrial revolution.

The advanced countries of both the East and the West are committed to the proposition that most of the ills of man can be traced to external environmental factors of one kind or another. As recent converts to the theory, the Soviets tend to go to greater extremes in stating their position than we do. The orthodox Marxists presumably still hold that the difficulties and distortions of the individual man are to be understood as the result of the difficulties and distortions of capitalism and the class society. While few of us in the Western world would go so far as this, it is almost as unfashionable in the United States as it is in the U.S.S.R. to attribute juvenile delinquency to original sin. In both societies the cure for such personal deviations is looked for in better housing, more appropriate schooling, higher community morale, and so on.

In spite of the immense prestige of science and the tacit assumption in many quarters that it can abolish many evils, Western Europe and the United States have never expressed *official* confidence in science as the solution for the major problems of human existence. In recent years doubt as to whether science is sufficient may actually be increasing. It is not that science cannot help to produce all the food, shelter, clothing, and atomic bombs that have come to be expected of it. Of course it can. The difficulty which is now emerging is of a different character. In those areas where there is enough bread, it is again being discovered that man does not live by bread alone. The world we think about seems to be drawing away from the world we see and feel. Our manipulative understanding seems increasingly uncoupled from either physical enjoyment or spiritual satisfaction.

The predicament should not after all have been unexpected. At the very beginning of the century, Henry Adams turned to musing on the conflict between the Virgin and the Dynamo, and wondering what would result from the fact that "in these past seven years man had translated himself into a new universe which had no common scale of measurement with the old. He had entered a supersensual world, in which he could measure nothing except by chance collisions of movements imperceptible to his senses."[4]

Let us look in more detail at some of the other ways in which the progress of science apparently makes it more difficult for human beings to adjust themselves to their condition. A decade before Adams made his gloomy observations one of the earliest empirical social scientists was demonstrating by a resourceful use of available statistics that modern scientific societies suffered from a new disease to which he gave the name *anomie*. It is characterized by a feeling of namelessness, of not belonging to anything or anybody, and finally by a fatal lack of belief in life itself. In this last state it carries a high mortality rate if one counts only recorded suicides. The rate is much higher if one adds the indirect self-destruction involved in heavy smoking, excessive drinking, fast driving, and the like. Everything that has happened since his time has borne out Durkheim's unhappy conclusion[5] that the more men become capable of controlling the external conditions of life, the less interested they become in living.

He attributed the disease largely to the disappearance of a sense of interdependence with the rest of society, and it is difficult though not impossible to argue with the conclusion. If he was right, it is at least interesting that this feeling should have become so common in a society in which the increasing division of labor had made individuals *in fact* more interdependent than ever before. The trouble we have in sensing the interdependence may probably be traced to that fact that many of the people we depend on are some distance away—in the wheat fields of Montana, the sheep runs of Australia, or the iron mines of Liberia, for example. Even though our continuing dependence on such remote figures is greater, we do not feel it with the same intensity as our grandfather felt his dependence on the farmer's wife down the road who came in with a bowl of soup when he was ill.

Another contradiction lies at the base of a further possible explanation for the lack of interest in living felt by many of our contemporaries. It could well be that our many technical triumphs over premature death have tended to diminish the significance of life. If so there are probably very good biological reasons for the apparent paradox, for it makes good sense that animals should become most aware of the importance of living when survival is most seriously threatened and conversely less concerned when life is more secure. The intensification of feeling under adverse conditions insures that the threatened animal will put forth the strongest possible effort to defend himself or escape from danger. As death has become less and less a part of our day-to-day existence, various devices have been invented to remind ourselves that nonetheless it lurks just around the corner. Formal religion abounds with examples, as does the literature of secular tragedy. In defending himself to the Countess Maffei for the number of deaths in "Il Trovatore," Verdi went so far as to assert ". . . after all, death is all there is in life. What else is there?"[6] Surely, Verdi's is an extreme view, but it includes a very real truth, since for those who don't go to church or the theatre, civilization has had to invent gladiatorial combat, prize fighting, and automobile races to reintroduce the life-giving sense of death. In any age but our own it would simply have been impossible for a school child not to have experienced the death of a near relative or a number of schoolmates. Probably he would have had several close brushes of his own. Now, perhaps a majority may have to wait until a high-school classmate kills himself in an automobile to find out how death looks. When death is considered at all by the contemporary adolescent, it is more than likely to be in the form of mass obliteration so that it becomes merely another aspect of the conformity in which we are said to spend so much of our lives.

It is not only through such practical results that technical advance has managed to erode man's sense of validity and excitement. As we suggested earlier, the kind of world science has chosen to talk about is in a way alien or at least uninviting to most men. For as noted earlier, the scientific method has achieved its successes by reducing the subjective individual component of experience to a minimum. In its unremitting effort to produce as wide agreement as possible, it is most successful when it has reduced natural phenomena to pointer readings. Most of what makes life worth living, its warmth, its color, its love and joy, as well as its pain and its tragedy —indeed all its immediately subjective presentations to consciousness—is deliberately circumvented or simply omitted. This is not to say that the scientist does not experience those human emotions. Of course he does. As many of them have often attested, the very process of scientific discovery induces in the discoverer a sense of joy, wonder, and beauty. Furthermore, as Jacob Bronowski, among others, has been at pains to make clear, the process of creating a scientific generalization has much in common with the process of creating great poems, paintings, or pieces of music. Nevertheless, the world science presents to us is in a very real sense alien to immediate experience, with its wave lengths in place of our tones and colors, its tropisms, drives, or conditioned responses in place of our loves, hates and free will.

Worst of all, when science trains its sights on man himself, it comes up with a diagram which is really very embarrassing. As the most recent summary of social science man puts it:[7] "In his quest for satisfaction, man is not just a seeker of truth, but of deceptions, of himself as well as others. (La Rochefoucauld said, 'Social life would not last long if men were not taken in by each other.') When man can come to grips with his needs by actually changing the environment, he does so. But when he cannot achieve such realistic satisfaction, he tends to take the other path: to modify what he sees to be the case, what he thinks he wants, what he thinks others want.

"The traditional images of man have stressed, as prime motivating agents, reason or faith or impulse or self-interest; the behavioral science image stresses the social definition of all of these. Here the individual appears less on his own, less as a creature of the natural environment, more as a creature making others and made by others."

The extremity of meaning to which the mild phrase, "made by others," can take us is found in the so-called isolation experiment. If one places the ordinary man in a room from which all auditory and visual patterns are excluded, and in which touch stimuli are reduced insofar as possible, it has been found that the subject's personality undergoes grave changes in a matter of hours. So disturbing is the disintegration caused by this isolation from a continuous flow of information that the experiments have rarely been continued for more than a very few days.

We are not, it seems, captains of our souls. The very substance of personality is critically and constantly dependent, not only on what has flowed into it in the past, but also on what is reaching it here and now. This is indeed an unflattering picture, and since relatively few are able to participate in the joy of scientific discovery or fully savor the kind of beauty and order revealed by it, there are many who deplore its tendency to detachment or, as Jacques Barzun says, its "abstractness." But abstract though it may be, it gives us the best clues we have to the actual behavior of what we believe to be the concrete world. The real difficulty is that, as we found above, the "new universe had no common scale of measurement with the old." In theory, the universe which Adams was looking at was really not new at all. Descartes had described both it and its incommensurability with the familiar world of sensation 350 years before. In practice, however, it was not until about Adams' time that men in large numbers began to seek their personal satisfaction in the new materialist world of extension. It is not only an intellectual urge toward epistemological tidiness that should now urge us on to find a "common scale of measurement" between the new universe and the old. To use Freud's term, our whole libidinal existence is tied to the old universe of immediate perception. It was the awareness of color and form, and not the orderly progression of wave lengths, that caused Wordsworth's heart to leap up when he beheld a rainbow in the sky, just as it was the sound, and not the sine waves of the Dorian mode that inspired Plato's guardians to deeds of valor. But it is not only the physical world that we perceive in this way. Man has long (possibly too long) relied on direct perception in developing his personal and social relations. Other people are perceived as friendly or threatening, beautiful or ugly, or above and below one in the pecking order. Derived from these basic perceptions are the emotions of love and hate, fear and faith, charity and greed which make up so much of the texture of man's social and political existence and minister to his will to live or drive him to an early grave. It is the failure to sense this texture that leads, as we have seen, to anomie.

How shall we set about developing the common scale? Largely it seems to me that we must look to the humanities and the creative arts. High culture may not have been very good at helping us understand how the physical world works, but it has been much better than science at making us feel its importance. Both science and art are concerned with giving some sort of order and form to our universe, refining our perceptions and putting them into some sort of order. Indeed, in an earlier day it was often difficult to distinguish the two. As late as the Renaissance anatomists were half graphic artists and the artist was often half an anatomist. A little later the learned and artistic world joined Newton in rejoicing over the order revealed by the planetary system. As time has gone by, however, science has become more and more preoccupied with discovering or inventing order purely as a means of understanding and control primarily of the external world, whereas art has retained its original preoccupation with experience and its orderly expression as a means of cultivating the individual personality. In this view, art not only sharpens our perceptions and reveals an aesthetic order among them. By so doing it makes the world and its ambiguities and conflicts not only more understandable but more tolerable. Milton was entirely explicit about the role of art in persuading man not only to understand but to accept the universe when he wrote *Paradise Lost* to "justify the ways of God to men."

Lying behind much great art is the assumption that there is a *moral* as well as an aesthetic and mechanical order in the universe. Science has not proved itself capable of discussing this type of order in more than the most rudimentary way. The clearest descriptions have been provided by two other procedures: revelation and the use of pure or right reason. As recognized methods of learning or knowing about the world, these are of course considerably older than science as we now understand the term. In most cultures they have occupied positions of far greater prestige and influence. It is unnecessary to discuss past differences in the picture of the tangible, material world provided by revelation and right reason on the one hand and by science on the other. These are of historical interest only. The much more difficult problem of determining the status of the natural law underlying the structure of the universe and accessible to reason and intuition, but not to experimental science, must be left to others. But the scientist may not renounce an interest and concern for the fine arts so easily; for he recognizes that the artist is concerned with the same tangible world that he himself sees and feels. Some scientists at least may also feel that there is something incomplete about the way they themselves see and feel it. Something important seems to be left out. Somehow the world science knows so well and so much more fully and precisely with every passing year does not seem fully satisfying. We seem to know more and more about how to live without finding out any more about why it is worthwhile to live. Even more disturbing is the thought that although the applications of science have abolished or controlled an astonishingly large number of the obvious causes of sorrow and tragedy, it is not obvious that the majority of men feel life to be any less sad or tragic than ever before. In the realm of human relations we apparently know much more about the Oedipus complex than our grandfathers did, but do we suffer any less from its effects?

When Thucydides said that men do what they can and suffer what they must, he seemed to imply that there was a reciprocal relation between the two sorts of activity. Now it is not so clear that this is so, for science has greatly increased what men can do, but it still seems that we must suffer almost as much as we did in the time of Pericles. It may in fact be that the welfare of the individual man is not quite so closely coupled to external circumstance as the scientist and the social reformer have liked to think. At least equally important may be the way the individual perceives events and the way he processes the perceptions into the emotions and the moods of his conscious experience. A few examples may recall the ways in which the best art helps us not only to understand but to accept with good grace the suffering which is such a standard part of life as we must live it. When we hear from Ivan Karamazov that every man wants to kill his father, we are at the very least reassured to find that we are not alone in our sinful wishes. When we share with Hamlet a certain indecision as to whether it is nobler in the mind to suffer or oppose, we begin to feel part of a decision process that involves not merely our individual dilemma, but a conflict of general principles which may be as broad as all mankind. Ultimately, we may find a certain grandeur in even the most sordid aspects of the human condition. If by mischance of inheritance or upbringing one of us is doomed to strangle his wife, he may take heart that he is not simply a jealous idiot but shares a tragic tendency to love "not wisely but too well." If we must suffer, and apparently we must, art (and revelation) help us to believe that it is in a good cause, inscrutable though that cause may presently seem. Because of this ability to endow ordinary human situations with a transcendent importance, art plays a significant part in the development of the ethical sense. The relation of art to good conduct was, of course, clearly recognized by the Greeks and perhaps somewhat more indirectly by the Christian clergy who commissioned the great works of art work of the Middle Ages and the Renaissance. It is less clearly discernible today when much of art seems devoted to demonstrating that human life is even more meaningless and trivial than appears at first glance.

On a somewhat different level, art may combine with revelation to persuade us (some of us, at any rate) that even though the material world fails us, supernatural help is at hand. The beauty of a well-sung "Miserere Nobis" has helped to convince many that there is such a quality as mercy if we will only believe it hard enough. The main point to bear in mind, however, is that the primary purpose of both revealed knowledge and of artistic knowledge is to make the individual feel better about the world as it is. The emphasis is on altering or enlarging the individual's experience of the world, not on changing the world itself to serve man's desires.

Having reviewed all these undoubted merits of the traditional high culture one may be tempted for a moment to ask why we should bother about anything else. The answer is that indispensable though the traditional means are for deepening and refining perception, for introducing a sense of order into the perceived world, and for justifying the ways of God to man, they have proved themselves seriously defective as a source of new knowledge. Somehow we must find ways of encouraging the humanist and the creative artist to confront the knowledge that science gives us, and to translate it into terms meaningful for the world of direct perception into which we were born.

Unless art is to degenerate into escapism, it must take into account the picture of man and his place in the universe which is currently presented by science. The picture is paradoxical, if not indeed self-contradictory, for as is well known, science has progressively reduced the prestige and status of man in the scheme of things, first, by showing that he lives on a small planet in a rather out-of-the-way part of the universe, second, by showing his close relationship with what are obviously lower animals, and finally, by showing that many, if not all, of his actions are determined by genetic and environmental variables over which he as conscious individual has little or no control. How odd it is that in the face of all this, man has through his own unaided efforts developed instruments for looking farther out and deeper into his universe than anyone could have imagined when he occupied his exalted position as the center of creation. Not only can he see and hear things no one ever thought of before, he has arranged them in ways that produce an extraordinary sense of order and predictability. Furthermore, the formulae which reflect the new-found order can be used to heal the sick, feed the multitudes and destroy one's enemies on a scale which even the avenging Jehovah would have regarded as pretentious. How do we bring these two individuals together in some coherent relationship—the peripheral, lowly, puppet-like figure described by science and the bold, pioneering, self-possessed, and apparently self-determining fellow who invented science and appears to control the scientific establishment?

The resolution of this paradox would seem to call for an art of a high order. Certainly it will not be accomplished by those who allow themselves to bog down in existential despair over the first of these two images even though they may for the moment appear more sophisticated than our eighteenth century ancestors who marveled smugly over the second.

The type of paradox we have shown to underlie the phenomenon of anomie may be more important to the immediate future of man than the one just discussed, and on its face it appears to be more easily resolvable. It should not lie too far beyond the power of artistic creation to make the majority of men feel what every economist and political scientist knows about the increasing interdependence of men. We are not increasingly alienated from one another; it only feels that way. But it is not reassuring to find that one of the finest writers of our time, who wrote one of his finest books to give twentieth-century currency to John Donne's seventeenth-century reflection that no man is an island, should have ultimately succumbed to a sense of loneliness and isolation.

The foregoing disjunctions and paradoxes, as well as others which might be mentioned, seem to be traceable to the difficulty we have in bringing into coherence the knowledge of the world we infer from the scientific method and the knowledge that comes to us directly through the senses. It is a gross oversimplification of the problem to hold that the fine arts and humanities are concerned with value problems while the sciences are not. Often both are concerned with the same problems, but they look at them in different ways. The scientist in his study calculating the effects of a new weapons system and Goya plotting out his sketches of the horrors of war are dealing with the same phenomenon and in a very real sense both are trying to communicate some of the values involved. Goya hoped to transmit his feelings about war by recreating them on canvas. The scientist may well seek to elicit the same feeling, but he follows a more elaborate process involving the use of abstract numerical symbols and the interposition of an intellectual process between symbolic presentation and the final excitation of an appropriate feeling or emotion.

To take a more homely instance, the Methodist ministers of my youth who inveighed against smoking cigarettes as a sin and the Surgeon General who promulgated the recent report on the physiological effects of smoking were both talking about the same phenomenon and both were ultimately concerned about the same value problem; but they elected to arouse the feelings of others on these important matters in very different ways. It is obvious that neither of these appeals succeeded in arousing motivation strong enough to halt the evil practice. It remains to be seen whether closer cooperation between the two approaches might be more successful. It is reasonable to suppose that the Methodist minister's approach failed in part because it lacked the support of any intellectually convincing evidence. There is, in fact, an increasing probability that value judgments unsupported by other sorts of evidence will be viewed by larger and larger numbers of people as crotchety and out of touch with reality. Quite recently, for example, the established church in Sweden has asked itself whether there is any real point in condemning premarital intercourse when many of Sweden's unusually intelligent and otherwise law-abiding citizens have regularly engaged in this practice without demonstrable harm.

Scientific evidence unsupported by more immediate appeals to the perceptive and emotive faculties is equally ineffective. The generality of mankind simply has not yet become capable of extracting much real subjective motivation out of statistical accounts of the effects of smoking, fast driving, marrying in haste, or overprotecting one's offspring. Even more remote are the evil results of certain sins of omission, such as failing to vote for adequate schools and health services. If scientific knowledge is to realize its potential for bringing us a better world, it will need all the help possible from those who can convert such remote, if not really abstract, bits of knowledge into sensations of clear and present danger.

It would be a mistake to become too preoccupied with the negative effects of scientific knowledge on values. On the contrary, scientists like to think of themselves as accentuating the positive. The very creation of science reflects credit on man and restores at least some of the stature taken from him when it threw doubt on his central position in the universe. And as apologists for science never tire of pointing out, the products of science have a very considerable esthetic value to those who take the trouble to familiarize themselves with the rules. Nor is it obvious that the required background is any more esoteric or abstruse than that necessary for the appreciation of many of the finest expressions of the arts. Here again, the problem seems one largely of translation from one realm of discourse to another.

It should now be a great deal easier to bring the two sorts of knowledge into some sort of conjunction than at any time since Descartes made it so difficult to attach any real importance to the world as perceived by the senses. In the first place, recent events have made us much more aware than any of our predecessors of the very real limitations and uncertainties involved in any way of knowing. If the subjective, perceived world is haunted by doubts about the reliability of the senses, the universe inferred by science is

Common Scale of Measurement

no more firmly founded on the shifting sands of the inductive method. Even the mathematics which so easily convinced Descartes of the absolute status of the extended or measurable world has now been shown to be no better than its essentially arbitrary assumptions. In a world where everything is at least a little bit doubtful, nothing can rule absolutely.

Some thoughtful people have even gone so far as to suggest that the basic uncertainty of our scientific knowledge in a certain way helps to establish the validity of faith and revelation. Even if the rest of us are unprepared to embrace so sweeping a view, we may at least allow ourselves to feel somewhat less foolish as we pay more attention to the world of subjective experience.

Finally, the revolution in physics has accustomed us to looking at the same phenomenon in two different ways, depending on the objectives we have in mind. It has proved convenient for some purposes to regard light as made up of discrete particles, while for other equally important purposes we can continue to regard it in terms of continuous waves. For a much longer time, but without being so explicit about it, physicians have observed a kind of informal law of complementarity. For some purposes a patient may be regarded as simply an unusually complicated chemical machine, and the doctor's attention may be focused on restoring chemical balances upset by disease. But the complete physician must also consider as best he can the subjective dislocations in the consciousness of the patient which come as an entirely different kind of result from the basic chemical disturbances.

Similarly there should be nothing disjunctive about a culture which sets out on the one hand to control the external world for man's welfare and at the same time attempts to adjust man to what is unadjustable in his condition. Experience has shown that he is not likely to do either one well enough to render the other superfluous.

REFERENCES

1. E. A. Burtt, S.T.M., Ph.D., *The Metaphysical Foundations of Modern Physical Science* (New York: Harcourt, Brace & Co., 1932) pp. 4-5.

2. René Descartes, *Philosophical Works*, Trans. Elizabeth S. Haldane, C.H., LL.D., and G. R. T. Ross, M.A., D.Phil., Vol. I, Part I, Principle 70 (New York: Dover Publications, Inc., 1955) p. 249.

3. Ibid., Principle 76, p. 53.

4. Henry Adams, *The Education of Henry Adams* (New York: The Modern Library, 1931) Chap. XXV, p. 381.

5. Emile Durkheim, *Suicide, A Study in Sociology*, Trans. John A. Spaulding and George Simpson (Chicago: Free Press, 1951).

6. George Martin, *Verdi, His Music, Life and Times* (New York: Dodd, Mead & Co., 1963) p. 301.

7. Bernard Berelson and Gary A. Steiner, *Human Behavior: An Inventory of Scientific Findings* (New York: Harcourt, Brace & World, Inc., 1964) Chap. 13, pp. 663 and 666.

The Integrity of Science

[This report was prepared by the Committee on Science in the Promotion of Human Welfare[1] of the American Association for the Advancement of Science, under the chairmanship of Barry Commoner.]

I. The Problem

SCIENCE HAS systematically created a powerful and rapidly growing body of knowledge. From this basic knowledge have come the spectacular feats of modern technology: space vehicles, nuclear explosives and power plants, new substances and electronic machines, and a significant increase in human longevity. This record of growth and achievement creates a widespread impression that science is a strong, well-established human enterprise. Confidence that science can continue to fulfill human needs is a distinctive characteristic of modern society.

But the ultimate source of the strength of science will not be found in its impressive products or in its powerful instruments. It will be found in the minds of the scientists, and in the system of discourse which scientists have developed in order to describe what they know and to perfect their understanding of what they have learned. It is these internal factors—the methods, procedures, and processes which scientists use to discover and to discuss the properties of the natural world—which have given science its great success.

We shall refer to these processes and to the organization of science on which they depend as the *integrity of science*. The term is a useful one, for it connotes the importance of a unified internal structure to the success of science, as well as its guiding imperative—the search for objective knowledge. On the integrity of science depends our understanding of the enormous powers which science has placed at the disposal of society. On this understanding, and therefore ultimately on the integrity of science, depends the welfare and safety of mankind.

The continued strength of science cannot be taken for granted. Although science has its own history and tradition, it is not wholly independent or self-sustained. Scientists are human beings, and science is a part of culture. What is the influence of changing social conditions, particularly the growing importance of science to society and the rapid approach of scientists to positions of power, on the search for new knowledge and on the system of scientific discourse? Can the very success of science and its closer interaction with the rest of our culture lay it open to the influence of new and possibly alien points of view which derive from other sectors of society: military, business, or political?

This is not a one-sided problem. As the success of science becomes more evident, its trappings and its personalities begin to make their appearance outside the laboratory: at international conference tables, in legislative chambers, in advertising appeals, and in the hue and cry of partisan politics. Are these appropriate uses of the methods of science? Can political life benefit from the viewpoint of science? Can the integrity of science safely withstand the invocation of science in political issues?

The importance of these questions and the absence of any immediate answers to them are the reasons for this report. In it we shall consider the effects of certain features of our culture on the integrity of science. These are problems which affect science wherever it exists, but in ways which vary with local circumstance. We are here concerned with the issues that arise in connection with the recent development of science in the United States.

II. Experiments in Space

Symbolic of the immense growth and power of modern science is the exploration of space. With the development of powerful rockets for military purposes it has become possible in the last decade to send vehicles and human passengers beyond the earth's atmosphere. With the concurrent development of highly efficient sensing devices and methods of communication, these vehicles have also served as important means of gathering scientific information. Elaborate basic research, a vastly expensive technology, and strong political and military motivation unite in nearly every venture into space.

The "Starfish" Experiment. One of the earliest discoveries of space research was the existence of belts of atomic particles surrounding the earth and trapped by its magnetic field in arcs between the north and south poles. Hardly had this "magnetosphere" been noticed and named for its discoverer, Van Allen, than *experiments*, rather than mere observations, were under way there.[2]

On April 30, 1962, the U. S. Government announced its intention to conduct nuclear explosions at high altitudes in order to ascertain the effects of artificially-injected electrons on the natural belts of the magnetosphere. The immediate motivation was military interest in the disruptive effects on radio communication of atomic particles produced by a high altitude nuclear explosion. The experiment—"Starfish"—was also of interest to scientists because its effects might reveal significant data about the magnetosphere itself.

Three high altitude tests had been set off secretly in August 1958 over the South Atlantic. When they were made public some six months later scientists in this country and abroad protested vigorously. The announcement of the new test brought renewed protests from scientists, especially radio-astronomers. Some scientists predicted that the experiment would cause large-scale, persistent changes and hamper further study of the still poorly understood Van Allen belts, but others disagreed. Resolution of these disagreements was difficult, for secrecy restrictions limited the exchange of information among the disputants.

The U. S. Government then announced that it had called together a group of leading scientists to consider whether the proposed tests would substantially prejudice astrophysical and geophysical science or create a radiation hazard to manned space flights. On May 28, 1962, the U. S. Government announced that this committee was convinced that the effects of the Starfish experiment would "disappear within a few weeks to a few months," and that there "is no need for concern regarding any lasting effects on the Van Allen belts and associated phenomena."[3]

The Starfish explosion took place on July 9, 1962, when a 1.4 megaton hydrogen bomb was detonated 250 miles above Johnson Island in the Pacific. Despite early confusion regarding the physical consequences of this explosion, it is now clear that it generated a long-lived belt of atomic particles in the magnetosphere and that it has obscured the properties of the natural radiation belts. According to a review of the experiment by McIlwain,

> ... it may be necessary to wait more than 30 years before the natural electron fluxes in the region around 1.5 earth radii can be measured with complete freedom from artificial effects.[4]

Several satellites, *Transit VIB*, *Traac*, and *Ariel*, were extensively damaged by the new radiation belt. *Ariel* is especially noteworthy as it was launched by the United States in order to carry British instruments, as a cooperative venture. *Telstar*, on the other hand, rode out the high radiation levels successfully for some time after the test, but radiation damage was noted in later reports.[5]

The Starfish experiment is a spectacular demonstration of present capabilities for human intervention into natural phenomena in space. It also reveals serious inadequacies in our present ability to predict the consequences of such interventions, and in the attendant experimental procedures.

Science involves not only passive observations of nature, but also experiments which influence natural processes, either to reveal new information or to provide a practically useful result. Scientific procedure provides for special rules to regulate experiments, designed to elicit from them observations of maximum validity. The scientist's experiments are disciplined interventions into nature. They are based on previously gained knowledge which is sufficient to estimate the practicality and usefulness of the operation. Experiments are designed not simply for the effect but to yield measurable results in interpretable form. Usually this requires the establishment of an experimental control, in which the particular alteration induced by the experiment is deliberately excluded, so that by direct comparison, one can determine the effect of the factor of interest.

Properly executed, the Starfish experiment would have been preceded by a survey of natural bands followed by general scientific discussion of the observations. Had this been done, the data derived from particles artificially injected by the explosion could have added to scientific knowledge without precluding information about the natural phenomenon. Instead, the Starfish experiment was carried out in the absence of adequate knowledge of the natural belts. By artificially injecting subatomic particles into the unique and worldwide magnetosphere, the experiment has limited the information which can be derived from inquiries into this aspect

The Integrity of Science

of nature. As Dr. Van Allen stated at our Committee's symposium at the annual meeting of the American Association for the Advancement of Science in Philadelphia:

> Our failure as a nation to produce a substantial study of the scientific consequences of these tests long before the decision was made that they were to be conducted, is, it seems to me, quite inexcusable. With tests such as this, studies should have been conducted in such a way that they were subject to publication and general scientific discussion.[6]

Free dissemination of information and open discussion is an essential part of the scientific process. Each separate study of nature yields an approximate result and inevitably contains some errors and omissions. Science gets at the truth by a continuous process of self-examination which remedies omissions and corrects errors. This process requires free disclosure of results, general dissemination of findings, interpretations, conclusions, and widespread verification and criticism of results and conclusions.

The principle of free dissemination and open discussion has not been fully honored in the Starfish experiment. Although an attempt was made to forewarn the scientific community of proposed experiments (through the IGY-AGIWARN network), insufficient time and secrecy restrictions inhibited the normal predictive and analytical processes of science. A detailed and unhurried discussion of the possible effects of the high altitude explosion in open scientific literature might have revealed—in advance of the experiment—a consensus contrary to the conclusion of the government's *ad hoc* committee that the effects would be short-lived.

The "West Ford" Experiment. A second example of recent space research, the West Ford project, further illuminates the hazards of large-scale experimentation and shows how they can be minimized by adherence to the proper procedures of science.[7]

In the summer of 1958, the U. S. Army Signal Corps convened a group of scientists to study, among other things, means of establishing an invulnerable worldwide military communications system. It was suggested that such a system could be established by encircling the earth with orbiting belts of fine copper wires. These would form radio mirrors for multi-channel microwave signalling, linking any two stations on earth if the heights of the belts were sufficiently great. The belts would be invulnerable to attack, since they would only reflect ground-controlled radio waves, and, unlike communications satellites, such as *Telstar* and *Echo*, would be physically indestructible.

COMMITTEE ON SCIENCE

The proponents of West Ford developed a technique for testing their idea experimentally on a small scale. By placing relatively few copper wires in a predetermined orbit, they could establish a temporary belt, which although not operational in a practical system of communications, could establish the feasibility of the full-scale scheme. Calculations showed that pressure from sunlight would gradually drive the proposed experimental belt down into the atmosphere and destroy it within a time dependent on location of the orbit.

The Department of Defense approved investigation of this approach and research on the project began at the Lincoln Laboratory. Because of its military importance, the project was "born classified." However, knowledge that some test of these ideas was planned soon became current among astronomers throughout the world. Many became concerned about the possibility that the bands would interfere with optical and radio observations. To be detected, a celestial object must yield a signal which stands out against the random optical or radio signals from the nearby regions of the sky. Contamination of the sky with metallic dipoles, if sufficiently dense to produce a signal which is discernible against the natural background, will hamper observations of faint celestial objects.

With the details of the proposed experiment under secrecy restrictions, actual knowledge about U. S. intentions and the possible effects of the experiment was scanty. As Dr. Edward Purcell of Harvard University reported later, regarding the decision to undertake the experiment:

In those days the project, directed as it was toward military communications, was secret. But the scientists in the project and the responsible officers in the government saw that the decision involved questions that could not be rightly disposed of by arithmetic in a classified report. To broaden the basis for a responsible decision, the Space Science Board of the National Academy was asked to assemble a group of scientists to analyse the planned test . . . Meanwhile the word was beginning to get around. Fragmentary knowledge and rumours naturally left many scientists apprehensive and suspicious. It was decided to meet the problem quite openly. The Defense Department and the Lincoln Laboratory, with the support of the President's Science Advisory Committee, effected a rapid declassification of all essential matters.[8]

After several meetings, including at least two that were restricted in size because of security requirements,[9] the *ad hoc* committee assembled by the Space Science Board concluded that while present astronomical experiments would not be seriously hampered, a per-

The Integrity of Science

manent belt—even of small size—might become a hazard in later years, as greater sensitivity is achieved in radio and optical instruments. The committee recommended that the dipoles be established in a temporary orbit, that a non-military spacecraft be used to launch the equipment, and that a ground-controlled fail-safe device be installed to prevent dispersal of the copper dipoles if the rocket happened to achieve an undesirable orbit. These conditions were not fulfilled in the government plans for the first West Ford attempt (in May 1961). The committee advised that the proposed launch be called off, and it was.[10]

Neither the *ad hoc* committee studies nor the resultant consideration by the Space Science Board has as yet been published. However, for the reason given by Purcell (see above) in September 1960, a large part, but not all, of the technical information about the project was declassified and presented to a meeting of the International Scientific Radio Union by Walter Morrow of the Lincoln Laboratory. Later, several detailed considerations of the problem were prepared for publication in the *Astronomical Journal* by members of the Space Science Board's subcommittee and by members of the Lincoln Laboratory.[11]

An examination of these open discussions reveals the following information of interest: (1) All discussants agreed that the brightness of the experimental band proposed by Morrow would not interfere with astronomical observations from the earth. (2) Certain parameters in the Morrow calculation (for example, rate of needle dispersion) remained classified, although these data are essential to a calculation of the life-time of the belt.[12] (3) The experimental belt could interfere with astronomical observations from satellites which might otherwise make novel studies of very faint celestial objects; this might be obviated by particular locations of the dipole orbit.[13] (4) A dipole band sufficiently dense to support an operational communication system would seriously interfere with optical and radio observations.[14]

In August 1961, the Space Science Board announced to the scientific community that it had received government assurance that no additional launches of orbiting dipoles would take place until results of the first experiment had been analyzed and evaluated. The Space Science Board asked that full scientific and operational information about the project be published as soon as possible. However, at the same time, the International Astronomical Union adopted two resolutions, one against the precedent of contaminating space, and the second, while thanking the U. S. Government for announcing the planned experiment, said that the IAU "... is completely opposed to the experiments until the question of permanence is clearly settled in published scientific papers with adequate time being allowed for their study."[15]

On October 6, 1961, an article in *Science* by Shapiro and Jones of the Lincoln Laboratory for the first time made public the altitude and inclination of the proposed orbiting dipole belt. Calculations for estimating belt lifetime in various orbits were described, leading to an estimate of seven years for the proposed orbit.

On October 21, 1961, the experiment was carried out. A military rocket was used. "Fail-safe" procedures were not provided. The dipole dispenser arrived not in the proposed seven year orbit, but in a different one, for which the calculated lifetime was "indeterminably longer than the seven years estimated..."[16] However, the dipole dispenser failed to work properly and the belt of dipoles was not formed. The hazard of a long-lived belt, which might have interfered with future astronomical observations, was avoided only because of an instrument failure.

A second attempt on May 10, 1963, succeeded. A belt was established in a short-lived orbit and subsequent observations suggest that it is disappearing at the predicted rate. The instrument included a "fail-safe" device. Data obtained from this experiment provide a basis for firmer conclusions regarding the possible effects of large-scale operational belts on astronomical research.[17]

The events associated with the West Ford experiment show that adherence to the principles of disciplined experimentation and open communication between those responsible for the project and the scientific community generally succeeded in preventing possible hazards to further astronomical research. However, a number of serious difficulties were encountered in achieving the final laudable outcome of the project.

Because of secrecy, astronomers were at first unable to develop a critical analysis of the proposed experiment. Some data essential to the calculation of the belt's lifetime (that is, mechanism of needle dispersion, altitude and declination of the proposed band) became available to astronomers only fifteen days before the first experiment was actually carried out, a period much too short to permit any necessary corrective effects of open scientific scrutiny to operate.

The Space Science Board committee succeeded in preventing a proposed launch which did not conform to its recommendations in the summer of 1961. However, when the experiment was actually

The Integrity of Science

carried out in October 1961, not all of the committee's recommendations were followed. The package of dipoles was launched into a long-lived orbit. If the unexpected failure of the package to disperse the dipoles had not occurred, this experiment might have realized the fears expressed by astronomers regarding its hazards to future astronomical research.

Experience with both Starfish and West Ford shows that the scientific procedures which must govern experimental investigations, if they are to further the accumulation of knowledge, can be broken down. Under pressure for results of military importance, the principles of disciplined investigation and of respect for necessary experimental controls may be, to a degree, neglected, if, because of attendant secrecy, the experiments are not open to the full scrutiny of the scientific community. In these experiments a predictive failure may be irreparable, for the experiments are not confined to a single laboratory, but intervene in phenomena which are unique on the planet.

III. Exploration of the Moon: Project "Apollo"

A considerable part of the U. S. space program is devoted to a particular mission, *Apollo*, which is designed to land one or more men on the moon and return them to earth.[18] The Apollo project is a technological enterprise in that it requires the application of basic scientific knowledge to the solution of a given problem—the accomplishment of a manned landing on the moon. However, since the project is to be achieved in an environment which is new to science it requires the acquisition of certain basic knowledge about the moon and interplanetary space: for example, the gross physical character of the moon's surface, chemical properties and radioactivity of surface materials, intermittent changes in cosmic ray intensity in interplanetary space.

The chief independent body which has advised the government on the scientific aspects of space research is the Space Science Board (SSB) established by the National Academy of Sciences in 1958. In the scientific considerations developed by the specialists serving on committees reporting to the Space Science Board, the scientific values to be derived from the manned exploration of the moon have been given relatively little importance, as compared with a number of other investigations of the moon which do not involve a manned landing.

For example, a discussion of lunar research by H. C. Urey (published in 1961 in *Science in Space,* edited by Lloyd V. Berkner and H. Odishaw, of SSB,[19] which summarizes SSB considerations during 1958–1961), proposes the following order of priorities: (1) a satellite of the moon; (2) a hard landing lunar probe; (3) a soft landing lunar probe; (4) the return of samples; and (5) manned landing. In an earlier SSB committee report, manned exploration of the moon was one of nine projects, in a total of twenty-one, assigned to the lowest of three priority categories.

In February 1961, the SSB discussed national goals in space research, and in a statement transmitted to the government in March 1961, stated:

As a result of these deliberations, the Board concluded that scientific exploration of the moon and planets should be clearly stated as the ultimate objective of the U.S. space program for the foreseeable future.[20]

In this statement the SSB did not discuss the time-table for carrying out manned exploration of the moon in specific terms, but commented:

The Board concluded that it is not now possible to decide whether man will be able to accompany early expeditions to the moon and planets. Many intermediate problems remain to be solved. However, the Board strongly emphasized that planning . . . must at once be developed on the premise that man will be included. . . .

. . . Planning for "manned" scientific exploration of the moon and the planets should be consummated only as fast as possible consistent with the development of all relevant information. The program should not be undertaken on a crash basis which fails to give reasonable attention to assurance of success or tries to bypass the orderly study of all relevant problems.

A time-table for manned lunar exploration was established for the first time by the decision of President Kennedy, announced on May 25, 1961, which concluded that ". . . this Nation should commit itself to achieving the goal, before this decade is out, of landing a man on the moon and returning him safely to earth."[21] The controlling reasons given for this decision by President Kennedy and by his scientific advisor, Dr. Jerome B. Wiesner, were not scientific, but social and political. Thus, in response to a question regarding his agreement with President Kennedy's decision to establish the project as a national goal, Dr. Weisner stated:

Yes. But many of my colleagues in the scientific community judge it purely on its scientific merit. I think if I were being asked whether this

The Integrity of Science

much money should be spent for purely scientific reasons, I would say emphatically "no." I think they fail to recognize the deep military implications, the very important political significance of what we are doing and the other important factors that influenced the President when he made his decision.[22]

The decision to accomplish a manned landing on the moon by 1970 established new priorities in space research which are clearly reflected in subsequent considerations by scientists of investigation of the moon. In these later considerations the importance of each proposed scientific investigation is usually evaluated in the light of the intention established by President Kennedy's decision. This can be seen in the report of the Summer Study Session at the State University of Iowa conducted under the auspices of the Space Science Board:

This report deals with the immediate future up to and in part including Apollo. Inasmuch as landing a man on the moon is an announced national goal, much emphasis is placed on those scientific experiments and observations which are vitally necessary to accomplish this mission or which might contribute to its success. Our specific recommendations are strongly influenced by this consideration.[23]

In general, scientific observations required for the planning of the manned landing are now assigned higher priorities than other studies which are of greater scientific interest but not essential to the development of the technology needed for the Apollo project. Therefore, the pattern for development of scientific research in space has been altered significantly by the essentially political decision to undertake the Apollo program.

This procedure is seriously at variance with important precepts of scientific experimentation and technology. The preferable order of events is: basic scientific investigation, technological application based on the resultant basic knowledge, social use of the technological innovations. In the Apollo program this sequence has been reversed, so that a program for a particular technological achievement has been committed, even as to the date of its accomplishment, in advance of the orderly acquisition of the related basic knowledge.[24] The Apollo program, in its present form, does not appear to be based on the orderly, systematic extension of basic scientific investigation.

The Apollo program is extremely costly in funds and in required personnel. The total projected budget for space research, a large part of which is devoted to the Apollo project, represents a considerable part of the nation's entire expenditures for research. In 1964, out of a total federal expenditure of $1,800 million for *basic research*, NASA accounted for $700 million, and the National Science Foundation about $300 million. Thus, more support for the nation's total program in basic research comes from a mission-oriented agency—NASA—than from NSF which is the agency established by Congress for the purpose of developing a science-oriented national program in basic research. At the same time NASA accounts for the federal government's largest expenditures in *applied* research. Since at the present time the Apollo program represents the bulk of NASA activities, these estimates apply with only a minor reduction to the Apollo program itself.

The demand of the space program for scientific personnel, which is in large part due to the Apollo program, has been the subject of some confusion. In 1962, Dr. Hugh L. Dryden, Deputy Director of NASA, stated:

It has been estimated that by 1970 as many as one-fourth of the Nation's trained scientific and engineering manpower will be engaged in space activities, although I cannot confirm the accuracy of this estimate.[25]

NASA testimony before the Senate Committee on Aeronautical and Space Sciences in November 1963 reduced this estimate to 5.9 per cent of the total supply of scientists and engineers in 1970.[26] Nevertheless a questionnaire sent to 2000 randomly selected members of the AAAS in July 1964 showed that the percentage of those answering who receive direct or indirect federal support in connection with space activities had already reached the level of 12 per cent.[27]

A recent analysis of scientific manpower utilization by a committee of the National Academy of Sciences reported that

... the NASA program will accentuate the shortage of personnel with specialties such as systems technology, stability and control, guidance systems and internal flow dynamics. Furthermore there will be a pronounced effect on the market for less experienced mechanical, electrical and aeronautical engineers and for physicists and mathematicians.[28]

Thus, the NASA basic research program erects, in parallel with the NSF program, a new national system of scientific support, which, in contrast to that of NSF, is mission-oriented rather than science-oriented. Its major program, Apollo, which is justified by a social rather than scientific purpose, will significantly influence the direction of basic scientific research in the United States.

The Integrity of Science

We are aware that there is a considerable precedent for such constraints in wartime research. An example is the World War II atomic bomb project, which represented one aspect of a far-reaching social decision to turn much of our nation's material and intellectual strength to the single task of winning World War II. However, in the present instance, there is no evidence that there has been an opportunity for our society to make a conscious choice to sacrifice the advantages of free development of basic scientific research, even temporarily, for the purpose of winning a purported race to the moon.

In this connection the following statement made by an NASA official in an address to the Annual Meeting of the American Association for the Advancement of Science in December 1962 is worth noting:

> At this stage, the scientific community has the opportunity to assist in determining what man will do out in space, and in particular what he will do when he gets to the moon. If the scientific community does not give this matter its thought and attention and proffer its suggestions and advice, its ideas will be missed. But this will not bring things to a halt. Someone else will make the scientific decisions.[29]

If the scientific community is subjected to pressure or blandishments designed to solicit research activity which conforms to the purpose of the space research program, the free pursuit of knowledge will suffer.

Finally, we find reason for concern in the confusion regarding the social and scientific justification of the Apollo project. In the scientific considerations of the Apollo program, we have found several instances in which scientific advisory groups assert, in their reports, that the Apollo program is justified by such nonscientific motivations as "man's innate drive to explore unknown regions," or "national prestige." We believe that such appeals, which are made by scientists who are acting in their professional capacities, or are closely attached to professional scientific judgments, are inherently dangerous both to the democratic process and to science. If a scientist, as an individual citizen, wishes to promulgate a particular political course, he is of course free to do so. However, in our view, when such advocacy is associated with his organized professional scientific activity, the political or social intent acquires a wholly unwarranted cloak of scientific objectivity. This tends to obscure the fact that the political issue, despite its association with science, is, like all matters of public policy, open to debate. Such action on the part of scientists is likely to inhibit the free public discussion of the issue, and delay the development of an independent judgment by citizens generally.

IV. Large Scale Technology and the Environment

Detergents and Insecticides. In the last twenty-five years there has been a dramatic improvement in the capability of chemical technology to produce commercially important quantities of a large number of useful new synthetic compounds: plastics, pesticides, herbicides, food additives, medical drugs, detergents, and a great many products for specialized industrial applications. This development reflects basic scientific advances in organic chemistry and chemical engineering. It is the basis of new heavily capitalized industries that have yielded important economic and social benefits.

These advances have resulted in the dispersal into the biosphere of numerous synthetic organic compounds, some in the amounts of millions of pounds annually. Some of these substances are not immediately degraded on entry into the biosphere. As a result, living things, including man, have absorbed varying amounts of newly synthesized substances, with which they have had no previous contact.

A number of problems have arisen recently which are characterized by the appearance of undesirable side-effects incidental to the application of some of the new products. Examples are: killing of animals and fish by insecticides, increasingly troublesome pollution of water supplies by agricultural chemicals and by industrial wastes, accumulation of synthetic detergents in water supplies. Two informative examples of these problems are experiences with synthetic detergents and insecticides.

Within a few years after the large-scale introduction of new synthetic detergents in the early 1940's, untoward effects, especially foaming, were noted in water supplies in various parts of the country. It was then discovered that the new detergents, unlike soap, were not degraded by the biological processes in sewage disposal plants. As a result, in certain areas detergents began to appear in streams and rivers, and in potable water supplies derived from these sources. Questions—as yet unanswered—arose concerning the possibly hazardous effects of ingestion of detergents by human beings.

It was then discovered that the resistance of detergents to degradation in sewage disposal processes was due to a particular

The Integrity of Science

chemical attribute—branched structure of the detergent molecule. Bacterial enzymes that degrade hydrocarbons are incapable of acting on branched molecules. (In contrast, common soap is a straight-chain molecule and is degradable.) The chemical industry is now making an intensive effort to develop economical, degradable, synthetic detergents. Legislation preventing sale of non-degradable detergents has been introduced into Congress, and the industry has announced plans to replace the non-degradable types.

The problems arising from the large-scale dissemination of pesticides, particularly insecticides, during the last twenty years are exceedingly complex and diverse. They have been the subject of intense discussion recently and have been considered in a report of the President's Science Advisory Committee.[30] We shall discuss briefly a relatively limited instance of the general problem—difficulties associated with the presence of insecticides in the waters of the Mississippi River.

In 1957 the first extensive spraying with the then relatively new pesticide endrin, a chlorinated hydrocarbon, began in the Mississippi Valley. It has since been used extensively by sugar cane and cotton farmers to control insects attacking these crops.

Between 1954 and 1958, investigators reported several instances in which dieldrin (an insecticide closely related to endrin and produced metabolically from the latter) was found to cause killing of fish following application of the insecticide to nearby land.[31] In March 1964, the U. S. Public Health Service and officials of the State of Louisiana announced that "water pollution involving toxic synthetic organic materials appears to be the cause" of fish-kills in the Mississippi River.[32] The fish, the river waters, and the river mud were found to contain endrin and dieldrin, as well as several unidentified organic compounds.

The Mississippi River fish-kills have had significant economic effects. A long-established fishing industry in the bayou country of Louisiana has been reported to be seriously hampered by the problem.[33] Investigations are under way to determine if levels harmful to humans have occurred, but little detailed information about chronic toxic effects in humans is available as yet. Fish containing measurable amounts of insecticide have reportedly reached the market in some Louisiana towns, and health officials have expressed concern about possible hazards from drinking water of Louisiana cities which is taken from contaminated rivers.[34]

The sources of the insecticides found in Mississippi River fish are not firmly established at this time. Possible sources are runoff from farmlands routinely treated with insecticides and industrial wastes from insecticide manufacturing plants.

Both of the instances cited above represent a defect in the method of introduction of technological processes based on large-scale synthesis of new types of organic substances. In both cases, the substance introduced was demonstrably effective for its intended purpose—as a washing agent or as a pesticide. In each case the hazard resulted from the substance's unanticipated secondary effects in the biosphere.

The effects of introducing these substances into the biosphere were not adequately studied, along with their other properties, when they were under laboratory development. For the case of detergents this conclusion has been stated explicitly by Mr. C. G. Bueltman, of the Soap and Detergent Association, before this Committee's symposium on December 30, 1962.

The development of synthetic detergents was aimed primarily at improvement of functional properties associated with the *raison d'etre* of the product—i.e., to wash efficiently in a broad variety of water supplies; to possess good shelf life; to be pleasing in appearance, odor, feel; to suds freely and to sell at a price acceptable to the consumer . . .

It is admitted that total consequences and more particularly susceptibility of biological decomposition, was not anticipated. In fact, so far as biodegradability goes, hindsight shows that this was universally overlooked as a factor requiring consideration.[35]

That similar limitations were operative in the case of chlorinated hydrocarbon insecticides is evident from a review in 1959, when these substances were already in wide agricultural use, which stated: "Except for DDT, little is known about the effects on fish and fish-food organisms of chlorinated hydrocarbon insecticides that have been used for a number of years."[36]

The introduction of synthetic detergents and insecticides into the biosphere represents a serious human intervention into natural processes. The evidence cited shows that this intervention was not based on an orderly, disciplined development of all the requisite basic scientific information. The full biological significance of the large-scale introduction of synthetic detergents and insecticides could have been discovered much sooner if there had been planned systematic studies of their effects on the water supply in small-scale field trials.

In the absence of such studies there was a large economic commitment in the production of these contaminants before their crucial faults were discovered. There has been inadequate contact between the scientific considerations operative in the development of these substances—their chemical structure and synthesis, and their efficiency as detergents or insecticides—and the equally well-known biological phenomena into which they are to intervene. In the development of these new products there has been a serious gap between the relevant branches of science.

Fallout. Experience with nuclear testing provides a further insight into these problems. Since 1948 nuclear explosions carried out for purely experimental purposes (that is, for the technological improvement of weapons) by China, France, Great Britain, the United States, and the U.S.S.R. have disseminated millions of curies of radioactive materials over the planet as fallout.

Considerable amounts of these materials have been absorbed by plants, animals, and man. Because radiation causes important damage to biological processes, this burden of radioactivity—added to radiation from natural sources and from medical procedures—increases the total risk of harm to man. The problem of estimating this medical risk has resulted in considerable confusion and controversy.

The Iodine-131 problem provides a useful example of the biological aspects of this complex and still-confused subject. This radioisotope is produced by all nuclear explosions. Beginning in 1957, fallout-monitoring procedures in the U. S., especially those carried out by the Public Health Service, included measurements of Iodine-131 in milk, which is a major source of human exposure to this isotope. The results show that in a number of regions in the U. S., Iodine-131 in milk reached levels in the range of 100-1000 pc/liter* during periods of active atmospheric testing. Although the precise medical significance of these levels is still a matter of debate, there is a common agreement that this degree of contamination results in a radiation dose to the target organ (the thyroid) considerably in excess of the biological dose from any other fallout isotope. Hence, Iodine-131 is now recognized as the most severe radioactive hazard from fallout, at least during a time when testing is under way.

To what extent was the predominance of Iodine-131 among the possibly hazardous consequences of nuclear testing known to the planners of the nuclear test program? The most comprehensive

* picocurie(pc) = 10^{-12} curie.

assemblage of data regarding nuclear explosions is "The Effects of Nuclear Weapons," published jointly by the Atomic Energy Commission and the Department of Defense in 1957, and in revised form in 1962. Both editions of this handbook discuss the possible biological hazards from fallout and describe the behavior of isotopes of chief interest in this connection. The 1957 handbook discusses Strontium-90 and Cesium-137; the 1962 edition discusses these radioisotopes and Carbon-14 as well. Neither edition mentions the possibility that Iodine-131 might contribute to the biological hazards from nuclear tests. There appears to have been no published notice of the Iodine-131 problem until 1957, when the issue was raised in testimony before the Joint Congressional Committee on Atomic Energy. Although a considerable number of fallout-producing nuclear tests had already been carried out by 1957, the agencies responsible for them were apparently unaware that Iodine-131 constituted the most severe immediate hazard.

It would appear that nuclear tests, like other recent interventions into the biosphere, were undertaken without an adequate understanding of their possible biological hazards. As massive experimental effects on the biosphere, nuclear explosions therefore represent operations which have not been carried out in keeping with disciplined scientific procedures.

An important cause for this technological failure is that discussion of the fallout problem by the general scientific community was hampered by secrecy. Until 1954, nearly all data about fallout were unavailable to the scientific community because of security restrictions. Following the declassification of these data, when the general scientific community had an opportunity to consider the problem, a number of important changes in the understanding of the fallout problem took place through contributions made by the general scientific community.[37] The corrective effects that followed partial declassification testify to the importance of an independent community of scientists to the effectiveness of science as a source of knowledge.

The problem of evaluating environmental hazards, which is particularly exemplified by experience with fallout, reveals another issue for the integrity of science. By 1958–59, sufficient evidence had accumulated to convince most scientists that there is a linear relationship between radiation dose and biological damage. This viewpoint has been adopted by the Federal Radiation Council (FRC), which has the responsibility of establishing standards for radiation exposure in the U.S.[38]

The Integrity of Science

If, as required by the linear theory of radiation damage, any increase in radiation exposure is accompanied by some added risk of damage, in determining the acceptability of the risk the hazard must be balanced against the benefit expected from the relevant operation. Such a balance between risk and benefit is a value judgment. Determination of a standard for radiation exposure which is based on such a judgment is no longer a scientific conclusion but a social one. This relationship is explicitly stated in FRC policy:

In establishing radiation protection standards, the balancing of risk and benefit is a decision involving medical, social, economic, political, and other factors.[39]

The subsequent history of the standards established by the FRC has been marked by chaos and controversy. This is illustrated by some recent events associated with exposures from Iodine-131 due to fallout. During the summer of 1962, atmospheric tests by the U.S.S.R. and the U.S. caused Iodine-131 levels in several areas of the U.S. to approach Range III (which according to FRC guidelines requires control measures), and local health authorities in Utah, Wisconsin, and Minnesota took appropriate action. However, on August 17, 1962, the Secretary of Health, Education and Welfare (also Chairman of the FRC) stated that control measures were not called for because the guidelines had been developed for "normal peacetime conditions" and were not applicable to fallout from nuclear tests. This view holds that the benefits to the nation from nuclear testing have not entered into the balance which led to the establishment of the radiation standards and that when these benefits are taken into account higher levels of radiation exposure and correspondingly greater risks are warranted. The FRC has recently announced new and higher standards applicable to fallout which also take into account the possible risks involved in the protective actions. Thus the guidelines have been revised, but without any indication as to the weight given to the benefits of nuclear testing.

These reinterpretations of the Iodine-131 standards have led to confusion and doubt regarding the inherent validity of the standards promulgated by the FRC. A challenge to a scientific body can ordinarily be met by analysis and discussion of its scientific findings by the scientific community. This process finally resolves the disagreement or leads to an equally acceptable statement of uncertainty. However, in the case of the revision of radiation exposure standards this procedure is not possible—for the question under discussion is not an evaluation of the risk from radiation (which is a scientific matter subject to scientific validation), but is rather the wholly nonscientific question of how the benefits of nuclear testing should be balanced against the increased medical risk from fallout. Such a challenge therefore cannot be resolved by the procedures of scientific discourse. Since the FRC is presumably a scientific body, an unresolved challenge to the validity of its conclusions will tend to be regarded—especially by the public—as a reflection on the ability of science to elucidate the problem.

Similar difficulties have occurred with disturbing frequency in the recent controversies regarding the effects of fallout, of nuclear war, and of environmental contamination in general. In a number of instances individual scientists, independent scientific committees, and scientific advisory groups to the government have stated that a particular hazard is "negligible," "acceptable," or "unacceptable"— without making it clear that the conclusion is *not a scientific conclusion, but a social judgment.* Nevertheless, it is natural that the public should assume that such pronouncements are scientific conclusions. Since such conclusions, put forward by individual scientists, or by groups of scientists, are often contradictory, a question which commonly arises among the public is "How do we know which scientists are telling the truth?" Regardless of its origin, such a doubt erodes the confidence of the public in the capability of the scientific community to develop objective knowledge about scientific issues of crucial importance to public policy. To arrogate to the science that which belongs to the judgment of society or to the conscience of the individual inevitably weakens the integrity of science.

V. *The Integrity of Modern Science*

The foregoing examples testify to the striking success of modern science. They show that science has developed powers of unprecedented intensity and world-wide scale. The entire planet can now serve as a scientific laboratory.

At the same time, new large-scale experiments and technological developments of modern science frequently lead to unanticipated effects. The lifetime of the artificial belts of radiation established by the Starfish nuclear explosion was seriously underestimated in the calculations which preceded the experiment. Synthetic detergents were committed to full-scale economic exploitation before it was discovered that an important fault—resistance to bacterial degradation in sewage systems—would eventually require that they be

The Integrity of Science

withdrawn from the market. The hazards of pesticides to animal life were not fully known until pesticides were massively disseminated in the biosphere; the medical risk to man has hardly been evaluated. Nuclear tests responsible for the massive distribution of radioactive debris were conducted for about ten years before the biological effects of its most hazardous component were recognized.

It is a major responsibility of science to provide society with a proper guide to its interaction with nature. Apparently, in modern circumstances, science has not adequately met this responsibility, and it becomes important to inquire into the possible reasons for this defect.

There is a common tendency in the execution of large-scale experimentation and technological operations to neglect the principles of disciplined experimentation, of consideration for experimental controls, and of open disclosure and discussion of results. These erosions in the integrity of science reflect important changes in the relationships between the acquisition of new scientific knowledge and its use for the satisfaction of social needs. What are these changes and how do they account for the disturbing tendency to use the enormous power of modern science in the absence of adequate knowledge?

In the last twenty to thirty years an important change has taken place in the relationship between basic science and its technological application to social needs. During the period of intensive industrialization in the nineteenth century, basic scientific investigation was a major source of the required fundamental knowledge, especially of mechanics, electricity, and chemistry. In this period, basic scientific investigation pursued a course largely separate from current industrial needs, and practical applications developed only as a by-product of basic research or through chance discovery and invention. The development of electric power is a useful example: about thirty-five years elapsed between Faraday's basic scientific discovery of electromagnetic induction (1831) and the development of the first commercial electric generators (1866–7). Power systems developed gradually thereafter, as their usefulness became increasingly evident. The first commercial power plant became operative in 1882, in New York City. Such delays permitted the development of a broad base of scientific knowledge in advance of its large-scale application. For this reason, and because the effects under scientific control in that period were, in any case, limited in intensity and scope, technological application of scientific advance was gradual and relatively disciplined. There are, of course, important exceptions to this generalization: the discovery of radium and x-rays led to certain abuses; the consequences of new industries for public health were often poorly understood; steam-boilers exploded, railroad bridges collapsed, and steamers foundered in the seas. But these defects were limited in effect and duration.

The present situation is very different. Now the origin of technology in basic science is clearly understood and consciously exploited. Major socially useful applications are no longer based on the fortuitous appearance of the relevant scientific knowledge. *Instead, a social decision to accomplish a particular technological aim is often made in advance of the necessary scientific knowledge, and the latter is sought for with the express purpose of achieving the desired technology and satisfying a stated social need.* The decision to land a man on the moon was hardly a fortuitous outcome of the search for knowledge. It was, rather, a conscious decision, largely on political grounds, to develop the basic and applied science necessary to achieve this particular technological accomplishment.

Under these conditions, the laboratory of basic science inevitably loses much of its isolation from cultural effects and becomes subject to strong social demands for particular results. This new relationship has, of course, greatly reduced the delays which previously intervened between discovery and application. However, the new relationship has also had a less fortunate effect: *it has resulted in technological application before the related basic scientific knowledge was sufficiently developed to provide an adequate understanding of the effects of the new technology on nature.*

Experience with nuclear testing provides an illuminating insight into this relationship. Nuclear weapons have been developed as a result of a strong social demand for a particular physical effect: an extremely powerful explosion. But a nuclear explosion is not only a physical process; it is also a vast ecological experiment. Since the ecological aspects of nuclear explosions had no apparent immediate relationship to the socially-determined goal of the program, the development of basic knowledge regarding the physics of nuclear explosions greatly outstripped what was learned about their complex biological consequences. As a result, the knowledge required for massive nuclear explosions was developed—and put to use—in the absence of an adequate understanding of the biological hazards that followed.

We are constrained to ask why the long-established precepts of science have not been sufficiently strong, despite insistent social demand, to prevent such hazardous use of partial knowledge.

Secrecy, which has become ubiquitous in modern, large-scale science and technology, hampers the processes of scientific discourse. In the normal procedures of science, errors or inadequacies in scientific information are detected and corrected through open dissemination of results and free discussion of their significance. When secrecy intervenes, such inadequacies are not subject to the scrutiny of the independent scientific community and may go uncorrected for relatively long periods of time; faulty action may result.

Another source of present weakness in the integrity of science is that the social agencies which are responsible for the pattern of research support—especially Congress—do not yet appreciate the hazards involved in developing support for science on the basis of immediate demands for particular results. Support for science which does not permit the free and balanced development of all aspects of a problem tends to narrow the range of available scientific information and dangerously unbalances our control of new interventions into natural phenomena.

The National Science Foundation was intended to provide just this sort of broad support for science. However, as a result of the rapid development of a massive space research program by NASA, the relative strength of science-oriented support has become significantly reduced. If this process is unchecked, it will further reduce the ability of science to develop a comprehensive understanding of large-scale interventions into nature, and constitute a further erosion of the integrity of science.

Even where an adequate balance of information regarding physico-chemical and biological aspects of modern science exists, inadequate inter-disciplinary communication often limits the effective use of this information. Had the developers of the present synthetic detergents been aware of available information regarding the relative resistance of branched molecules to biochemical degradation, they might have hesitated to impose a massive burden of such substances on the biosphere.

We see in some recent developments a noticeable tendency toward the separation of "modern" aspects of science from more traditional fields. There is a tendency to look upon synthetic chemistry or the biophysics of radiation effects as "modern science" while the fields of biology that are more closely related to natural phenomena—for example, ecology—are often regarded as old-fashioned and outmoded. Nevertheless, it is the complex natural system which is disturbed by the untoward secondary effects of massive physicochemical technology. Derogation of the sciences devoted to the study of natural systems is hardly conducive to the proper understanding of the consequences of the large-scale experiments that are so typical of modern science.

The scientist's position in society has changed considerably in the last decade and some of these changes have influenced the integrity of science. Because of the rapid increase in the importance of science to major national needs (military, economic, international), scientists have been drawn into extensive participation in business, government agencies, and public affairs generally. The public has become willing to accept, with the respect accorded scientific conclusions, the scientist's views on numerous topics that have nothing to do with his special area of competence, or with science as a whole.

The scientist now often finds himself, by virtue of being a scientist, in a powerful position to influence social decisions which are not solely matters of science. For example, most major policy decisions about the space program require social judgments. Although scientists, as a group, have no greater competence or rights than other citizens in such matters, their close association with the space program has afforded them opportunities to exert disproportionate influence on these decisions. Scientists have also played a major role in advising the government on the development of the nation's military strength and on important international negotiations. Since such advice almost always involves nonscientific matters, which are not subject to the self-correcting effects of scientific discourse, there are often serious disagreements on these issues among different scientists and groups of scientists.

When scientists serve as advisors to a governmental or private agency which is committed to a particular point of view on a public issue, questions also arise concerning the influence of the parent agency's viewpoint on the advice given to it. Where such advisory bodies operate under rules of secrecy, or for some other reason do not make their deliberations accessible to the scrutiny of the scientific community, the normal self-correcting procedures of scientific discourse cannot be brought to bear. Conflicts may develop between the advisory group and other members of the scientific community regarding scientific matters, or the significance of nonscientific considerations. Such disagreements are difficult to resolve be-

The Integrity of Science

cause, in the absence of open discussion, they do not become explicitly stated.

The growing interaction between science and public policy requires considerable attention to the problem of distinguishing scientific problems from those issues which ought to be decided by social processes. An example of the tendency to confuse scientific evaluation with social judgment is the matter of radiation standards. Here a scientific body, the Federal Radiation Council, is engaged in setting standards of acceptability which are basically social judgments regarding the balance between the hazards and benefits of nuclear operations. These judgments are, or ought to be, wholly vulnerable to political debate, but their appearance in the guise of a scientific decision may shield them from such scrutiny.

VI. *The Responsibilities of the Scientists and of Society*

Under the pressure of insistent social demands, there have been serious erosions of the integrity of science. This situation is dangerous both to science and society. If society is to enter safely into the new age of science, steps must be taken to strengthen the competence of science as a reliable guide to nature at its source—the integrity of science. Scientists have an inescapable responsibility to maintain the integrity of science; this is required by their duties to their own discipline and toward society.

The set of principles and processes which comprise the integrity of science have been developed in a long and sometimes difficult history. The scientific community has a strong tradition of protecting this system of inquiry against insistent pressure or overt attack. This history has its heroes, its martyrs, its defeats. The lesson of both victories and defeats is the same. Wherever science has succumbed to social pressures that would subvert the objectivity of scientific data, foster perverted or undisciplined experimentation, or restrict the freedom of scientific discourse, the price has been paid in a costly coin—knowledge. The relationship between the integrity of science and knowledge is evident in each of the instances we have cited. In each of them, defects in the integrity of science have led to inadequacies in our understanding of nature.

What can be done to strengthen the integrity of science? In our view, replacement or even any extensive modification of the system of inquiry which science has developed is not required. On the contrary, each instance which has led to an erosion of the integrity of science has arisen not because the system was tried and failed, but because it was *not fully used*. We must find ways to ensure that this system of discourse is fully engaged in the development and social use of modern science.

Some will assert that the only effective way to ensure that science adheres to the principles of objectivity, of open discussion of results, and of disciplined experimentation is to see to it that all scientists develop a personal devotion to these principles. This view suggests that to strengthen the integrity of science we need but to promulgate a suitable code of ethics for scientists.

However, despite the importance of the scientist's personal outlook in sustaining the integrity of science, this viewpoint is largely a reflection of the system of discourse in which the scientist must operate. We believe, therefore, that steps to strengthen the integrity of science should be centered, to begin with, on the *system* rather than on its participants.

The basic problem which we now face is the effect of the rapid expansion in the scope of scientific research and technology on the integrity of science. The scale of new scientific and technological operations places new strains on the process of scientific discourse. What are required are means for bringing these new activities into more effective contact with the system of discourse that science has already established. Large-scale experiments and technological operations that might lead to violations of the principles of disciplined experimentation, or which might interfere with controls necessary to other research, need to be exposed to open consideration by the scientific community *before* they are undertaken.

Such operations are important parts of governmental or industrial programs, and we recognize the difficulties which may inhibit their open discussion. Nevertheless, we see no way to ensure that these activities can be carried out without jeopardizing their ultimate value to the government or to industry, and to society generally, unless they *are* subject to the corrective effects of open discussion. Military or commercial secrecy seriously hampers proper development of large-scale scientific intrusions upon the natural world, and we believe that our society must now take decisive steps to reduce these restraints.

Any effort to minimize such secrecy will, of course, be confronted with serious and complex difficulties. Nevertheless, the need for open scientific discussion of the consequences of modern experimentation and technology is so urgent that the task, despite its difficulty, should now be undertaken.

The Integrity of Science

To correct the difficulties which arise from present confusions between scientific opinion and social judgment, we can again rely on the principle of open discussion. In such discussion, the scientific community should require that any public assertion, whether made by a scientist, by a government agency, or by a political figure, which makes use of scientific considerations, include, if only by reference, verifiable sources for the latter. If a scientist, whether speaking professionally or as a citizen, asserts that fallout represents a calculable risk to health, he should be expected to indicate what scientific observations support this conclusion. If a public official declares that a particular public policy, such as exploration of the moon, is required for the advancement of science, he should be expected to indicate where the supporting scientific considerations may be found. The development of this type of discourse should do much to reduce the confusion between scientific evidence and social judgment and thereby help to restore the slackening public faith in the integrity of science.

All citizens bear serious responsibilities toward maintenance of the integrity of science. The basic social function of science is the development of objective knowledge about the natural world and of means for directing this knowledge toward the satisfaction of human needs. As we have emphasized, science has developed a set of principles and procedures which are designed to maximize the search for such knowledge, which is therefore the unquestioned goal of science. But in the rest of society, not every person or every institution may be equally well served by a particular scientific conclusion. A physician who asserts that smoking is harmful to health will gratify many parents, but will also displease certain farmers and manufacturers. A recitation of the hazards of nuclear testing or of the untoward effects of a government-sponsored experiment in space on science may be resented by those who wish to promulgate these activities. Science needs to be protected from such constraints by being permitted to develop and disseminate knowledge in keeping with its own procedures, so that the usefulness or desirability of this knowledge to society may be determined by that society. This is a responsibility of all citizens, including those who are scientists.

In its own self-interest, society must respect, and indeed encourage, the integrity of science. Too often science is regarded only as a means of satisfying immediate social demands, and such demands sometimes produce pressures which erode the integrity of science. Society must recognize more clearly than it now does that such pressures are self-defeating and, given the hazards involved in a faulty understanding of the power of modern science, exceedingly dangerous as well.

If scientists work to strengthen the integrity of science, and if citizens learn to respect the importance of the integrity of science to society, we can enter the new age of science in the hope that it will properly serve the welfare of man.

Appendix I—The "Starfish" Experiment

The following provides further details regarding considerations, by scientists and various agencies, of the possible effects of the Starfish experiment.

The U.S. Government announced the impending Starfish explosions in April 1962. The first test was to be a detonation of a one megaton nuclear bomb at a height of "hundreds of kilometers" above the Pacific Ocean. The announcement said:

> Public notice will be given approximately four days in advance of each detonation. This will permit geophysicists and other scientists throughout the world to make measurements of interest to the scientific community.

An *ad hoc* committee of the Space Science Board met in May 1962 to consider whether the tests would substantially prejudice astrophysical and geophysical research and create a nuclear hazard to manned space flights. According to one of the committee members, Dr. Van Allen, the committee decided that neither hazard was present in the proposed experiment. He reports that estimates of the expected lifetimes of artificially-injected particles were controversial, and the least settled point in the committee's considerations. At a symposium of the Committee on Science in the Promotion of Human Welfare of the American Association for the Advancement of Science in Philadelphia, December 30, 1962, Dr. Van Allen stated that "The lifetime at higher altitudes would become progressively greater and the most sanguine expectations of lifetime were not over a few years."

On July 19, 1962, Dr. Van Allen was quoted in the New York *Times* to the effect that the predictions of the *ad hoc* committee indicated that an explosion 100 times greater than that employed in the project would be needed to seriously disrupt the radiation belts. He added, however, that data regarding the actual effects of the explosion were being accumulated and would prove the point one way or another.

No information regarding the effects of the explosion was released by the U.S. Government at this time. However, on August 19, 1962, newspaper stories reported that: (a) Dr. James Warwick of the Atmospheric Research Corporation in Boulder, Colorado, had observed radio-emissions indicating that the explosion had produced a new, rather intense and persistent radiation belt and that (b) Dr. Van Allen confirmed the existence of a new belt. (Minneapolis *Tribune*, August 19, 1962). Dr. Van Allen added that at lower altitudes the radioactivity due to the artificial belt was already declining, while the new belts formed at higher levels would be "impossible to detect in a year."

On August 20, 1962, the government officially acknowledged the existence of an artificial belt but stated that it was disappearing rapidly. On September 1, 1962, the AEC and the Department of Defense announced that data from the satellite Telstar revealed the presence of a more intense and persistent belt than at first had been thought to exist. This conclusion was challenged by Dr. Van Allen. He said that the Telstar results strongly resembled the values of natural radiation belts, which would indicate negligible artificial radiation at high altitudes.

Dr. Wilmot Hess, who provided the early estimates based on Telstar data, more recently has pointed to the fact that Injun (the Van Allen satellite) flew at altitudes up to 1000 kilometers while Telstar had an apogee of 5630 kilometers. Further, the particle counters on neither satellite distinguished between high and low energy electrons. In a paper in *International Science and Technology*, September 1963, Hess agrees that much of the radiation flux observed by Telstar was due to low energy electrons, and states:

But whether they are fission electrons directly from the burst, with their energy somehow diminished, or electrons from some other source, somehow triggered by the burst, is uncertain and may remain so forever.

He further notes that some physicists believe that such electrons may have been present but undetected before the burst. More recently, Dr. Van Allen revised his estimates for the new belt's lifetime at high altitudes. On March 15, 1963, he announced that the new belt might last ten years or more, as shown by data from new satellites Injun 3 and Explorer 14.

Some evidence as to the reason for the inadequate predictions made for the life of the Starfish effects is given by McIlwain (*Science*, **142**, 360, October 18). He notes that the 1958 test series was carried out on lines of magnetic force for which the L values were 1.2, 1.7, and 2.1. (L values are lines of magnetic force numbered by the altitude, in earth radii, through which they pass at the equator.) Each time, the intensities were observed to decrease rapidly. Rapid decrease was then thought to occur between L values of 1.2 and 1.7. But McIlwain states,

> This is unfortunately not the case . . . Had this been known earlier, the 9 July nuclear test might have been carried out at a high altitude so that the electrons would have been injected on high lines of force where they would have been more rapidly removed.

The new radiation bands created by the Starfish explosion have had significant effects on other space experimentation. It was the influence of the experiment upon radioastronomy which brought early announcement of the belt by Dr. Warwick. He detected emissions from the new radiation belt very soon after the explosion took place. In his initial announcement, reported in the Minneapolis *Tribune,* August 19, 1962, Dr. Warwick said of these effects:

> One problem is that the signal imitates in major aspects the signal we get from the galaxy, and some kinds of observations may be impossible to distinguish. I think it is highly unlikely that the signal will interfere with observations at any major radio-telescopes except possibly India's and not necessarily there. It depends on what type of observations are being made. I am afraid, however, that some people will be concerned with the accuracy of some of their recent measurements.

At this committee's symposium at the annual meeting of the American Association for the Advancement of Science in Philadelphia on December 20, 1962, Dr. Van Allen noted that there has been a significant increase in the radio noise level in the 10 to 100 megacycle region. He said at the time:

> My understanding is, however, that it has not been observed at all in any mid-latitude observatory, and that it is dwindling away at about the rate we anticipated.

Later, Hess reported in his paper referred to above that radio noise was 2½ times background several hours after the blast and that:

> Thereafter, the excess noise decreased with agonizing slowness . . . expectations are that at least 15% of the original excess noise will remain after 1 year, and perhaps 8% still will remain 2 years after Starfish.

Concerning the lasting effects of the Starfish explosion upon scientific investigation of the Van Allen belts, Dr. McIlwain finds that on the high lines of force the electrons accelerate during natural magnetic storms, and he states:

The Integrity of Science

Since the rate of complete removal (not just deceleration) may be very slow, a more appropriate question may be: How many times do artificially injected particles have to be accelerated and decelerated before they are to be considered natural?

And, at this committee's symposium in December 1962, Dr. Van Allen pointed out:

> The injection of energetic electrons into the radiation belt has prejudiced the investigation of the question of whether there are electrons of energy of the order of Mevs already present there naturally. This is a question of considerable interest and it is difficult to say at what time in the future it will be possible to investigate this definitely.

Appendix II—The "West Ford" Experiment

Additional details on several relevant aspects of the West Ford experiment are provided in what follows.

For a number of years scientists have recognized the limits imposed on long distance (intercontinental) communication by certain natural phenomenon. Relatively low frequency, long radio waves can span intercontinental distances because they are reflected from the ionosphere (a zone of charged particles surrounding the earth). However, such long waves are much less efficient message carriers than high frequency radio waves. Moreover, the ionosphere is not a dependable medium; sun spots, solar flares, and plasma streams all create magnetic storms affecting its reflectivity. Although high frequency radio waves are capable of carrying large quantities of messages they are not reflected by the ionosphere and are therefore restricted to line-of-sight transmission over short distances.

To counteract these difficulties, satellites have been developed to orbit the earth and redirect high frequency radio communications through line-of-sight paths capable of connecting any points on the surface of the earth. Such satellites, for example Telstar, can handle very large numbers of messages. However, satellites have a limited usefulness for *military* communication. They travel along set paths and their position cannot be kept secret; Telstar contains complicated electronic equipment which can be readily damaged, for example, by high altitude nuclear explosions.

On May 10, 1963, the Lincoln Laboratories made a successful attempt to establish a dipole belt. Alterations in design to avoid previous malfunctions and to provide "fail-safe" controls and changes in design of the parent spacecraft, which was under Air Force control, reduced the weight of the dipoles to 18 kilograms. The experiment established a dipole belt at 3650 Km., inclination 87.4°.

Concerning the lifetime of the orbit achieved, Jones et al. (*Science,* **140,** 1173) reported:

> Before the command was given to eject these radio reflectors from the parent satellite, orbital parameters were carefully determined from many observations . . . not a single individual dipole would remain in orbit longer than 5 years.

William Liller of the Harvard Observatory has been serving as recipient and analyst of all optical observations of the West Ford Belt. His final report (*Science,* **143,** 437–441, 1964) concludes that "Photographic and photoelectric observations show that the West Ford dipole belt was no brighter than had been predicted."

In a report dated February 7, 1964, the Space Science Board reached the following conclusions about the last West Ford launch:

> (a) We conclude, as was originally forecast, that as of the time of this statement and with the observing techniques in use today the present West Ford experiment has not been harmful to either optical or radio astronomy. (b) The predictions of the effects of the experiment have been reasonably well borne out by the observations. We may therefore rely on essentially the same methods to predict the effects of any experiments similar to the West Ford experiment which may possibly be proposed in the future, suitable allowance being made for the increased vulnerability that may be associated with future advances in observing technique.

Appendix III—Project Apollo

The following presents in greater detail the background of the decision to attempt a manned landing on the moon, with respect to social motivation and scientific considerations.

President Kennedy's message to Congress (May 25, 1961), in which he proposed the establishment of the program, reflects the strong social and political motivation of the Apollo Program. He stated:

> Finally, if we are to win the battle that is going on around the world between freedom and tyranny, if we are to win the battle for men's minds, the dramatic achievements in space which occurred in recent weeks should have made clear to us all, as did Sputnik in 1957, the impact of this adventure on the minds of men everywhere who are attempting to make a determination of which road they should take . . . Now is the time to take longer strides—time for a great new American enterprise—time for this Nation to take a clearly leading role in space achievement which in many ways may hold the key to our future on earth. . .

The Integrity of Science

... Recognizing the headstart obtained by the Soviets with their large rocket engines, which gives them many months of leadtime, and recognizing the likelihood that they will exploit this lead for some time to come in still more impressive successes, we nevertheless are required to make new efforts on our own...

... I believe that this Nation should commit itself to achieving the goal, before this decade is out, of landing a man on the moon and returning him safely to earth. No single space project in this period will be more exciting, or more impressive to mankind, or more important for the long-range exploration of space; and none will be so difficult or expensive to accomplish...

The considerable size of the project and the rather concentrated location of its major facilities in a particular region of the country (the Southeast) inevitably bring into play additional social factors. An article in the New York *Times* (August 25, 1963) states:

The United States moon program is producing a quiet economic revolution, especially in the southeast . . . It is producing a new basic industry built on applied physics, mathematics, chemistry, medicine, astronomy and electronics . . . The moon program, Project Apollo, is to be concentrated along a 1,500 mile crescent, beginning 22 miles south of Houston, Texas, sweeping through New Orleans and south Mississippi and ending 35 miles south of Miami in a Florida swampland.

The Space Science Board (SSB) and its affiliated committees have evaluated the scientific goals of space research. Considerations relevant to investigation of the moon are summarized in what follows.

The SSB began its work in 1958 and by 1961 had developed an extensive series of proposals for scientific investigation in space, based on recommendations by various subcommittees. This material was summarized in a book, *Science in Space,* edited by L. V. Berkner and Hugh Odishaw of SSB (New York: McGraw-Hill, 1961). Recommendations regarding investigation of the moon are given in Chapter 9, written by Dr. H. C. Urey, who served as Chairman of the SSB Committee on Chemistry of Space and Exploration of Moon and Planets. This chapter lists twenty-one specific projects for lunar exploration in order of their relative importance from the standpoint of scientific knowledge. This order is based on earlier committee considerations in which the projects were assigned priority ratings of 1, 2, or 3. The project for manned landing on the moon was among nine projects assigned the lowest of the three priority ratings. The complete list of recommended projects for investigation of the moon, in the order given in Chapter 9 of *Science in Space,* is as follows:

Operational Category	Specific Projects
a) Satellite of the moon	1) Radioactive determination of potassium, uranium, and thorium. 2) Television viewing of moon surfaces. 3) Mass and mass distribution. 4) Atmospheric density and composition. 5) Reflectivity of the lunar surface. 6) Exploration of the lunar magnetic field.
b) Hard landing of instrument on moon	1) Atmospheric density. 2) Surface hardness.
c) Soft landing of instruments on moon	1) Televised microscopic examination. 2) Tests for magnetic materials. 3) Hardness tests. 4) Seismic observations. 5) Radioactive detection of potassium, uranium, and thorium. 6) Mass spectrometer analyses. 7) Temperature measurements. 8) X-ray fluorescence analyses. 9) Spectroscopic analyses of surface rocks. 10) Volatilization of surface materials. 11) Measurements of moon's gravity.
d) Return of samples from the moon	1) Return of surface and core samples.
e) Manned landing on the moon	1) Geological exploration.

Manned exploration of the moon is discussed in only one other place in *Science in Space*. An introductory chapter devotes about three and one-half pages to the problem of exploration by man of space as a whole. After discussing human exploration of the moon and planets, it states:

No proper answer [i.e., to alternative technical plans] can be given to the question until suitable studies are made and the concerted development of automatic equipment is undertaken. . . . During this necessary research period, also, the problem of planetary exploration will be better understood as a result of space probe studies and soft landings of relatively simple instrumental payloads. Yet we can conjecture that ultimately, for detailed exploration of the planets, man will be needed to define the useful range of instrumentation and to direct complicated technical operations. The success of these prospective ventures of man into space—from orbital flights about the earth to landings on planets—is far from simple or, at present, assured in spite of the pronouncements of space enthusiasts. [p. 19].

The Integrity of Science

During the ninth meeting of the SSB on February 10 and 11, 1961, presentations were made by NASA representatives concerning the status of plans for a manned landing on the moon. This was followed by a discussion of the national goals of space research, which dealt chiefly with man's role in space. The outcome of this discussion was summarized in a statement, "Man's Role in the National Space Program," which was transmitted to the government in March 1961 and made public on August 6, 1961. The chief conclusions contained in this statement relative to manned exploration of the moon are the following:

At its meeting on February 10 and 11, 1961, the Space Science Board gave particular consideration to the role of man in space in the national space science program. As a result of these deliberations the Board concluded that *scientific exploration of the moon and planets should be clearly stated as the ultimate objective of the U.S. space program for the foreseeable future.* This objective should be promptly adopted as the official goal of the United States space program and clearly announced, discussed and supported. In addition it should be stressed that the United States will continue to press toward a thorough scientific understanding of *space*, of solving problems of manned space exploration, and of the development of applications of space science for man's welfare.

The Board concluded that it is not now possible to decide whether man will be able to accompany early expeditions to the moon and planets. Many intermediate problems remain to be solved. However, the Board strongly emphasized that planning for scientific exploration of the moon and planets must at once be developed on the premise that man will be included. Failure to adopt and develop our national program upon this premise will inevitably prevent man's inclusion, and every effort should be made to establish the feasibility of manned space flight at the earliest opportunity.

From a scientific standpoint, there seems to be little room for dissent that man's participation in the exploration of the moon and planets will be essential, if and when it becomes technologically feasible to include him. Man can contribute critical elements of scientific judgment and discrimination in conducting the scientific exploration of these bodies which can never be fully supplied by his instruments, however complex and sophisticated they may become. Thus, carefully planned and executed scientific expeditions will inevitably be the more fruitful.

With respect to the timing of a project for manned lunar exploration, the SSB statement recommended:

Broad programs designed to determine man's physiological and psychological ability to adapt to space flight must likewise be pushed as rapidly as possible. However, planning for "manned" scientific exploration of the Moon and the planets should be consummated only as fast as possible consistent with the development of all relevant information. The program should not be undertaken on a crash basis which fails to give reasonable attention to assurance of success or tries to by-pass the orderly study of all relevant problems.

On May 25, 1961, President Kennedy announced that manned exploration of the moon was adopted as the immediate goal of the national space program, to be accomplished at a specified time (1970) although this schedule for accomplishment of the project does not appear in the SSB statement which presumably provided the scientific basis for the announcement.

Following the foregoing events, the next major consideration of the scientific motivation for manned lunar exploration is to be found in "A Review of Space Research, Report of Summer Study Session conducted under the auspices of the Space Science Board at the State University of Iowa, June 17–August 10, 1962." The chief conclusions of this study relative to justification of the Apollo program and its relationship to the scientific investigations associated with the program are summarized in the introductory chapter of the report as follows:

The Apollo program was acknowledged as an integral part of the NASA effort, based on the President's decision that this undertaking be established as a national goal. The objectives of the Apollo mission and its inter-relationships with fundamental scientific research were discussed on many occasions during the Space Science Summer Study, and a number of working groups gave consideration to the opportunities for carrying out scientific research which the Apollo program would afford. These discussions also formed the basis for a more detailed consideration of the role of man in space exploration by a working group convened specifically to consider this topic.

Discussion of this topic revealed that there is considerable confusion about the Apollo mission and its proper justifications. Because of this confusion it is pertinent to present here the conclusions of the Summer Study on this subject.

In the first place, the Apollo program is related to man's innate drive to explore unknown regions, to national prestige, and to national security. These elements are of concern not only to scientists but also to all other segments of our society.

In the second place, there are important scientific objectives in the Apollo program, and it is in terms of science and scientific opportunities that the program appears to have been most widely misunderstood. It is in this context that the Summer Study conclusions concerning the Apollo program deserve elaboration.

The Integrity of Science

Put in the simplest terms, the objective of the Apollo program is to place a man on the moon and return him safely. Thus the current program is primarily a technological and engineering effort, and this fact ought to be generally recognized. When it becomes clear, however, that these ends will be achieved, a strong scientific validity immediately follows. By his presence, man will contribute critical capacities for scientific judgment, discrimination, and analysis (especially of a total situation) which can never be accomplished by his instruments, however complex and sophisticated they become. Hence, manned exploration of space *is* science in space, for man will go with the instruments that he has designed to supplement his capacities—to observe what is there, and to measure and describe phenomena in terms that his scientific colleagues will clearly understand. A scientifically trained and oriented man will be essential for this purpose.

In this context the Apollo program indeed acquires scientific validity. Scientists should recognize that Apollo is the first phase in a continuing engineering enterprise that will ultimately enable man to move about in space and provide him with the capacity for conducting his scientific investigations. It must always be remembered that as the earlier phases of the Apollo program proceed, engineering for the craft and for man will always assume the highest priority and the engineers must be protected in their ability to do their jobs. As the engineering tasks are accomplished, however, scientific investigations and missions will also be phased into the program; and, as flexibility and sophistication are achieved, scientific investigations will become the primary goals.

Appreciation of these concepts is of critical importance to the acceptance of the current Apollo program by scientists throughout the country. The proper exposition of these concepts by the federal government should go far toward allaying misunderstandings of the Apollo program which are currently prevalent among many members of the scientific community. [pp. 1–21, 22]

Detailed considerations relative to the scientific importance associated with the Apollo project are given in Chapter 11, "The Scientific Role of Man in Space Exploration." The scientific work to be accomplished by manned exploration of the moon is summarized as follows:

The scientific exploration of space has been proclaimed a national goal, and manned lunar landing is a major step in the implementation of this program. Man's opportunities for scientific exploration of the moon are practically unlimited. The lack of adequate scientific endeavor could invite serious criticism of the program, while the impact of a successful scientific mission by means of a lunar landing will enormously enhance the importance of the Apollo program in the eyes of the world.

Among the most important *scientific tasks* foreseeable for manned lunar landings are: (i) observation of natural phenomena, including micro-

COMMITTEE ON SCIENCE

and macro-structure and composition; (ii) collection of representative samples; and (iii) enplacement of monitoring equipment. For a more extensive statement of the objectives which we endorse, we refer to "Draft Report of the Ad Hoc Working Group on Apollo Experiments and Training on the Scientific Aspects of the Apollo Program" (July 6, 1962), prepared under the chairmanship of Dr. C. P. Sonett, NASA. [p. 11–3]

The Sonett report has not been made public by either the National Academy of Science or NASA.

In view of the stated cardinal importance of achieving a manned landing on the moon, the Study's working group on lunar and planetary research found it necessary to set a specific pattern of priorities for the types of investigations of the moon to be carried out in the immediate future. The relevant statements (from Chapter 4, which constitutes the report of this working group) follow:

Finding: The acquisition of information about the lunar environment and surface must be accelerated if responsible engineering decisions are to be made in time for a successful manned lunar landing and return by 1968 or by 1970. To this end it is necessary that NASA step up both the number and information-gathering scope of unmanned flights as planned as prerequisites to the manned landing, and that it also give increased support to earth-based experiments and observations designed to provide information bearing on the probable conditions to be met and coped with during a manned landing and return. The philosophy of the Apollo program should be to utilize to a maximum contributions feasible from earth-based experiments and unmanned space craft. [p. 4–2]

Finding: Other experiments were recognized to be of great scientific importance, though necessarily of lower priority than the practical information in support of the Apollo mission. A most significant achievement would be the return of a sample, or samples, of lunar surface material. A review of the importance of the unmanned programs and perhaps of the schedule for the Apollo manned lunar landing may well justify a decision to return a lunar sample from an unmanned landing. [p. 4–7]

Hearings before the Senate Committee on Aeronautical and Space Sciences, June 10, 1963, presented further opinion on Project Apollo from the scientific community. Of the dozen scientists testifying, the majority's views were substantially the same as those in the SSB report of August 6, 1961, quoted above. Among the dissenters was Dr. Polykarp Kusch, who felt that the main purpose of basic research—the orderly acquisition of knowledge—would be poorly served by the Apollo Project:

It is my belief that the present space program attempts too much too fast. There is not enough time for profound thought, for imagination to play over the demanding problems that occur. Someone has said to me, in a discussion of the space program, that the attempts that are being made to explore space are similar to those that would have been made had the physicists of the prewar era attempted a program of research involving a billion-volt proton accelerator. The scientific ideas that allow us presently to build such machines had not yet appeared; conceivably that machine could have been built, but only with very much greater difficulty than present machines propose. The important problems that have engaged in mind and efforts [sic] of the generation of physicists now in their prime were too dimly understood to allow the kind of effective inquiry currently undertaken. Much of the auxiliary gear that is central to the observation of high energy phenomena had not yet been invented. Finally, the extraordinarily effective guidelines that the theorists of physics develop had not yet begun to appear. [Hearings, p. 68]

On November 17, 1964, the SSB issued a new statement on space research goals. The section of the recommendations contained in this statement which refers to manned lunar exploration is as follows:

Aware of the parallel criteria of scientific and intellectual importance *and* of significance to the national interest, the Board summarizes its recommendations on the primary national objectives in the field of space science for the 1971–1985 period as follows:

1. *Exploration of the planets with particular emphasis on Mars*
    (a) This objective includes both physical and biological investigations, and especially the search for extraterrestrial life.
    (b) The experimentation should be carried out largely by unmanned vehicles while the solution of difficult biomedical and bioengineering problems proceeds at a measured pace so that toward the end of this epoch (1985) we shall be ready for manned planetary exploration.
    (c) Alternatives to the Mars and planetary exploration goal—(i) extensive manned lunar exploration (possibly including lunar base contruction) and (ii) major manned orbiting space station and laboratory program—are not regarded as primary goals, because they have less scientific significance. However, both have sufficient merit to warrant parallel programs but of lower priority.

REFERENCES

1. Members of the Committee during the preparation of the report (as released on December 31, 1964) were: Barry Commoner (Chairman), Washington University; Robert B. Brode, University of California, Berkeley; T. C. Byerly, United States Department of Agriculture; Ansley J. Coale, Princeton University; John T. Edsall, Harvard University; Lawrence

K. Frank, Belmont, Massachusetts; Margaret Mead, American Museum of Natural History; and Walter Modell, Cornell University Medical College. William T. Kabisch was the staff representative of the American Association for the Advancement of Science, and Gorman L. Mattison and Sheldon Novick were administrative assistants to the Committee.

Responsibility for statements of fact and expressions of opinion contained in this report rests with the committee that prepared it. The American Association for the Advancement of Science Board of Directors, in accordance with Association policy and without passing judgment on the views expressed, has approved its publication as a contribution to the discussion of an important issue.

Acknowledgments: The Committee is especially grateful to the following for valuable assistance in developing information relative to the report: Dr. Leo Goldberg, Dr. William Liller, and Dr. A. E. Lilley, all of Harvard University, and Dr. J. A. Van Allen of the State University of Iowa. The report does not, of course, reflect their opinions, nor are they to be regarded as responsible for any errors of fact which may appear in the report.

2. Further information on several aspects of Starfish appears in Appendix I to this report.

3. Press release issued jointly by the Atomic Energy Commission and the Department of Defense, Washington, D.C., May 28, 1962.

4. C. E. McIlwain, "The Radiation Belts, Natural and Artificial," *Science*, Vol. 142, No. 3590 (October 18, 1963), p. 361.

5. The importance of these satellites for early data on the effects of Starfish is discussed in Appendix I.

6. Paper by James Van Allen, presented on December 30, 1962, at the Symposium on "The Integrity of Science," sponsored by this Committee, American Association for the Advancement of Science Annual Meeting, Philadelphia.

7. For additional information on several aspects of the West Ford experiment, see Appendix II.

8. E. M. Purcell, "The Case for the 'Needles' Experiment," *The New Scientist*, Vol. 13, No. 272 (February 1, 1962), p. 246.

9. J. W. Findlay, "West Ford and the Scientists," *Proceedings of the IEEE* (Institute of Electrical & Electronic Engineers), Vol. 52, No. 5, special issue on West Ford (May 1964), p. 455.

10. *Ibid.*, p. 457.

11. *Astronomical Journal*, Vol. 66 (1961), pp. 105–18. (More recent and extensive material has been published in the special West Ford issue of the *Proceedings of the IEEE*, noted above.)

The Integrity of Science

12. *Ibid.*, p. 115.
13. *Ibid.*, p. 114.
14. Space Science Board, "A Summary Report on Project West Ford," August 11, 1961, p. 2.
15. "Resolution No. 2," 11th General Assembly, International Astronomical Union, Berkeley, California, August 24, 1961.
16. *Proceedings of the IEEE, op. cit.*, p. 565.
17. Results of the West Ford belt established on May 10, 1963, are presented in more detail in Appendix II.
18. A more detailed presentation of considerations relative to the decision to undertake Project Apollo appears in Appendix III.
19. L. V. Berkner and H. Odishaw (eds.), *Science in Space* (New York: McGraw-Hill, 1961), p. 195.
20. Space Science Board, "Man's Role in the National Space Program," National Academy of Sciences, Washington, D.C., August 18, 1961.
21. Message to the United States Congress by President John F. Kennedy, May 25, 1961. A more extensive quotation, detailing social motivation for Project Apollo is given in Appendix III.
22. Senate Committee on Aeronautical and Space Sciences, Hearings, November 21–22, 1963, p. 34.
23. "A Review of Space Research," the Report of the Summer Study Session at the State University of Iowa, 1962, publication No. 1079, National Academy of Sciences, Washington.
24. See statement by Polykarp Kusch, Appendix III.
25. Proceedings of the NASA—University Conference on the Science and Technology of Space Exploration, Volume I, 1962, p. 90.
26. Senate Committee on Aeronautical and Space Sciences, Hearings, November 21–22, 1963, p. 134.
27. "Space Program: Results of Poll of AAAS Members," *Science*, Vol. 145, No. 3630 (July 24, 1964), p. 368.
28. Report of the Committee on Utilization of Scientific and Engineering Manpower, publication No. 1191, National Academy of Sciences, Washington, 1964, p. 86.
29. Paper by Homer E. Newell, Director, Office of Space Sciences, NASA, at American Association for the Advancement of Science Annual Meeting, Philadelphia, December 26, 1962.
30. "The Use of Pesticides," President's Science Advisory Committee, Washington, May 15, 1963.

31. See, for example, *ibid.*, and M. Katz and G. C. Chadwick, *Trans. Amer. Fish. Soc.*, 90:394, 1961.

32. Department of Health, Education and Welfare, press release, dated March 19, 1964.

33. New York *Times*, March 29, 1964.

34. *Ibid.*

35. Paper by C. G. Bueltman, at the American Association for the Advancement of Science Annual Meeting, Philadelphia, December 30, 1962, Symposium on "The Integrity of Science."

36. See summary in C. H. Hoffman, Technical Report W60-3, Taft Sanitary Engineering Center, 1960, p. 56.

37. Proceedings of the National Conference for Scientific Information, Scientists' Institute for Public Information, New York, February 1963, p. 11.

38. Federal Radiation Council, "Staff Report No. 1," May 13, 1960.

39. *Ibid.*, p. 24, paragraphs 4.5 and 4.6.

Notes on Contributors

JAMES ACKERMAN, born in San Francisco in 1919, is chairman of the Fine Arts Department of Harvard University and currently resident historian at the American Academy in Rome. He is the author, among others, of *The Architecture of Michelangelo* (1961) and, with Rhys Carpenter, of *Art and Archaeology* (1963). He is at present engaged in studies on the relationship of art and science from 1400 to the present.

DANIEL BELL, born in New York City in 1919, is professor of sociology in Columbia University and chairman of the department in Columbia College. An associate editor of *Dædalus* and a member of the editorial board of the *American Scholar*, he taught at the University of Chicago 1945-1948, and was director of the seminar program of the Congress for Cultural Freedom (Paris) in 1956-1957. His publications include *The End of Ideology* and, as editor, *The Radical Right*. His essay "Twelve Modes of Prediction" appeared in the Summer 1964 issue of *Dædalus*.

HARVEY BROOKS, born in 1915, is dean of the Division of Engineering and Applied Physics at Harvard University. His association with that institution began with his election as a Junior Fellow of the Society of Fellows in 1940. Leaving in January of 1942, during World War II he worked with the Harvard Underwater Sound Laboratory. Since his return to Harvard as Gordon McKay Professor of Applied Physics in 1950, most of his research has been in the field of solid state physics. The author of many contributions to scientific publications, he has since 1956 been editor-in-chief of the *Physics and Chemistry of Solids*, an international journal which he founded under the sponsorship of the Pergamon Press in Oxford, England.

RENÉ DUBOS, born in 1901 in Saint Brice, France, is professor at and member of The Rockefeller Institute, with whose faculty he has been associated since 1927. In addition to important achievements in microbiology and experimental pathology, he is also a student of the ecology of disease and of the effects on man of environmental forces. Among his recent books are *Pasteur and Modern Science* (1960), *The Dreams of Reason* (1961), and *Torch of Life and Unseen World* (1962). His essay "Medical Utopias" appeared in the Summer 1959 issue of *Dædalus*.

OSCAR HANDLIN, born in Brooklyn, New York, in 1915, teaches American social history at Harvard University, where he is director of the Center to Study the History of Liberty in America. Besides having edited the Library of American Biography and the *Harvard Guide to American History*, he has published numerous volumes, including: *The Uprooted* (awarded the Pulitzer Prize); *The American People in the Twentieth Century; The Americans;* and *Firebell in the Night.* His last contribution to *Dædalus* was "Historical Perspectives on the American Ethnic Group" in the Spring 1961 issue.

GERALD HOLTON, born in 1922, is professor of physics at Harvard University; from 1957 to 1963 he was Editor of the American Academy of Arts and Sciences and, until 1961, Editor of *Dædalus.* His research interests are in the physical properties of materials under high pressure and in the history and philosophy of science. Among his book publications are: *Introduction to Concepts and Theories in Physical Science;* and (as editor) *Science and the Modern Mind.*

GYORGY KEPES, born in 1906, Selyp, Hungary, painter and designer, worked in Berlin and London on film, stage, and exhibition design (1930-1936). In 1937 he came to the United States to head the Light and Color Department at the Institute of Design in Chicago. Since 1946 he has been professor of visual design at the Massachusetts Institute of Technology. His writings include: *Language of Vision* and *The New Landscape in Art and Science,* and he was editor of *The Visual Arts Today.* His paintings are in permanent collections of the Albright Knox Art Gallery in Buffalo, Boston Museum of Fine Arts, Brooklyn Museum, Corcoran Gallery of Art, Fogg Art Museum at Harvard University, Houston Museum of Fine Arts, Kansas City Art Museum, Phoenix Art Museum, San Francisco Museum of Art, Whitney Museum of American Art, and others.

EDMUND RONALD LEACH, born in Sidmouth, England, in 1910, is reader in social anthropology and Fellow of King's College in the University of Cambridge. He spent the war years of 1939-1945 in service in and around Burma. He is the author of *Social Science Research in Sarawak* (1950); *Political Systems of Highland Burma* (1954); *Pal Eliya: A Village in Ceylon* (1961); and *Rethinking Anthropology* (1961).

HARRY LEVIN, born in 1912, is Irving Babbitt Professor of Comparative Literature and presently chairman of the Department of Comparative Literature in Harvard University. His extensive publications include many critical articles and books. His most recent are *The Power of Blackness: Hawthorne, Poe, Melville* (1958); *The Question of Hamlet* (1959); and *The Gates of Horn: A Study of Five French Realists* (1962). His essay "Apogee and Aftermath of the Novel" appeared in the Spring 1963 issue of *Daedalus.*

HERBERT MARCUSE, born in 1898 in Berlin, Germany, is professor of politics and philosophy and chairman of the History of Ideas Program in Brandeis University, with which institution he has been associated since 1954. In 1951 and again from 1961 to 1962, he was Directeur d'Etudes, Ecole Pratiques des Hautes Etudes, in Paris. He is the author of *Reason and Revolution: Hegel and the Rise of Social Theory* (1941); *Eros and Civilization: A Philosophical Inquiry into Freud* (1955); *Soviet Marxism* (1957); and *One-Dimensional Man: Studies in the Ideology of Advanced Industrial Society* (1964).

MARGARET MEAD, born in 1901 in Philadelphia, has been associate curator of the American Museum of Natural History since 1942, and professor of anthropology at Columbia University since 1954. Her books include: *Coming of Age in Samoa; Male and Female; New Lives for Old;* and *Soviet Attitudes toward Authority.* Her most recent contribution to *Dædalus,* "Work, Leisure, and Creativity," appeared in the Winter 1960 issue.

ROBERT S. MORISON, born in Milwaukee in 1906, has, since October 1, 1964, been professor of biology and director of the Division of Basic Biology at Cornell University. From 1944 until that date, Dr. Morison was attached to the Rockefeller Foundation, where, beginning in 1959, he served as director of medical and natural sciences. His special interests are neurophysiology (specifically, the electrical activity of the central nervous system), on which he has written extensively, and the advancement of scientific education and research, particularly in underdeveloped countries.

TALCOTT PARSONS, born in Colorado Springs, Colorado, in 1902, received his education at Amherst College, the London School of Economics, and the University of Heidelberg. Since 1927 he has been associated with Harvard University, where he became professor of sociology in 1944. Among his extensive publications are: *Structure of Social Action* (1937); *Toward a General Theory of Action* (1951); *Structure and Process in Modern Societies* (1959); *Social Structure and Personality* (1964). His most recent contribution to *Dædalus,* "Youth in the Context of American Society," appeared in the Winter 1962 issue.

DON K. PRICE, born in Middlesboro, Kentucky, in 1910, is professor of government and dean of the Graduate School of Public Administration at Harvard University. He has served in a number of administrative and advisory posts in Federal government, and from 1954 to 1958 was vice-president of the Ford Foundation. His publications include *Government and Science; The Secretary of State* (as editor and co-author); and *City Manager Government in the United States* (with others). His essay, "Administrative Leadership," appeared in the Fall 1961 issue of *Dædalus.*

ERIC WEIL, born in 1904, is the holder of degrees from the University of Hamburg and from the Sorbonne. He is presently professor of philosophy at the University of Lille. In addition to writing articles for such periodicals as *Critique, Revue de Métaphysique et Morale,* and *Confluence,* he is the author of *Logique de la Philosophie, Hegel et l'Etat, Philosophie Politique, Philosophie Morale* and *Problèmes Kantiens.*

INDEX

Abstractism, 134, 148
Académie Française, 12
Academy-Institute of Arts and Letters, 12
Ackerman, James S., xii, xiii
Acton, Lord John, 214
Adams, Henry, 5, 282; the Virgin and the Dynamo, 279
Adams, John Quincy, 117
Adler, Mortimer, 123, 124
Administration, study of, 119–121
Africa, 167
Aged persons, 180–181
Age of Reason, 210, 267
Agriculture, 117, 121, 277
Alienation, xvii, xx, 224–226, 236, 241, 245, 258, 266–272, 287; of experience, 279–281; of nonscientific culture, 233; social, 36–37. See also Disjunction
American Academy of Arts and Sciences, xi, 12
American Association for Advancement of Science, xxii, 133–134, 295, 303, 318, 320; Committee on Science in Promotion of Human Welfare of, xxii, 133
American Institute of Biological Sciences, 134
Americanization of culture, 5
American Philosophical Society, 12, 113–114, 133
American Society of Biological Chemists, 134
Analysis: social, 44–69; scientific, 95–98, thematic, 98–107
Anaxagoras, xx–xxi
Anna Karenina (Tolstoy), viii

Anomie, x, xxiv, 28, 280–283, 287. See also Disjunction
À nous la liberté (Clair), 196
Anthropocentrism, 203, 207, 213
Anthropology, 7–9, 67, 77; defined, 29–30; origins of, 50–54; and social cohesion, 24–37
Anthropomorphism, 203, 207
Anticipations (Wells), 188
Antiscience, 256–259, 271, 272
Anxiety, 257–258
"Apollo" project, 299–304, 322–329; justification of, 325–327. See also Moon; Space
Aquinas, St. Thomas, 41, 252, 253
Archimedes, 201
Architecture, 152–153
Ariel (satellite), 294
Aristotle, 26, 41, 128, 213, 274
Arnold, Matthew, viii, 3–4, 7, 9
Art, 171–172, 283–284; environmental, 151, 159–161; modern, 248; universality of, 169
Artist, 148–149, 154
"Art of Science, The," (Snow), 10
Arts, the, xix, 10, 39–41, 74, 219, 223–225, 283–287; and culture of future, 169–170, 172; Freud's influence upon, 73; visual, 145–161
Ashby, Eric, xxii
Associations, professional, 39. See also Organizations; names of associations *passim*
Astronomical Journal, 297
Astronomy, 292–299, 321–322
Atmospheric Research Corporation, 319
Atomic Bomb, 206, 214, 279; World

337

Index

Atomic Bomb *cont'd*
  War II project of, 303. *See also* Nuclear weapons
Atomic Energy Commission, xxii, 232, 308, 318
Attitudes, moral, 83–84
Audience, educated, xviii, 74–75, 221
Authority: moral, and Durkheim, 62–63; political, and social scientist, 131–133, 138; subordination of science to, 110–116
Automation, 36–37, 267

Bacon, Francis, 12, 16, 111–113
Bailyn, Bernard, xxix
Bar Mitzvah, 239
Barth, Karl, 136
Bartók, Béla, 148
Barzun, Jacques, 282
Becket, Thomas, 23
Beckett, G. A., 249
Behavior, 22, 24, 33, 38, 43, 45, 56, 66, 219, 256; biological, 50; and Freud, 73–74
Bell, Daniel, xx, xxiv
Bellamy, Edward, 188, 196
Benedict, Ruth, 51
Berkner, Lloyd V., 300, 323
Biology, 130–134, 275, 276, 304–309; and evolution, 253–254, 260–261; as natural history, 50. *See also* Ecology; Traits, organizational
Boas, Franz, 51
Boehme, Jacob, 111
Bohr, Niels, 94, 104, 130
Books, 13, 25. *See also* Literature; Novel
Born, Max, xxiii, xxviii, 104
Borneo, 169
Boulding, Kenneth, 23
Boyle, Robert, 12
Braithwaite, W. S., 105
Brave New World (Huxley), 196
Bridgman, Percy W., 128–129, 137
British Academy (1902), 12
Bronowski, Jacob, 281
Brookings Institution, 40
Brooks, Harvey, xviii, xxix
Bruno, Giordano, 105, 204
Bueltman, C. G., 306
Bulletin of the Atomic Scientists, The, 110
Bureaucracy, 71–73, 241–242, 245
Burtt, E. A., 274
Butler, Samuel, 11

Butor, Michel, 249
Buttrick, Wallace, 119
Byron, George Gordon, 192

Cabet, Étienne, 187
Camus, Albert, 249
Cannon, W. B., 54
Capek, Karel, 196
Capitalism, 51–52, 60
Carbon-14, 308
Carnegie, Andrew, 118
Cartesians, 90
Caste, 34, 35
Catholicism, 35
Catlin, George, 178
Causality, 46, 274–275; and "uncertainty," 78–79
Cervantes, Saavedra de, 1
Cesium-137, 308
Change, cultural, 70–86
Chaplin, Charlie, 196
Chardin, Teilhard de, 131, 255
Charles I, 113
Charles II, 113
Chemistry of Space and Exploration of Moon and Planets, committee on, 323
Chesterton, G. K., 122
China, 237, 238
Churchill, Winston, 256
Church of England, 115, 121
City planning: and environmental art, 159–161; and light, 152–159
Civilization: and culture, xxii, 219–221, 251; modern technical, 237
Civil Service, British, 120, 121
Clair, René, 196
Clarke, Samuel, 92
Coherence-making, xvii, xviii, xx, xxix
Cohesion, social, 29–30; language as index of, 32
Collaboration, artistic-scientific, 145–161; Kepes' proposal for, 150–152; three basic conditions for, 160
Collingwood, R. G., 106
Colonialism, 167–168
Commitment, 40–41; artistic, 149; scientific, 265
Commoner, Barry, 291
Communication, 19, 266, 270–272; artistic-scientific, 149–151; and culture, xv–xvi, 3, 32, 164–170; difficulties in, 70; and glyphs, 175; growth in systems of, 36–37; and information, 85–86; intercontinental,

338

Index

Communication *cont'd*
321; and space technology, 292–293, 296. *See also* Secrecy
Communism, 205
Community: nineteenth century disrupted, 189–192; scientific, 110–116, 271, 303, 308, 315; social, 264–266; solidary, 36, 185–186, 189; world, xiii, 164–170
Compton, Arthur, 135
Computers, xvii, 55; and information feedback, 82–83, 103
Comte, Auguste, 61; and spectrum of sciences, 112, 131, 132, 138–139
Conant, James B., 130
Concepts, scientific, 95
Condorcet, Marie Jean, 253
Confirmation, social, 239–240
Consciousness, 170, 172
Conservation, 268, 269; Descartes' laws of, 99–100
Consistency, 209–210, 215, 217
Contingency analysis (x-y plane), 95–97, 99, 103, 104, 106
Contract, 60–61
Cooley, Charles Horton, 65
Copernicus, xxviii, 16, 97, 101, 105, 112, 234
Cornford, F. M., 102
Cosmology, 204, 207, 247, 254; mechanical, 246; thema in, 101–102
Cotes, Roger, 91
Council for a Livable World, 110
Cowley, Abraham, 12
Creativity, xix, 160, 171
Criticism, artistic, 40, 71, 245
Crystal Palace, 158, 187
Cubism, 17, 147
Culture, 1–13, 277–278; anthropological view of, 7–9, 24–37; change in, and science, 70–86; and communication, xvi, 25, 70; concept of, vii; definition of, xiii, xv, 1–2, 24, 30, 218; diremption of, 241–247; for educational purposes, xv; and the future, 163–182, 252; nature of, 14–19; redefinition of, 218–235; and social cohesion, 26–30; as social heritage, 27; and social sciences, xvi–xvii, 67–69; Stalin-Trotsky clash over, 2; traditional, 283–286
Culture: A Critical Review of Concepts and Definitions (Kroeber and Kluckhohn), vii, 8–9

"Culture and Anarchy" (Arnold), viii, 4
Custom, 32–34
Cybernetics, 54; in public administration, 120

Daedalus xi; "A New Europe?" 71
Dalton, John, 115
Dante, Alighieri, 169
Darwin, Charles, 47, 76, 105, 178, 254
Death, 280–281
Decision-making, 120
Degradation, biological, 304–305, 313
Democritus, xxvii–xxviii
Depersonalization, 241–243
Descartes, René, xxviii, 17, 94, 99–100, 128, 199, 201, 202, 204, 282, 288, 289; dichotomy of, 42, 45; and Durkheim, 61; and universe, 275–276
Dessauer, Friedrich, 88–89, 91
Detergents, 304–305, 306, 310, 313
Determinism, 51–52, 129–130, 135, 137; classical, 78–79
Dewey, John, 65, 245, 258, 259
Dialectic, 47
Dictionary of Occupational Titles, 243
Diffusion, cultural, 30–31
Dijksterhuis, Eduard Jan, 97, 99–100
Dilthey, Wilhelm, 48–49, 56
Dipole belt. *See* Westford experiment
Disciplines, intellectual, xv, 39–68; effect of scientific themes on, xviii–xix, 76–86; medieval concept of, 14–16; principal conceptions of, 43–49; scholarly standards of, 39–41; *scientia* in, 15–19
Discrimination, racial, 26–27
Disjunction, cultural, xvii, xx, xxiv, 27, 28–29, 37–38, 163–170, 275; of artist and science, 145–161; and custom, 32–33, 34; of knowledge and senses, 273–289; of role and person, 241–243; of science and mankind, 266–270; of science and philosophy, 199–217; of science and scholar, 6; of science and technology, 184–198; of social structure and culture, 236–249; of vocabulary, 245–247
Distance: esthetic, 248–249; psychic, 249

339

Index

Divine Purpose, 111–113, 135–136. See also Theology
Division of Labor (Durkheim), 239
DNA, 85–86
Dodds, E. R., 262, 263
Donne, John, 287
Dostoyevsky, Fëdor, 211
Drugs, xii
Drummond, Henry, 135
Dryden, Hugh L., 302
Dryden, John, 11–12
Dualism, 42, 47, 276
Dubos, René, xx, xxiv, 130–131
Durkheim, Émile, 28, 36, 43, 55, 60–65, 241, 242, 280; *Division of Labor*, 239

Ecclesiasticism and science, 114–116
Echo (satellite), 295
Ecology, Ecosystems, xvi, 76–77, 269–270, 271, 313–314; and nuclear testing, 312
Econometrics, 132
Economics, 44; classical, 50, 51; laissez-faire, 83; Marx's interpretation of, 51–52; and Weber, 55–60, 63
Eddington, Arthur, 135
Education, 14–15, 165–182, 221, 227–229, 233–234; divergence in, xii, 163; government subsidy in, 116–117; liberal vs. scientific, 1–4, 6, 11–13, 222–223; priority of human concern in, 257; role of social sciences in, 39–69; and *scientia*, xiv–xv, 19–23
"Effects of Nuclear Weapons, The," 308
Einstein, Albert, xiv, 78, 104, 105, 127, 255
Eisenhower, Dwight D., 122
Electricity, 195, 311
Electronics, 291
Elementary Forms of the Religious Life (Durkheim), 62
Eliot, Charles, 42
Eliot, T. S., viii, 5
Elite: and culture xiii, 3, 7–8, 164–165, 228–229; as educated artists, 178; and *scientia*, 19; scientists as, 37
Emancipation, political, x
Emerging nations, 163, 167, 178
Empathy, 59, 67

Empiricism, 15, 43, 66, 226; scientific, 95
Encyclopédie (Diderot), 2
Endogamy, 34–36
Energy, xviii, 3, 80, 99–100. See also Nuclear energy
Engineer, xvii; defined, 203
England, 34–35
Environment, xii, 26, 37–38, 43, 44–45, 66, 260–261; and art, 159–161; adaptation to new, 268–269; and Durkheim, 61; and ills of mankind, 279; and technology, 195–196, 252, 263–264, 304–310
Epistemology, 42, 43, 66, 90–91; and Cartesian dichotomy, 45
Equilibrium, 77
Essay on Philosophical Method (Collingwood), 106
"Establishment": academic, 222–225; scientific, xix, 109, 121–122, 137–139, 221, 269; social, 227
Estrangement, scientific, 251–272
Etranger, L' (Camus), 249
Evelyn, John, 11
Evidence, scientific, 70–71, 287–288
Evolution, 47, 165, 253–254, 261–262; as scientific theme, 76, 77
Existentialism, xxvii–xxviii, 130, 229, 246
Experience, 42, 46, 226, 229–230, 239–241, 245; alienation of, 279–281; and esthetic distance, 248–249; and Hegel, 237; and hypothesis, 88–89; and scientific knowledge, 264–266
Expertise, 36, 71–73
Explorer (satellite), 319

Factory, 186–188, 194–195
Fallout, nuclear, 307–310, 317
Faraday, Michael, 115, 127, 311
Far East, xiii
Febvre, Lucien, 237
Federal Radiation Council, 308–310, 315
Federation of American Scientists, 134
Feedback, 80–85, 86, 103; stability and response of, 82, 84; unstable, 83
Fight and flight responses, 262, 268–269
Firth, R., 30
Force, 95, 98–99
Ford, Franklin L., xv–xvi, xxix

Index

Forrester, J. W., 81, 83
Forster, E. M., 268
Foundations, philanthropic, 118, 121; and social scientist, 123; subversives in, 124
Fragmentation, xvi, xxv; economic and social, 163–167; of knowledge, 193–194; scientific, 264–266. *See also* Specialization
Frankenstein, 37, 191
Franklin, Benjamin, 113–114, 115, 253
Frazer, J. G., 8
Freedom, individual, 218, 227, 240, 241–243
"Free will," 78
French Revolution, 76, 113
Freud, Sigmund, xiv, 43, 64, 105, 282; *Moses and Monotheism*, 101; psychoanalytic theory of, 73–74
Fromm, Erich, 242
Futurists, 146; Italian, 147

Gabo, Naum, 146
Galen, 16
Galileo, xxviii, 42, 96, 105, 201, 202, 203, 234; on scientific themes, 100–101; trial of, 204
Gasset, Ortega y, 249
Gates, Frederick G., 119
Gaugin, Paul, 178
Geist, 46–47, 48, 53, 67
Genesis, 101
Genetics, 76, 85–86
Gestalt, 49, 51, 57, 58
Gilbert, William, 101
Gilson, Emile, 265–266
Gleichschaltung, xiv
Glyphs, 174–175, 181
Gogol, Nikolai, 2
Government, xii; and education, 19, 116–117; and science, 110–139
Goya, Lucientes, 287
Granet, Marcel, 237
Graubard, Stephen R., xxix
Gravitation, Newton's theory of, 92–93, 95, 98–99
Great Britain, 115
Greeks and the Irrational, The (Dodds), 262
Griffith, Mary, 187
Gross National Product, 73, 278

Halévy, Judah, 44
Hall, A. R., 92–93
Hall, M. B., 92–93
Hamilton, Alexander, 117
Handlin, Oscar, xx, xxi
Harvard Observatory, 322
Hatch Act, 120
H-Bomb, x, 293–294. *See also* Nuclear weapons
Hegel, Georg Wilhelm, 29, 56, 67, 215, 236–237; and *Geist*, 46–47, 48, 52–53
Heidegger, Martin, 210
Heisenberg, Werner, xxv, xxvii, 94, 104, 105; "uncertainty principle," 78–79, 128
Helmholtz, Hermann, 99
Hemingway, Ernest, 256
Hess, Wilmot, 319, 320
Hilbert, David, xxviii
Historicism, 166–167, 213, 217; and Dilthey, 48–49; and Hegel, 47, 48, 52, 67; and Weber, 55
History of the Royal Society (Sprat), 12
Hitler, Adolph, 210
Hobbes, Thomas, 1, 42, 43, 137; and utilitarianism, 45
Hoggart, Richard, 5
Holton, Gerald, 23, 130
Homeostasis, 54
Hooke, Robert, 113
House Committee on Un-American Activities, 124
Humanism, 3, 8–11, 15; *scientia* of, 16
Humanities, viii, 41, 223, 283; man as measure of, 9; and politics, 109; and sciences, xi–xii, xviii, 9–10, 106–107
Humanization. *See* Values, cultural
Hume, David, xxvi, 44, 97, 208; and Kant, 46
Hutchins, Robert M., 123, 124
Huxley, Aldous, 10, 196
Huxley, Thomas, viii, xxi, 3–4
Huyghens, Christian, 201
Hypothesis, 88–89; Newtonian, 90–94, 107, 203; science as system of, xxvii–xxviii; thematic, 92–94, 105

IBM, xxii, 232
Idealism, German, 46–49, 66–67; and Marx, 51; and Weber, 55–60
Identity, modern, 145–146, 239–240
Ideology, xii, 218; political, 71
Illumination, 152–153
Impressionism, 17

341

Index

Inclusiveness, 167–168
Incoherence, cultural, xvi, 29, 260, 270. *See also* Disjunction
Induction. *See* Science, inductive method of
Industrialization, x, xiii, xxii, 103, 186–187, 194, 311
Industrial Revolution, 58, 268
Inequality, 218; financial, x
Information, 85–86
Injun (satellite), 319
Insecticides, 304, 305, 306, 310
Inspiration, 19
Instrumentalism, 206, 210
Integration, cultural, 29, 164–165, 259–264, 270–272
Intellectualism, ix, 228; and science, 121
Interaction, 18, 238–239
Intercommunication: future, 169–174; historical, 164–169; among specialists, 2, 182. *See also* Communication
Interdependence, social, 280–283, 287
Interests, cultural, 7
Internalization, 63–64
Internal Revenue Code, 120
International Astronomical Union, 297–298
International Science and Technology, 319
International Scientific Radio Union, 297
Iodine-131, 307–308, 309
Isolation, xiv, 282

Jaeger, Werner, 8
James, Henry, 5, 196
James, William, 65, 97, 242
Jeans, James, 135
Jefferson, Thomas, 111, 112–114, 115, 116–117
Jews, 35, 239
Johns Hopkins University, 118
Johnson Island, 293
Joyce, James, 249

Kafka, Franz, 249
Kant, Immanuel, 46–48, 53, 66, 200, 211, 215, 234, 265
Kelvin, William, 103, 115, 127
Kennan, George F., 123, 124
Kennedy, John F., 122, 300, 301, 322–323, 325

Kepes, Gyorgy, xviii–xix
Kepler, Johannes, xxiv–xxv, 203, 204
Keynes, John Maynard, 53
King, Martin Luther, 178
Kluckhohn, Clyde, vii, 8
Knowledge, 171–174, 244; and communication, xv–xvi; cultural absorbtion of modern, 253–256; and human experience, 264–266; scientific, and social pressure, xxii, 315–318; structure of, 11; unity of, xiv, xxv
Kooning, Willem de, 23
Koyré, Alexandre, 90, 201
Kroeber, A. L., vii, 8
Kusch, Polykarp, 328–329

Labor, division of, 35–36, 61; Marx's attitude toward, 237; and social interdependence, 280
Language, xvi–xvii, 12–13, 17, 20, 28, 174–177; and glyphs, 175; as index of social cohesion, 32; as science, 54; as vehicle for cultural transmission, 25; and vocabulary, 245–247
Laplace, Pierre S., 70–71, 78, 79, 112, 246
Larmor, J., xxvi, xxvii
La Rochefoucauld, François, 282
Law, 56, 109; and Durkheim's theory of contract, 60–61
Lawrence, T. H., 249
Lawrence Scientific School (Harvard), 116
Leach, Edmund R., xii, xvi
Leadership, political, 109–111, 114, 120
Leavis, F. R., viii, 3
Leisure, 220–221
Lessing, Gotthold, 248
Leviathan (Hobbes), 1
Levin, Harry, xii, xxix
Levi-Strauss, Claude, 54
Libraries, future, 13
Liebniz, Gottfried Wilhelm, 90, 93
Life on the Mississippi (Twain), 4–5
Light, creative use of, 151, 152–159
Liller, William, 322
Lincoln Laboratory, 296, 297, 321
Linguistics, mathematical, 85, 200. *See also* Language
Literacy, x
Literature, 219, 223–225; and Freud,

Index

Literature *cont'd*
73; modern, 249; as "nonscientific" culture, 232
Literature and Science (A. Huxley), 10
Location, social, 238, 240
Locke, John, 42, 43, 44, 45
Lodge, Oliver, xxvii
Logic, 54–55
Longevity, 280–281
Looking Backward (Bellamy), 188
Louis XIV, 203
Louisiana, 305
Lowell, A. Lawrence, vii
Luminescence, 159
Luther, Martin, 210

McCarthyism, 124
Macdonald, Dwight, 6
Machines, 186–198; literary protest and, 188, 191–192, 196; as threats, xxi
"Machine Stops, The" (Forster), 268
McIlwain, C. E., 294, 319–320
McLuhan, Marshall, 13
Macnie, John, 188
Magnetosphere. See Van Allen Belt
Maine, Henry, 242
Malinowski, Bronislaw K., 8, 27–28
Mallarmé, Stephané, 248
Malthus, Thomas R., 45
Management, industrial, 195
Mann, Thomas, 2
Mannheim, Karl, 236
Manpower, scientific. See Personnel, scientific
Marcuse, Herbert, xvii, xx, xxii, 23, 242
Marey, E. J., 147
Marinetti, Fillippo, 146
Maritain, Jacques, 135, 136
Marshall, Alfred, 53
Marx, Karl, 51–52, 67, 76, 237, 279; and the Law, 56
Massachusetts Institute of Technology, 39
"Masscult and Midcult," (Macdonald), 6
Materialism, 51; as synthesis, 52–53
Mathematical Principles of Natural Philosophy (Newton). *See Principia*
Mathematics, xxii, 41, 85, 200, 202–204, 231, 246–247, 275; and logic, 55

Matter, 92
Matthiessen, Peter, 8
Mauss, Marcel, 43
Maxwell, J. Clerk, 102, 103, 127
Mayer, Johann, 99
Mayr, Ernst, 131
Mead, George Herbert, 65
Mead, Margaret, xiii, xix, xx
Measurement, 274, 276, 282; Adams on, 279; social, 79
Mécanique Céleste (Laplace), 246
Mechanical Arts, 14
Media, mass communication, 238, 239. *See also* Communication
Medicine, 190, 261, 268; for space age, 263
Meiklejohn, Alexander, 23
Meillet, Antoine, 54
Melville, Herman, 8
Memoirs (Academy of Arts and Sciences, 1785), xxiii–xxiv
Mercantilism, 203
Metaphor, 246–247. *See also* Disjunction; Vocabulary
Metaphysics, 221, 225; and theology, 42
Michelson, Albert, 154
Middle Ages, xiii, 14–15, 41, 154, 161, 164, 201; art in, 285
Middle East, xiii
Military, xxii. *See also* Apollo project; Nuclear testing; Space
Mill, James, 44
Mill, John Stuart, 53
Milton, John, 283–284
Minneapolis *Tribune*, 319, 320
Mississippi River, 305
Mobility, social, 241–243
Modern Prometheus, The (Shelley), 192
Modern Times, 196
Modern Utopia (Wells), 261
Moon, exploration of, 299–304, 312, 317; projects' priority for, 324–328. *See also* Apollo project
Moore, G. E., 208
More, Thomas, 1
Morison, Robert S., xx, xxiv
Morrow, Walter, 297
Moses and Monotheism (Freud), 101
Motion pictures, 152
Motivation, 178, 273
Motives, 44; Weber's analysis of, 57
Motte, Andrew, 90, 92
Movements, artistic, 147–148

343

Index

Music, 245, 248–249; and humanism, 16; and quadrivium, 14

NASA, 302, 313, 325, 326, 328
National Academy of Science, 12, 110, 114, 134, 299, 302, 328
National Aeronautics and Space Administration. *See* NASA
National Cultural Foundation, 7
National Register of Scientific and Specialized Personnel, 243
National Science Foundation, xi, xxix, 302, 313
Natural Sciences, xviii, 41, 42, 166–167, 200–204, 221–223, 230–231, 267
Nature, xxv–xxvi, 93–94; effect of new technology on, 293–299, 303–310, 312; and man, 267–268; Newtonian view of, 90; scientific mastery over, 200–207; unity of 254–255
Negro, 238
New International Dictionary (Merriam-Webster), 12–13
Newton, Isaac, xxvi–xxviii, 12, 42, 75, 104, 105, 201, 203, 283; *Principia*, 89, 90–94, 99, 128
New York, 238
New York Times, 318, 323
Niebuhr, Reinhold, 136
Nietzsche, Friedrich, 210
1984 (Orwell), 196
Noise, 85, 86
Notes Toward a Definition of Culture (Eliot), 5
Novel, 248–249; as agency of expression, 244–245
Nuclear: energy, 3, 166; testing, 307–310, 311, 312, 317; weapons, x, 198, 206, 214, 226, 258, 267, 291

Objectivity, scientific, 204–207, 259; and philosophy, 208–211; and social pressure, 293–299, 303, 304–310, 312–315. *See also* Value freedom
Odishaw, Hugh, 300, 323
Oppenheimer, J. Robert, xiv, 2, 256
Optiks (Newton), 90
"Optiman," 263
Organizations, scientific, 133–134, 244. *See also* names of organizations *passim*
Orientation, future-time, 240–241

Orwell, George, 7, 196
Ostwald, Wilhelm, 155
Overpopulation, x

Paine, Thomas, 113
Panofsky, Erwin, 23
Paradise Lost (Milton), 284
Paris Universal Exposition (1867), 187
Parmenides, 102
Parsons, Talcott, xii, xvi–xvii, xxix, 242, 247
Patronage, xviii, 118–124, 206, 228, 234, 267, 313
Patterns of Culture (Benedict), 51
Paul, Pope, 178
Pauli, Wolfgang, 104
Pauling, Linus, 256
Peabody Museum, Harvard, 8
Pepys, Samuel, 11
Perception, 18, 273–278, 283; esthetic, 248
Personnel, scientific, 302
Pessimism, 126–128
Pesticides. *See* Insecticides
Pevsner, Antoine, 146
Phaedo (Socrates), xx
Phenomena, 264–265; and Kant, 46, 265
Philippines, 169
Philology. *See* Language
Philosophy, xxvi, 41, 112, 219, 223–225; dualistic, 42, 47, 276; and epistemology, 42; moral, 109; and science, xvii, xxi, 127–129, 134–138, 211–212, 216–217; twentieth century, 18
Photography, 17, 152, 154
Physicists, xiv, xxii, 74, 126–129. *See also passim*
Physics, xxii, 74–75, 77; as true science, 204–205
Physics in My Generation (Born), xxiii
Physiology, xii
Picasso, Pablo, 256
Planck, Max, xxvi, 33
Plato, 206, 207, 213, 215; and perception, 274, 283
Plymouth Brethren, 35
Poetry, 74, 248
Poincaré, Jules Henri, xxvii, 100
Political science, 119–120. *See also* Administration; Politics
Pope, Alexander, 246

Index

Politics, 71, 109–139, 227–228, 235; academic, 115; effect of on "pure science," xxii–xxiii; and scientific community, 109–111, 125–126, 291, 312
Popper, Karl, xxvii, 98
Population, 238
Positivism, xxvii, 226, 229
Pound, Ezra, 5
Power, science as instrument of, xxi, 207–208, 214–215, 277, 314
Pragmatism, 64, 65, 206
Prelude, The (Wordsworth), 178
Presbyterians, 116
President's Science Advisory Committee, 110, 296, 305
Price, Don K., xviii–xix
Priestley, Joseph, 115
Primitive Culture (Tylor), 9, 24
Principia (Newton), 89–94, 96; "Hypothesis non fingo," 91, 92; Regulae Philosophandi, 90–93, 107
Progress, 253; and Jefferson, 117–118; technical, 220–224
Propositions, scientific, 95
Protestant Ethic and the Spirit of Capitalism (Weber), 56–57
Psychoanalysis, 73, 77, 105; and religion, 74
Psychology, xii, 42, 44, 131; and public administration, 120; thematic approach to, 104; and values, 208–209
Publication of scientific experiments, 292–295, 298–299, 316–317
Public opinion, 79
Purcell, Edward, 296, 297
Puritan Revolution, 76, 113

Quakers, 35
Quantum theory, 70, 75, 79, 128
Quine, W. V., xxix

Rabelais, François, 237
Radicalism: Jeffersonian, 111, 114–116; philosophical, 44
Radioactivity, 293–295, 307–310, 315, 318–321
Read, Herbert, xix, xxii, 5
Realism, 164, 166, 204–205
Reality, 70, 71; in art and poetry, 74; social, 218, 236–249
Rebellion, social, 240–241, 271
Rede Lecture (1959), viii, ix, 2, 3
Reece, B. Carroll, 122, 124, 125

Reformation, 58
Regulae Philosophandi (Newton), 90; Fifth rule, 91–93, 107
Relationship functions, 17; social, 43, 63, 236, 244
Relativism, xvii, 8
Relativity, 77, 78, 79
Religion, 74, 135–137, 166, 204, 219, 280; and commitment, 41; as status symbol, 225. See also Theology
Renaissance, 202, 252–253, 283; art in, 285; and intellectual discipline, 14, 41; *scientia* in, 17
Reports on Manufactures (Hamilton), 117
Research, xxvii, 206, 305–307; and Apollo project, 302–303; and atomic bomb, 303; and development, federal, 110, 234; and scientific integrity, 291–329
Responsibility, scientific, 310, 314–318
Revolution, scientific, ix–x; Huxley's view of, 4
Rhythm, 147
Ricardo, David, 44, 51, 52
Rickert, Heinrich, 49
Rimbaud, Arthur, 248, 249
Robbe-Grillet, Alain, 249
Rockefeller, John D., 119
Rose, Wickliffe, 119
Rousseau, Jean Jacques, 61, 214
Royal Academy of Arts, 12
Royal Society of London for Improving Natural Knowledge, 11–12, 113
R.U.R. (Capek), 196
Russell, Bertrand, xxviii, 98, 274
Russia, Czarist, 238

Saint-Simon, Claude, 206
Sameness, xvii
Sapir, Edward, 54
Sartre, Jean-Paul, 6
Satellites, 294, 321. See also names of satellites *passim*
Saussure, Horace de, 54
Schiller, Johann, 236
Schoenberg, Arnold, 248
Scholarship, 70–72, 275; humanistic-scientific dichotomy in, 88
Schrödinger, Erwin, 104, 135
Science, 3, 189–192, 219; abstractism of, 134–139; compatibility within, 255–256; and cultural change, 70–86, 251–272; and culture, vii–xxviii,

345

Index

Science *cont'd*
  30–31, 199–217; inductive method of, 88–89; integrity of, xxii, 291–329; modern, 313–314; and philosophy, xxi–xxvi, 127–129, 134–138, 211–212, 216–217; and political influence, 109–125; popular, 197–198; and religion, 134–136, 166; self-restraint of, 125–134; and technology, xx–xxiii, 184–198, 266–270; thematic imagination in, 88–107
Science (magazine), 298, 322
Science and Hypothesis (Poincaré), 100
Science in Space (Berkner and Odishaw), 323, 324
Scientia, xiii, xiv, xv, xvii, 14–23; and discipline, 15; and education, 19–23; medieval concept of, 14–15; in Renaissance, 17
Scientific American, xiv, 17
"Scientific method," 18, 70; Descartes', 99; inductive, 88–90; Newton's, 90–94; Russell on, 98; and social pressure, 294–295, 298, 299, 301, 306, 311–312, 315–318; "themata" in, 101–107
Scientism, 213–214
Scientists, 32–33, 36–38, 273–274; and artists, 283–284; as dissenters, 109–139; and intellectuals, ix; nineteenth century view of, 42; responsibility of, 315–318
Secrecy, 313, 314, 316; and radioactive fallout, 308; and "Starfish" experiment, 293–295; and "West Ford" experiment, 296–298
Segregation, racial, 132
Selections from the Unpublished Scientific Papers of Sir Isaac Newton (A. & M. Hall), 92
Self-consciousness, artistic, 145–149, 241; and personal identity, 239; and Zen Buddhism, 249
Self-restraint, scientific, 125–134
"Semantics of Culture" (Levin), xii, 1–13
Senate Committee on Aeronautical and Space Sciences, 302, 328
Sensibility, 237–241
Sequence, 147
Seward, William H., 187
Shakespeare, William, 169
Shannon, C. E., 85

Shape of Things to Come, The (Wells), 196
Shelley, Mary, 192
Shils, Edward, 242
Signs, visual: and artistic communication, 151–152; and glyphs, 174–175
Simmel, Georg, 63
Simpson, George Gaylord, 150–151
Sinnott, E. W., 131
Smith, Adam, 44
Snow, Charles P., viii, 2–4, 9–10
Soap and Detergent Association, 306
Social action, 41
Social Gospel, 136
Social Sciences, 28, 41, 42, 47, 191, 207; and culture, xvi–xvii; methodology of, 55–65; and political policy, 131–133; role of, 39–68; and technology, 191–192; vocabulary of, 246–247
Society, 27–31, 219–220; "affluent," 220, 226, 228, 231; defined, 31; mass, 238–239; responsibility of, 317; technological, 227
Sociology, 55, 76; and Durkheim, 61–63; and public administration, 120; thematic approach to, 104; and Weber, 55–60; and values, 208–209
Socrates, xx–xxi, 215, 262
Sonnett Report, 328
Soviet Union, ix, 71, 279; culture in, 2
Space, 197, 235, 259, 263, 292–304, 314, 317; man's role in, 325–328
Space Science Board, 296–297, 298–300, 301, 318, 322–323, 325–326, 328–329
Specialization: functional, 243–245; and generalization, 11; professional, xiv–xv, 241–242; and refinement of techniques, 15; of roles, 242–243; scientific, xxv, 192–194
Spencer, Herbert, 60, 242
Spengler, Oswald, 2
Sprat, Bishop, 12
Stability, social, x
Stalin, Josef, 2
Stammler, Rudolf, 56
Standards, cultural relativism of, 8
"Starfish" experiment, 293–295, 299, 310, 318–321
Statesmanship, 71, 72
Statistics, 55
Steele, Richard, 9

Index

Strontium-90, 308
Structure of Social Action (Parsons), 247
"Study of Administration, The" (Wilson), 120
Subjectivity, xvi, 273, 281–289
Subsidy, educational, 116–117. *See also* Foundations; Patronage
Subversion, political, 123
Sumner, William Graham, 76
Support, financial. *See* Patronage
Swift, Jonathan, 4
Szilard, Leo, 85

Tagore, Rabindranath, 178
Taylor, E. B., 9; defines culture, 24, 27
Taylor, Frederick, 195
Teaching machines, 13; and feedback concept, 82
Teamwork, artistic, 150–152, 156
"Technique," xiii–xiv, 14–15; and *scientia*, 20
Technology, ix–x, xxi–xxiv, 184–198, 206, 259–264; and economics, 44; and environment, 304–310; Hamilton's proposal on, 117; as independent force, 266–270; intellectual, 247; and social responsibility, 291–329; and workman, 36–37
Technology and the Academics (Ashby), xxii
Television, 152
Telstar (Satellite), 294, 319, 321
Tennyson, Alfred Lord, 8
Testing, educational, 79
Themata, scientific, xviii, 88–107
Themes, scientific: effect of on culture, 76–86; energy, 80; feedback, 80–85; relativity, 78; uncertainty, 78–79
Theogony (Hesiod), 101
Theology, 41, 190, 246; and metaphysics, 42; Kant's concern for status of, 46; and Newtonian physics, 93–94; Protestant, 136–137; traditional, and politics, 109–110, 124, 134–135
Theory, scientific, 73–75, 90–107; and calculation, 202; construction of, 88–90
"Theory of Popular Culture, A" (Macdonald), 6
Thoreau, Henry David, 214

Three Contributions to Sexual Theory (Freud), 64
Three Hundred Years Hence (Griffith), 187
Thucydides, 1, 284
Tillich, Paul, 136, 242
Tocqueville, Alexis de, xvii
"To Hell With Culture" (Read), xix, 5
Tolstoy, Leo, viii–ix
Tower of Light, Baltimore, 156–158
Traac (Satellite), 294
Tradition, 185–186, 189
Training vs. education, xv
Traits, organizational, 50–51, 53–54
Transformations, xviii; and artistic creation, 145–161; and the future, 163–182; and political decision, 109–139; scholarship and practical affairs in, 70–86; and thematic decision, 88–107
Transit VIB (satellite), 294
Transplantation, surgical, xii, 263
Transportation, xxi, 252
Transylvania College, 116
Trilling, Lionel, 3, 249
Trotsky, Leon, 2
Twain, Mark, 4–5
Two Cultures and the Scientific Revolution (C. P. Snow), 2. *See also* Rede Lecture
Two Cultures? The Significance of C. P. Snow (Leavis), 3

Uccello, Paolo, 248
"Uncertainty Principle," 78–79, 128
Under the Mountain Wall (Matthiessen), 8
Unitarians, 35, 115, 116
United Nations, 163, 205
United Nations Committee for International Cooperation, 175
United States: Army signal corps, 295; Department of Defense, 296, 308, 319; Department of Health, Education and Welfare, 309; Public Health Service, 305, 307
Unity, 3, 151, 265–266; complementary, 147–148; intellectual, 65–66; philosophical, 127
Universe, xxviii–xxix, 74, 111, 171, 172, 252; Descartes' conception of, 275–276; modern conception of, 286; specific vs. foreign, 219
University, 39, 122; "elite," 228. *See*

347

Index

University *cont'd*
  also Education; Politics, academic
University of Chicago, 123
Urbanization, 36, 268–269. *See also* City planning
Urey, H. C., 299–300, 323
U Thant, 178
Utilitarianism, 45–46, 47–48, 66; and Durkheim, 55, 60–64

"Value-freedom," Weber, 59, 204, 205, 207, 208, 212. *See also* Objectivity
Values, 41, 63, 208–212; cultural, 218–225, 228, 230; and Plato, 215
Van Allen, James, 293, 318, 319, 320–321
Van Allen Belt, 293–295, 320–321
Verdi, Giuseppi, 281
Versatility, artistic, 161
Vesalius, 16
Vinci, Leonardo da, 15, 16, 201
Violence, 219
Vocabulary, 245–247. *See also* Language
Voyage en Icarie (Cabet), 187

Wald, George, xxix
Warwick, James, 319, 320
Washington, George, 116, 238

Water, 268, 269; pollution of, 304–305
Weber, Max, 49, 55–60, 203, 211–212, 216, 241–242, 248
Weil, Eric, xx
Wells, H. G., 188, 192, 196, 261
"West Ford" experiment, 295–299, 321–322
Weyl, Hermann, xxvii, xxviii, 137
Whitehead, Alfred North, 53, 58, 107, 246, 247
Whorf, Benjamin, 54
Why War? (Einstein-Freud correspondence), xiv
Wiesner, Jerome B., 300–301
Williams, Raymond, 5
Wilson, Woodrow, 120
Wissenschaft, 11, 39, 48
Wittgenstein, Ludwig, 23
Woolf, Virginia, 6
Woolwich, Bishop, 166
Wordsworth, William, 178, 283
World Council of Churches, 137
Wren, Christopher, 12

x-y plane. *See* Contingency analysis

Yeats, William Butler, 249

Zen Buddhism, 246, 249
Zola, Émile, 232